D0504651

Agricultural Pollution

AUSTRALIA
LBC Information Services
Sydney

CANADA AND USA
Carswell
Toronto

NEW ZEALAND
Brooker's
Auckland

SINGAPORE AND MALAYSIA
Thomson Information (S.E. Asia)
Singapore

Agricultural Pollution

by

John Blackhurst, FRICS, FAAV.
Planning and Land Advisor

and

Michael Payne, B.SC.
Environmental Consultant

Published in 1997 by
Sweet & Maxwell Limited of
100 Avenue Road
London NW3 3PF
(http://www.smlawpub.co.uk)
Phototypeset by LBJ Typesetting Ltd
of Kingsclere
Printed and bound in Great Britain by
MPG Books Ltd of Bodmin, Cornwall

No natural forests were destroyed to make this product;
only farmed timber was used and replanted

A CIP catalogue record for this book is available from the British Library

ISBN 0421 526106

ABOUT THE AUTHORS

John Blackhurst has been involved with farming and pollution control for over 30 years. He has been a Dairy Farmer and was Regional Farm Waste Adviser for MAFF. Like Michael Payne, he was Head of the NFU's Environment Department. This was followed by some ten years as NFU County Secretary for Derbyshire, specialising in a wide range of rural law including Planning and Environmental issues. On joining Flint Bishop & Barnett in 1990 he set up a Planning and Land Use Department and has fully utilised his skills of negotiation and advocacy. He is a Chartered Surveyor, a Fellow of the Association of Agricultural Valuers and a Member of the British Institute of Agricultural Consultants.

Michael Payne has been advising farmers on environmental issues for the past 17 years. He has been closely involved with the development of legislation, as well as casework, in his work for the National Farmers Union where he was Head of the Environment Department and Assistant Director of the Parliamentary and Professional Services Division for eight years, before setting up his own environmental consultancy. He has the benefit of a scientific background, and is also actively involved in a Norfolk family farming business. He specialises in environmental issues affecting agriculture, particularly air and water pollution, odour problems, environmental aspects of the planning system and management agreements with conservation agencies. He is a member of the British Institute of Agricultural Consultants and the National Farm Waste Management Register, and acts as an expert witness in court and at arbitrations, planning enquiries and appeals.

ACKNOWLEDGMENTS

Neither of us thought that writing a book of this type together would be so challenging. It has, however, been both exciting and time consuming. So there are a number of people who we must thank. Firstly, my wife Ruth for her perseverance and restraint when yet another weekend disappeared under the pen. Next Flint, Bishop & Barnett who have so kindly provided their extensive library and word processors. Thanks particularly go to Carol Waring, my secretary at Ashbourne and to Jean Buxton at the Derby office for their tremendous help with the text. **J.B.B.**

The preparation of this book has been a labour which sometimes seemed likely to produce little more than a mouse! Whether it has been worthwhile is for the reader to judge. Any merit which may be found in "my" part is due in no small measure to my wife Liz who encouraged and organised me throughout. She also read numerous drafts and suggested many improvements and corrections. **M.R.P.**

PREFACE

The subject of agricultural pollution is potentially so wide that it would be impossible to contain its scope wholly within a volume of this size. Whilst it is important to define the term in its broadest sense, the scope is narrowed to examine principally the pollution caused by most normal farming activities. To a lesser extent the impact on agriculture of external sources of pollution is also included. It generally excludes health and safety legislation and food, sales and processing, bed and breakfast or holiday accommodation, agricultural shows and many of the diverse enterprises current in, or related to, farming in England and Wales. Hazardous substances and radioactive waste are also largely excluded, as is much detail on "controlled" or non-farm waste management, which is a subject in itself. So far as law is concerned, detailed procedures through the courts are not encompassed within the scope of this volume.

"Pollution" is capable of several meanings and definitions, two of which are found in the Environmental Protection Act. Section 29 has a definition relating to waste on land but perhaps the word can best be described as the release into the total environment of any substance or energy which may cause harm or nuisance to mankind or any living organisms supported by the environment. It will be seen from this that there is a huge potential for causing pollution or permitting it to happen whether knowingly or otherwise. The word "contamination" has no statutory definition but may be taken to indicate that there is present, in any environmental medium, a substance which would not normally be found there. There is no necessity for that substance to be harmful.

The word "environment" should necessarily include the widest possible interpretation. So it consists of air, water and land, all living organisms, buildings, plants and trees and sometimes mere perception. The last concept may be difficult to interpret but, if one looks at the common law right to quiet enjoyment of one's own property, it is the perception of the scope of that right which influences the degree of concern towards it.

A further problem is that although much of the law in the U.K. is the same, there are variations between England, Wales and Scotland. The references in this book relate strictly to England and Wales and, for ease of understanding, we merely speak of England or English, so references apply to Wales except where stated. Scottish readers therefore may need to consult further specific legislative measures. The European Union has its measures referred to as E.C. or European Community legislation. The text is up to date as at December 1996.

The impact of any action or scheme of development within the countryside is bound, by definition, to have some environmental impact. The text concentrates on the environmental harms which are likely to arise on, over, in or under agricultural land, irrespective of whether they are caused by farming or not. Off-farm pollution caused by agriculture is also included.

One further point about this book. It is written in the style which intermingles law with practice and tries to make them indistinguishable. The underlying rationale for this is so that lawyers will have a better understanding of the practicalities of on-farm environmental pollution. By so doing they will be able better to advise, to mitigate and to defend civil and criminal actions. Farmers will be better aware of the legal principles which form the backdrop to their activities, or inactivities, so helping them to protect both themselves and the environment against damage. It is a holistic approach.

CONTENTS

TABLE OF CASES

TABLE OF STATUTES

TABLE OF STATUTORY INSTRUMENTS

TABLE OF EUROPEAN LEGISLATION

Treaties

1957 Rome Treaty establishing the European Economic Community 2–01
  Art. 130(r) 5–17
  (x) 5–17
  Art. 189 5–18
1971 Convention on Wetlands (Ramsar Convention) 2–06, 2–19, 4–25
1979 Convention on the Conservation of European Wildlife and Natural Habitats 2–06
  Convention on the Conservation of Migratory Species of Wild Animals 2–06
1985 Convention for the Protection of the Ozone Layer 2–06
1992 Convention on Biological Diversity 2–06
  Convention on Climate Change 2–06
  Maastricht Treaty on European Union 2–01, 2–02
  Art. 100(a) 2–02
  Art. 130(s)(1) 2–02
  (2) 2–02

Directives

1975 Dir. 75/440 (Surface Water Abstraction Directive) [1975] O.J. L194/26 .... 2–07, 5–20
  Dir. 75/442 [1975] O.J. L194/39 .... 2–07, 7–07, 7–38
  Art. 2(1)(b) 7–07
1976 Dir. 76/160 [1976] O.J. L31/1 2–03
1979 79/409 [1979] O.J. L103 .... 2–16, 2–19
1980 Dir. 80/68 [1980] O.J. L20/43 2–07
  Dir. 80/778 [1980] O.J. L299/11 .... 2–03, 2–07, 2–43, 2–44, 5–14, 5–18, 5–19, 5–20, 5–38, 5–42, 5–43
  Art. 7 5–19
1985 Dir. 85/337 [1985] O.J. L175/40 2–08

Directives—*cont.*

1986 Dir. 86/278 [1986] O.J. L181/6 2–07, 2–08, 7–26, App. 3
  Reg. 8(2) 7–27
  (3) 7–27
  (4) 7–27
1990 Dir. 90/219 [1990] O.J. L117/1 2–07
  Dir. 90/220 [1990] O.J. L117/15 2–07
  Dir. 90/313 [1990] O.J. L158 2–08
1991 Dir. 91/156 [1991] O.J. L78/32 .... 2–07, 7–07, App. 3
  Dir. 91/271 [1991] O.J. L135/40 2–08
  Dir. 91/676 [1991] O.J. L375/1 .. 2–08, 5–14, 5–15, 5–18, 5–20, 5–21, 5–22, 5–23, 5–24, 5–25, 5–26, 5–29, 5–32, 5–34, 8–27, 10–02, 10–04, App. 3
  Art. 1 5–20
  Art. 2(j) 5–20, 5–24
  Art. 3(1) 5–20, 5–22
  Art. 4 5–20
  Art. 5 5–20
  (3) 5–26
  (5) 5–26
  Art. 6 5–20
  (1)(b) 5–20
  Annex 1 5–20
  Annex 2A 5–21
  Annex 2B 5–21
  Annex 3 .... 5–20, 5–21
  (2)(b) 5–26
1992 Dir. 92/43 [1992] O.J. L206 ... 2–08, 2–09, 2–16, 2–19, 4–04, 4–05, 4–11
  Art. 4 2–16
  Dir. 92/72 [1992] O.J. L297/1 2–08
1996 96/61 [1996] O.J. L257/26 8–02, 8–15, 8–16, 8–18
  Art. 3 8–15
  Art. 9(4) 8–16
  Annex 3 8–15

TABLE OF PLANNING POLICY GUIDANCE NOTES

Chapter 1
Introduction

Today the emphasis is on sustainability and environmental awareness. Whatever our actions and developments, we should always have an eye to the needs and aspirations of future generations. In "the good old days", one always farmed as if one was going to live for ever, but lived as if one would die tomorrow. Or, to put this another way, farmers farmed in a way which caused the least long term damage to their land. There was always a tomorrow, and every farmer wanted to leave his farm in a better state than when he started. A steady build up of fertility would provide a sound basis for future profits, either for the farmer himself or his successors. The latter were nearly always from the same family. This practice allowed also for improvements around the farm which were not directly related to profitability. Latterly, there appears to be a society built on the shifting sands of immediacy and short-termism. However, the reality of sustainability is to force society to look beyond the artificial constraints of such policy and to envision a constantly improving outlook. Hence the circle of thinking has fully turned. **1–01**

There is clearly a strong moral basis for the concept of sustainability. The Bruntland[1] definition is "Development that meets the needs of the present without compromising the ability of future generations to meet their own needs." It is that basis which forms the platform for modern legal constraints to which both the law and government direction has given rise. Some management systems and techniques have, in many cases, yet to catch up with this concept. Certain methods of livestock and arable farming are proving environmentally unsound.

The nature of farming

The purpose of agriculture is to obtain natural products in greater quantity or more reliably or efficiently than can be achieved by harvesting wild plants or animals. The difference is illustrated under modern conditions by the farming and marine fishing industries. The livelihoods of farmers depends on the value by which his inputs to his crops or livestock are exceeded by the crop available for sale. The fisherman puts nothing into producing his "crop", merely providing harvesting equipment to take the surplus natural production. **1–02**

The fundamental method of the farmer is to foster the natural reproduction and growth of plants and animals. This involves protection from predators, parasites and disease, and management of nutrients to enable full natural growth potential to be achieved. Selective breeding is also an

[1] Bruntland, "Our Common Future" (1987).

important principle practised since earliest times to increase the suitability and level of production of plants and animals for human needs.

The farmer obtains more from his activities than he puts in, because he uses natural materials which he does not have to provide in order to fuel the growth and reproduction of his stock and crops. These basic "fuels" of the agricultural system are air, water, soil and sunlight. They are generally available on a renewable sustainable basis, and it is crucial to the future of agriculture that they should remain so. Agriculture is essentially a sustainable process (although questions might be raised about certain aspects of modern practices), dependent on the maintenance of air, water and soil in good condition. However, since agriculture operates in such an intimate relationship with the environment, and on such a large scale, it has an enormous potential to cause pollution if it is not properly carried out.

Historical view

1–03 As we write this book our country has not known war for 50 years. From time to time we receive sharp reminders that the world is a very unstable place. The basic requirements of life suddenly start to become more focused. Those with long memories will remember the drive for food following the end of the First World War with the provision of small parcels of land for soldiers in the form of statutory allotments. There was the "Dig for Victory" campaign following the Second World War and the race towards self-sufficiency. If a country does not have to rely too heavily on imports, then, in time of trouble, it can look after itself far more easily and concentrate its resources into its war effort.

Agriculture has altered dramatically over the past 50 years with the industry becoming mechanised and the development of the agri-chemical support industries providing fertilisers, pesticides and new crop varieties. The development of the service infrastructure of transport, power and water has also played a major rôle, as in other areas of the economy, in allowing concentration of sectors of the industry in favourable locations. Technology, through research and development, is a further factor which has facilitated the development of the industry, aided by effective systems for disseminating information and ideas to farmers.

Increasing food production became a goal all over Europe. In France particularly vast numbers of "peasant" farmers were able to make a living off the land with a handful of cows and an acre or two of corn. The French government saw a future whereby not only was the quantity of food substantially increased, but the focus was to retain very large numbers of farmers engaged in agriculture. There were social as well as economic benefits from this.

1–04 In the U.K. the government encouraged this drive towards more production by an increasingly sophisticated range of grants and subsidies. The technical development of agriculture has accompanied, and been largely driven by, the policies of successive governments to provide the U.K. population with plentiful and cheap food and to become self-sufficient in temperate products (although these aims have been somewhat distorted by the Common Agricultural Policy). These were aimed at the enlargement of individual farms in addition to ensuring an adequate basic income. Bigger was better and the economies of scale were sought. In the 1960s, for example, grants were available for hedge removal and the piping of ditches, giving larger fields. Farm woodlands were grubbed out with grant aid and very large scale drainage systems, not only on the better land but also on marginal and hill land, were installed. At the same time encouragement was given for growing shelter belts to allow stock to be kept out longer in the winter, higher up on the hill.

One of the effects of technical development has been the increasing specialisation of farms. In place of traditional mixed farming, many have now concentrated, sometimes exclusively, on a single enterprise, be it combinable crops, dairy farming or intensive housed livestock. This specialisation allows the industry to exploit both the economies of scale and the characteristics of each part of the countryside, for example soils and climate. As a result, the dairy industry is now predominantly located in the wetter and milder western parts of the country where grass growth is greatest, while cereals, being deeper rooted and more resistant to drought, tend to dominate farming in eastern parts of the country. Instead of cereals being grown on each farm for consumption by its own livestock, they are now grown in one part of the country and transported to another where the animals are kept. On a smaller scale, daffodil production illustrates the position of the industry to take best advantage of climate. Blooms are grown in the extreme south west of the country in Cornwall and the Scilly Isles where early springs allow Easter markets to be supplied, while the best quality bulbs for planting are grown in the excellent soil around the Wash.

While the average size of holdings increased and there was much greater efficiency, the numbers of farmers continued to fall. It was a time of rapid technological change and innovation, coupled with improved yields, matched by a vast research programme. Substantial government funding was pumped into the production of better strains of crops, careful selection and genetic improvement of livestock. The result has been that cattle have produced more milk and meat, pigs and sheep have been better converters of food and the increasing speed of production meant that the aspirations of those in government, charged with ensuring the security of their nation's food supplies, were met. Exactly the same process occurred in the arable sector with crops of winter wheat yielding four tons per acre rather than one ton as previously.

The concentration of production into specialist units, together with **1–05**
sustained pressure on the profitability of the industry, has led to the amalgamation of farms and the continuing trend to the larger size of individual units. The average farm size in the U.K. is substantially greater than in countries of continental Europe, where social factors, legislation and government policies are different, both in ethos and effect. Clearly, increasing size has an influence on the seriousness of potential pollution should things go wrong. In addition, problems may arise in particular areas where an unusual concentration of a particular type of business occurs. The

pig industry is an example of this, with high densities occurring near certain ports such as Hull and Rotterdam, where cheaper feedstuffs are imported. Some such areas have experienced particular problems, and have had to evolve particular policies in response. The planning policy for intensive livestock units in the county of Humberside is an example.

At the same time mechanisation of agriculture began to lift off, much the same was happening in other industries. This meant that fewer and fewer workers were required to look after more and more livestock and acres. So, as production grew, the numbers of workers involved in the industry began to fall. one of the results of this was that those tasks once carried out routinely over the winter period tended to be overlooked, such as the repair and maintenance of buildings and machines, hedging, ditching and drainage. At other times there was a squeeze in agricultural incomes and men were laid off for purely economic reasons.

Farmers were exhorted to borrow money to put up new buildings with the aid of substantial grants. The equations often made sense but, as with all investments, it was the timing which was critical. Those who put up buildings, at the latter end of the economic cycle, relying heavily on borrowed money, were unable to survive when interest rates escalated and incomes plunged.

There is no doubt that the changes which farming has undergone have increased pollution, both actual and potential, from agriculture. Initially, many of the changes were undertaken without consideration of the consequences. The classic example is the emergency ploughing of extensive areas of grassland during wartime to produce more crops for human consumption, leaving the legacy of increased nitrate levels which we still experience today. There is currently a need to modify some of the practices and facilities which were established or developed before the consequences were realised. Inevitably, this need to make retrospective alterations causes difficulties, in particular in communicating messages which have little or no financial benefits for the recipients.

It is clear that farming has been revolutionised during the course of the twentieth century in ways in which our forebears could scarcely have dreamed. But, in its wake, it has brought about the seeds of potential trouble by the very concentration of large numbers of livestock into areas where previously there were perhaps half or quarter the numbers. Increasingly complex cocktails of pesticides had to be used to control crop production, especially in mono-cultural systems.

The growth of pollution

1–06 It surely is a misconception that nature is infinitely adaptable. If it were so man would be able happily to continue polluting his environment. Nature would take care of it and absorb all the ill effects. Instead the sequential or knock-on effects from pollution can take many forms.

At a simple level, livestock produce faeces and urine which are normally spread on the land. Land is a very effective filtering medium and biological decomposition begins to take place immediately. Any liquid is filtered through the soil and most of the chemical constituents are removed by the plant's root system. Certain chemical constituents such as nitrogen, phosphate and trace elements are absorbed back into plants through the roots. Others, like potash, may be locked up by clay particles. Some liquids, in the warmer months, are drawn up immediately by plants or into the atmosphere by evapo-transpiration. Solids suffer the same fate but have to be broken down initially by the action of wind and weather, insects and microbes, and the general action of "nature". The nutrient value of both solids and liquids is utilised by the plant. The correct balance is one where there is no excess and no under-application so that the cycle is consistently sustainable. So, ideally, adequate amounts of organic fertiliser, preferably produced by the stock themselves, sustain the total requirements of the plants. There is no overload which cannot be utilised and which then runs off to cause pollution, or which sinks into ground water to contaminate aquifers. While a weed is a flower where it is not wanted, pollution can merely be nutrients which are in the wrong place at the wrong time. In other words "farm waste" is bad terminology when it refers to organic manure. It is a valuable resource which needs careful planning, storage and disposal, but properly used it creates no environmental hazard. It can substantially reduce the bill for bought in inorganic fertilizer. The essential balance of organic renewal to the relevant area of land is increasingly difficult to achieve, especially where there are intensive and specialist enterprises in place.

With the intensification of farming practices, the balance may be lost. **1–07**
There may be inadequate land to absorb the amount of effluent which is available. It may be in a high rainfall area, the land may slope sharply towards a watercourse and it may have a clay soil producing fast run-off. So, take the case of a very large dairy unit with a slurry system on limited acreage. Slurry is a mixture of faeces and urine which combine to form a semi-solid amorphous bulk. The quantities of slurry produced are more than the land can "naturally" absorb. Slurry tends to be largely anaerobic, meaning that its degradation takes place without the presence of air-loving organisms. These live only where there is no air present. (This is in contrast to the "aerobic" system where the microbes live in the presence of air and are generally much "sweeter".) Anaerobic digestion by these organisms tends to produce unpleasant smells, of which more later. It becomes a problem because the land area is insufficient to take the sheer volume of slurry, to break it down and to absorb it back, incorporating it fully as a fertiliser. So very careful management must come into play otherwise the surface can become clogged and natural breakdown of constituents cannot occur. In turn this may give rise to a saturation of the land to the extent whereby the application of more slurry is liable to cause run-off from the surface, particularly in times of heavy rainfall. This technique was intensified when farmers had "sacrifice" fields which were very heavily manured.

Where sewage sludge is applied, whether in its digested or undigested form, it is often spread on large areas of land by water undertakers with the consent of farmers. One of the difficulties with this form of treatment is that, particularly in some of the industrial areas, there is a high proportion of heavy metals in the composition of the sludge. Trace elements such as cadmium can build up quickly to highly toxic levels. They are absorbed both within the plant and the top soil layers. They cannot be removed by normal processes of nature, that is to say by biological degradation, and their build-up becomes cumulative. It eventually reaches such levels as to be highly dangerous and toxic to animals and can sterilise a whole area. There are built-in safeguards under statutory regulations by the use of strict limits for the application of sewage sludge to guard against such build-up.

We abuse nature at our peril and if a sensible balance is not maintained, the environment inevitably suffers the consequences. These can be slight or may be very dramatic but in every consideration of a pollution incident we should always have regard for what should be the natural order and the best way to rectify the imbalance which has occurred.

1–08 Farmers are driven by the economic need to make a living and show a profit. Although farming is still a way of life for many if not most farmers, like other citizens they need to feed and clothe their families. So, if one or other farm enterprise is in economic decline, others will be sought out and tried in order to keep the farm viable. With the tightening, in recent years, of the Common Agricultural Policy support regime, farmers have sought to diversify themselves from mainstream farm activities. Buildings have been transformed into craft centres, holiday lets or even sold off for housing: land is used for car boot sales, paint ball games and clay pigeon shooting. These are but a few of the very wide range of enterprises which are now found on the modern farm. Each, however, tends to bring a separate set of problems to bear in relation to environmental pollution.

A noticeable trend is found when farm buildings are sold away from the farm for residential purposes. These may become "protected" buildings (see Chapter 4). Many are situated on the edge of working farmyards and the various odours arising are often not understood or appreciated by ex-town dwellers. Lead poisoning from intensive clay pigeon shooting can sterilise an acre or so of ground. There is also the noise impact of cartridges being fired and complaints can and do arise. The impact of weather is one of the major factors in all pollution cases. If the ground is too hard or too saturated, run-off can occur in times of flash floods, causing water pollution. Periods of intense high pressure with thunder building up and no air movement can mean that odours linger and accumulate within an area and are unable to disperse. On the other hand a light pollution loading in a watercourse with large flows will gain no dilution effect of consequence.

Finally, the impact of governmental encouragement into the use of non-fossil fuels to reduce carbon and sulphur emissions had led to the testing of different crops such as willow and coppice for bio-fuel production. The ban on straw burning, together with encouragement for straw burning power stations again leads to radical re-use of straw. But there is no doubt that the chopping of straw following a combine and its re-integration in the ground can lead to the production, in time, of different soil structures.

These have different holding capacities by way of their ability to absorb liquids and indeed their ability to act as natural filters.

The nature of the problems may be acute pollution incidents, such as the escape of highly polluting silage liquor. But, increasingly, it is being recognised that diffuse pollution arising from numerous minor escapes of pollutants or from the general effects of farming activities, is having a damaging effect on water quality and the atmosphere. **1–09**

The scene is constantly changing and always evolving and circumstances will inevitably alter cases. If farmers and contractors are able to give more thought to pollution prevention, to take more care in their daily operations and in the planning stage of those activities, then when an accident or incident occurs, there will be more opportunity to mitigate in defence. Furthermore, it must surely be in the interests of all for pollution, in general terms, to be reduced and for more sustainable activities and developments to take place. The first aim of all farmers should be to use all practicable, sensible and economic means to prevent all forms of environmental pollution from taking place.

The record of the farming industry in recent years has been one of great improvement in environmental management. This may be seen in the statistics on pollution incidents and prosecutions. There is no room for complacency and evervone concerned needs to play their part. Farmers should all have a farm waste plan. This is so even if they do not carry livestock themselves but merely import organic wastes for use as fertilisers on their land. The plan itself would give rise to management practices which should be adopted, written down, and impressed both in writing and verbally upon employees. Agents and advisers should keep abreast of current developments. Solicitors are able to give forewarning of impending changes in legislation as well as strengthening advice should an incident ever occur. For pollution itself is likely to be very expensive by way of fines, remediation and bad publicity. It is also time-consuming, and time itself is a very precious commodity.

Chapter 2

Legislative Overview

The influence of Europe

2–01 The interaction of E.C. and U.K. environmental legislation is complex. A deep understanding of E.C. structure and procedures is largely outside the remit of this book, as is the operation of European Institutions such as the Parliament, the Commission, and the underlying Committee Structure. Nonetheless, some appreciation of underlying principles is essential.

The fundamental concepts which are enshrined in the Treaty of Rome, and subsequently the Maastricht Treaty of 1992, provide the base layer of authority which govern the actions of Member States and provide for first principles for European law. The second tier of authority is provided both by E.C. directives and E.C. regulations. These are examined in turn.

Directives

2–02 These normally give broad effect to the proposals of the legislative bodies, which are the Commission and the Parliament. They provide a skeleton for Member States upon which the flesh of national regulations can be clothed. The intention is for them to be interpreted in ways which are most appropriate for the Member States concerned and there will be variations of interpretation across the Community as a whole. The principle which permits such flexibility has been given additional endorsement following acceptance of the "subsidiarity" principle under the Maastricht Treaty. Certain articles under the Treaty provide for the Council to act by qualified majority voting, under Article 130(s)(1) and Article 100(a), whereas others instruct the Council to act without dissent, Article 130(s)(2), after consulting the European Parliament.[1] However, it must be remembered that where a Member State fails to comply adequately with the principles, then it is likely that complaints will be laid. Where a case comes before the European Court, if it is found against the Member State, it will reach a decision and order the State's Government to conform. Of importance to individuals is the ability to seek an initial ruling from the ECJ under specific circumstances.

In a very few cases only there are Directives which are so precise that they may have direct effect in Member States. This happens rarely but there have been instances[2] where a State has been challenged in the European Court for non-compliance with such a Directive. A person is able to claim, by way of a defence under a prosecution, that the State has not

[1] Case C–155/91 *Commission of the European Communities v. Council of the European Communities* [1993] E.C.R. I–939.

[2] Joined Cases C 6 & 9/90 *Francovich v. Italian Republic* [1991] E.C.R. I–5357; [1993] 2 C.M.L.R. 66.

complied with the spirit of a Directive. He may be able to claim compensation from the State under this circumstance, should he succeed, but it should be remembered that there are few Directives which have such direct effect.

Where there are wide areas for Directives to cover, often the initiating directive is called a "framework" Directive. That essentially sets the scene and, in turn, so called "daughter" Directives deal with the various areas of concern. These clusters of Directives form a very complex overlay of legislation. Often there will be even more Directives, particularly in the environmental field, in draft or preparation. Some which have been in draft fall by the wayside and have never been brought into force and others have been substantively modified. It is currently proposed that environmental Directives should be largely consolidated, partly for the sake of simplicity and partly in order to save time and paperwork. **2–03**

There are a number of draft Directives and Initiatives which are under consideration by the E.C.; apart from the Council Directive which proposes to introduce a tax on carbon dioxide emissions and energy, a proposal was made in 1996 by the E.C. Commission to round off the protection of water resources. This will be by means of a framework Directive and it would complement the two Directives on bathing water and drinking water. There have also been proposals relating to ground water which will cover three main areas. Polluted waters will be decontaminated, land uses which might contaminate will be controlled and there will also be some form of fiscal or economic weapons employed. Although this is likely to take some time before coming into operation, the impact on farming practices might be substantial.

E.C. Regulations

E.C. Regulations are the means by which the will of the E.C. is given direct effect in all Member States. They are directly applicable without any need for further legislation to be passed. Furthermore they may not be interpreted in a way which a Member State might consider to be more appropriate for its own circumstances in the same way that a Directive could be interpreted. Some environmental regulations give strict guidelines and parameters and, on occasion, very specific levels for compliance. An E.C. Regulation overrides national law and is only challengeable at the European Court of Justice under very limited circumstances. **2–04**

E.C. *dicta*, whether by means of Directive or Regulation, may seem somewhat remote from the man on the farm. But, as with safe car driving, one of the most fundamental tenets of environmental awareness is anticipation. So it is as well to keep a weather eye on proposals which may emanate from Europe in due course, since these are likely to have effects, directly or indirectly, on farming businesses. Such effects are important when considering long term capital investment plans. For example, there is a tighter regime operating in Holland than in England and Wales for the storage and spreading of farm slurries. If there were to be a move towards more universal constraint within the E.C., this would clearly affect existing farming operations and also might have some impact on expansion or updating projects. So, even though the effects of the proposals within the E.C. may not crystallise as drafted, it is likely that some regimes may in fact do so.

E.C. legislative structure

2–05 The institutional structure within the European Community consists of the E.C. Council, the E.C. Commission, the Directorates General, the European Parliament and the European Court of Justice. Of particular importance to agriculture is DG XI where there are four sub-directorates. Directorate B examines environmental protection on a long-term and strategic basis. Directorate D covers agriculture, water and soil, nature conservation, the quality of air, including noise, together with global warming. Directorate E covers certain pesticide and animal controls.

A further body is the European Environment Agency which is a supranational body ensuring that Member States operate European Environmental Directives and Regulations properly.

The European Court of Justice has a number of functions. It interprets E.C. law and it may also deal with complaints from individuals. An English court may ask the ECJ for a ruling based on interpretation of E.C. legislation.

International conventions

2–06 There are a number of conventions which have been agreed amongst European Union Members which have some relevance. In 1971 came the Convention on Wetlands of international importance (especially as waterfowl habitat). This is otherwise known as the "Ramsar Convention". It indicates especially sensitive wetland areas where environmental assessment for development is essential and where there is a more restrictive regime applicable.

The 1979 Convention on the Conservation of European Wildlife and Natural Habitats provided for the specific protection of certain species of flora and fauna. In the same year came the Convention on the Conservation of Migratory Species of Wild Animals. In 1992 there was agreement on a Convention on Biological Diversity.

More relevant to the question of global warming are the Vienna Convention for the Protection of the Ozone Layer 1985 and the 1992 Convention on Climate Change. The U.K. Parliament was a signatory to each of these conventions. This indicates a self-binding obligation which should be pursued by way of various legal instruments in order to put into practice the principle.

Directives and Regulations

2–07 There are many of both of these which touch on various areas of environmental importance but below are listed the main ones which directly affect agriculture. In 1990 there were two directives which dealt with genetic modification. This practice is likely to become widespread in animal and plant culture and the E.C readily understood the need for proper control and monitoring systems. Hence the Directive on Contained Use of Genetically Modified Micro-organisms (90/219/EEC); and the Directive on Deliberate Release into Environment of Genetically Modified Organisms (90/220/EEC).

There is a tranche of Directives dealing with waste streams of various sorts (largely omitted from this book) with agriculture on the fringe. The 1975 Directive on waste (75/442/EEC) was amended by the Directive Amending Directive 75/442/EEC on Waste (91/156/EEC). Of particular importance is the 1986 Directive on Protection of Environment, and in particular of Soil, when Sewage Sludge is used in Agriculture (86/278/EEC).

The water environment gains considerable attention of which the most relevant Directives are:

> 1975 "Directive Concerning Quality Required of Surface Water Intended for Abstraction of Drinking Water in Member States" (75/440/EEC);
> "Directive on Protection of Ground Water against Pollution caused by Certain Dangerous Substances (80/68/EEC); and
> The Directive relating to Quality of Water Intended for Human Consumption" (80/778/EEC).

The spreading of sewage sludge on land is governed by regulations which **2–08** effected the Directive on the Use of Sewage Sludge on Agricultural Land 1986 (EEC/86/278).

Two further Directives came in 1991, the Directive concerning Urban Waste Water Treatment (91/271/EEC) and the Directive concerning Protection of Waters against Pollution caused by Nitrates from Agricultural Sources (91/676/EEC).

Of more background concern relative to global warming came the 1992 Directive on Air Pollution by Ozone (92/72/EEC), and Regulation 3093/94 concerning the substances that deplete the ozone layer.

The 1985 Directive on Assessment of Effects of Certain Public and Private Projects on Environment (85/337/EEC) deals with the need for environmental assessment and has been brought into effect by the Town and Country (Assessment of Environmental Effects) Regulations 1988 (S.I. 1988 No. 1199). DoE Circular 15/88 provides guidance on its interpretation and operation.

The 1990 Directive on Freedom of Access to Information on Environment (90/313/EEC); certain environmental information is now available on register under Environmental Information Regulations 1992 (S.I. 1992 No. 3240).

The 1992 Directive on the Conservation of Natural Habitats and of Wild Fauna and Flora (92/43/EEC) is concerned to maintain the range of species in the Community. It is noteworthy for its effects on permitted development rights where there is a special area of conservation or a special protection area and the development which is proposed might have a significant effect on the area. There is then a requirement to seek a planning consent.

2–09 There are very few E.C. regulations of relevance to this book. The E.C. will establish a European Environment Agency which will effectively produce and monitor information on the quality, on the pressures relating to, and on the sensitivity of, the environment with particular emphasis on pollution. The EEA is able to assist the E.C. Commission through a wide range of environmental tasks by the monitoring of data.

An E.C fund known as LIFE was established under E.C. Regulation 1973/92 which provides funding for public and private enterprises within the ambit of E.C. environmental policy. Any application must be made to the Department of the Environment. It is largely concerned with assisting campaigns or actions which are designed to implement the "polluter pays" principle, and for assisting sites within the Habitats Directive.

Over the years there have been a large number of statutes and regulations (U.K.), aimed at pollution control, which had on-farm application. The more recent have leaned heavily on European Directives through means of statutes which have effect either directly or by means of U.K. Regulations, Codes of Practice, Mandatory Guidance and other forms of advice including ministerial direction. The underlying principles of the European legislation must be met and this creates a hierarchical structure.

2–10 The broad mix of E.C. and U.K. legislation, as it bites at the farm level, does not merely permit the regulatory bodies, the enforcers, to take action where a problem is perceived. There are four main spheres of influence. The first is by the use of preventative measures under the "precautionary principle". The intention is to prevent any pollution from taking place by putting into effect proper procedures and structures. The second concerns management. The management of a business or an operation or indeed a building, will all involve measures to ensure that plant and equipment, buildings and land are up to date and unlikely to prove unsound, whilst using systems to ensure that operational use is in accordance with guidelines and codes of practice, and also that staff are fully aware of their responsibilities. Successful prosecution or civil action in the courts indicates a failure to prevent the incident from occurring. The deterrent effects of sentencing, fines and compensation orders, imprisonment or community service orders, clean-up costs and personal liability through the criminal court system, together with injunctions and civil damages, have had the effect of reducing the number of pollution incidents. A final piece in this environmental jigsaw is the use of fiscal or economic instruments. So, for example, from October 1, 1996, the "landfill tax" was introduced. The intention is to reduce those waste streams being disposed of in landfill sites. Where they are so disposed, then financial penalties apply. In that case, there is also a reduction in National Insurance contributions with the purpose of neutralising the effects of the tax, thus fine-tuning the direction and effect of this "smart" weapon. Another economic pressure which has been discussed from time to time is "carbon tax". Whilst this latter has not yet risen to the top of the agenda, there is a clear means of targeting specific areas of concern, both by E.C. and U.K. legistation.

National Legislation

As members of the E.C., individual States must not create laws or regulations which are contrary either to the spirit or the letter of superior E.C. legislation. If a State attempts to promote such legislation it is liable to suffer the scrutiny of the ECJ, which may order compliance. The English Parliament is now no longer supreme. It enacts laws which follow the guidelines of E.C. Directives and International Conventions. Thus statutes comprise the first layer of national legislation. The principle of subsidiarity following the Maastricht Agreement in 1992 does mean that the E.C. should not produce such legislation as is best dealt with at national level. **2–11**

A statute may be free-standing or it may be designed to be inserted into another statute. Examples are the Planning and Compensation Act 1991 whose provisions became a part of the Town and Country Planning Act 1990: similarly parts of the Environment Act 1995 become subsumed within the body of the EPA 1990. Sections of statutes may modify or revoke sections of other statutes. Once an Act receives the Royal Assent it must become effective only, in whole or in part, by commencement orders. It is not uncommon for sections of statutes never to be brought into effect. An example is the inability to claim costs in the case of written representations for planning appeals. The power to do so was introduced into the 1971 Town and Country Planning Act, the Housing and Planning Act 1986 Schedule 11, paragraph 9 and the later 1990 version (section 322), but neither clause has yet been brought into effect.

Water legislation, relating to pollution control measures, is principally found in the Water Resources Act 1991. The Water Resources Act 1991 has been amended by the EPA 1990 and the Environment Act 1995. The Environment Agency has taken over the functions of the National Rivers Authority, as from April 1,1996. It has general functions over the entire water environment including licensing of abstraction and impounding works and discharges to controlled waters. It is concerned also with the classification of water quality and water quality objectives. It deals with main water pollution offences and now has substantial powers to prevent and to control pollution. It also has powers of compulsory purchase and works orders together with a variety of powers of entry. It may create byelaws. **2–12**

Another statute of relevance in the area of water is the Salmon and Fresh Water Fisheries Act of 1975. Section 4 allows a specific charge to be made against a person who "causes or knowingly permits . . . any liquid or solid matter . . . to cause the waters to be poisonous or injurious to fish or the spawning grounds, spawn or food of fish. . .". There is also a defence of "best practicable means" available.

The 1991 Water Industry Act provides for the duties of water and sewerage undertakers and also consents for trade effluent discharge into a public sewer. It carries over compulsory powers and compulsory works orders from the days of the predecessor water authorities. The Water Consolidation (Consequential Provisions) Act 1991 made some amendments to certain Acts including the Water Resources Act 1991 and the Water Industry Act 1991.

2–13 The pollution of land by waste is dealt with in Part II of the Environmental Protection Act 1990 which provides for the whole waste management regime. (A detailed analysis is not included within the scope of this title.) Part I of the EPA 1990 is concerned with prescribed processes of which relatively few relate to agriculture (but see the Chapter on soil). The Control of Pollution (Amendment) Act 1989 continues to deal with the offence of unregistered transport of controlled waste (agricultural wastes are not "controlled" waste). It covers contaminated land in Part IIA, which has direct relevance to agriculture. Part III of the EPA covers statutory nuisances. Part VI covers genetically modified organisms and Part VIII provided for public registers of land which may be contaminated. The Environment Act 1995 made substantial modifications to the 1990 EPA. There is still carry-over legislation of relevance including the Control of Pollution Act 1974, sections 60–74 and Schedule 1 which relate to noise levels and, in particular, noise from plant or machinery.

Noise control is covered by a number of statutes. It is one of the statutory nuisances under sections 79 to 82 of the EPA 1990. The EPA was amended by the Noise and Statutory Nuisance Act 1993 which covers audible intruder alarms. The noise and vibration caused by aircraft are dealt with under the Civil Aviation Act 1982, whereas claims for disturbance and damage to livestock caused by low flying military aircraft should be made to the Ministry of Defence, supported by a veterinary certificate.

2–14 Odours, as nuisances, are found under Part III of the EPA 1990. Section 79 describes the scope of those causes of statutory nuisances (see Chapter 9).

Statutory planning control is now consolidated largely into the Town and Country Planning Act 1990, as amended by the Planning and Compensation Act 1991, with conservation areas and listed buildings covered by the Planning (Listed Buildings and Conservation Areas) Act 1990.

Flora and fauna, together with the conservation of the countryside, fall within the ambit of the Wildlife and Countryside Act 1981, the Environmental Protection Act 1990, Part VII, the Protection of Badgers Act 1992 and the Environment Act 1995. An earlier statute is the Countryside Act 1968 which specifically confers a duty on all Ministers of the Crown, the Countryside Commission and English Nature "to have due regard to the needs of agriculture and forestry and to the economic and social interests of rural areas".

Pesticides storage and use is controlled by the Food and Environment Protection Act 1985 Part III, under which codes of practice may be issued. It also provides a general defence of due diligence. The storage of large quantities of certain chemicals is controlled by the Planning (Hazardous Substances) Act 1990 and the Planning (Hazardous Substances) Regulations 1992 (S.I. 1992 No. 656).

The above statutes are broadly those which impact on agricultural pollution lying within the scope of this book.

Statutory Instruments

In order to create the necessary detail, regulations are brought into effect either by a positive or negative resolution of Parliament, which provides the necessary orders. To ensure the smooth running of legislation, and so that the main body of a statute does not require changing, amendments may be made from time to time to S.I.s updating them in the light of new circumstances. They may also be revoked and superseded by further S.I.s as required. Below are listed the main S.I.s concerned with our subject. Those which are key in connection with water are the 1989 Water Supply (Water Quality) Regulations (S.I. 1989 No. 1147); the Surface Waters (Classification) Regulations (S.I. 1989 No. 1148); and the Controlled Waters (Lakes and Ponds) Order (S.I. 1989 No. 1149). **2–15**

The Habitat (Salt-Marsh) Regulations 1994 (S.I. 1994 No. 1293) are applicable to England only and provide aid for the establishment of salt-marshes subject to certain management requirements. These include, under the Schedule Regulation 3(b), that "the beneficiary shall not apply any inorganic or organic fertilisers (including farmyard manure, pig and poultry manure, slurry and sewage sludge). He shall not apply any fungicides or insecticides—nor herbicides except those necessary to control spear thistle, creeping or field thistle, curled dock, broadleafed dock or redwort (see Weeds Act 1959), and then only by means of a hand-held weed wiper or by spot treatment; he shall not store or dump any materials or dispose of any pesticides including sheep dip."

The Private Water Supplies Regulations 1991 (S.I. 1991 No. 2790 ensure that such supplies are wholesome and potable. Sampling and monitoring takes place and charges may be made.

The 1990 Nitrate Sensitive Areas (Designation) Order (S.I. 1990 No. 1013) and The Nitrate Sensitive Areas Regulations 1994 (S.I. 1994 No. 1729) affect England only. These affect specific areas detailed in Schedule 1. The intention is to provide protection to areas with boreholes or underground aquifers where nitrate levels are up to or near the maximum permitted level of 50 milligrams per litre. The basic requirements, in return for compensation, are that no more than 250 kilograms of nitrogen per hectare shall be applied in any year and no nitrogenous fertiliser shall be applied within 50 metres of a spring, well or borehole which supplies water for human consumption or for use in a dairy, or within 10 metres of any watercourse. (See chapter on nitrates.) The Control of Pollution (Silage, Slurry and Agricultural Fuel Oil) Regulations 1991 (S.I. 1991 No. 324) are of particular note. The Water (Prevention of Pollution) (Code of Practice) Order 1991 (S.I. 1991 No. 2285) gave approval to the "code of good agricultural practice for the protection of water". The 1991 Private Water Supplies Regulations (S.I. 1991 No. 2790) provide for maximum concentrations of contaminants. The Nitrates Sensitive Areas Regulations (S.I. 1994 No. 1729) of 1994 cover agreements with farmers in the relevant areas. **2–16**

Environmental assessment is becoming a key feature of larger development and is governed by the 1988 Town and Country Planning (Assessment of Environment Effects) Regulations (S.I. 1988 No. 1199), the Town and Country Planning (Environmental Assessment and Permitted Development) Regulations 1995 (S.I. 1995 No. 417). This S.I. extends the requirements for environmental assessment under the 1988 Regulations. Schedules 1 and 2 which are referred to in the former are found in the latter (see chapter on planning). The Town and Country Planning (Environmental Assessment and Unauthorised Development) Regulations (S.I. 1995 No. 2258) of 1995. The Town and Country Planning (General Permitted Development) Order 1995 (S.I. 1995 No. 418) (see chapter on planning).

The Conservation (Natural Habitats, etc.) Regulations 1994 (S.I. 1994 No. 2716). This provides under section 18 for the notification of operations which are potentially damaging. This S.I. implements the "habitat directive"—Council Directive 92/43/EEC. It is effective in England and Wales. It affects special areas of conservation, SPA under Article 4 of the Habitats Directive and areas classified under the Wild Birds Directive—Council Directive 79/409/EEC (Special Protection Areas—SPA). SPAs and SACs combine to form a conservation interface under "Natura 2000". In broad terms these are known as "European Sites". Where an application for planning permission is sought then the LPA must consult the appropriate competent conservation body. Where there is a deemed planning consent under the General Development Order the work shall not begin until written consent from the LPA has been granted under Regulation 62.

2–17 The Environmental Information Regulations 1990 (S.I. 1990 No. 3240) provide for public access to public registers and from a quite wide range of other "relevant persons". These include under section 2(3) government ministers and departments, local authorities and those "carrying out functions of public administration at a national, regional or local level". Information may be restricted only where it is taken to be "confidential" and this may, particularly under section 4(2)(b), be "information relating to, or to anything which is or has been the subject matter of, any legal or other proceedings (whether actual or prospective)". This information is in addition to that which is available under a variety of registers:

1. Register of Private Water Companies (Water Industry Act 1991, section 195)
2. Environment Agency—Discharge Consents to Control Waters (Water Resources Act 1991, section 190)
3. Discharge Consents for Trade Effluent to Sewers (Sewerage Undertakers)—Water Industry Act 1991, section 196
4. Registers of Contaminated Land—section 78R EPA 1990 containing details of remediation notices, appeals, remediation statements or declarations, appeal against charging notices, notices of land as a special site, etc.

There is no national register for successful prosecutions in regard to planning matters. An enforcement notice, however, lies on the land as a charge.

Noise regulations are numerous and include the 1975 Control of Noise (Appeals) Regulations (S.I. 1975 No. 2116); the 1981 Control of Noise

(Code of Practice on Noise from Audible Intruder Alarms) Order (S.I. 1981 No. 1829); the 1984 Control of Noise (Code of Practice for Construction and Open Sites) Order (S.I. 1984 No. 1992) and the 1987 Control of Noise (Code of Practice for Construction and Open Sites) Order (S.I. 1987 No. 1730). Civil aircraft fall within the Aeroplane Noise (Limitation on Operation of Aeroplanes) Regulations 1993 (S.I. 1993 No. 1409).

The Farm and Conservation Grant Scheme 1989 (S.I. 1989 No. 128) has a closing date for claims for grants of February 19, 1996. This included, under Schedule 1, (B), facilities (except those specified in sub-paragraph (C) below) for the handling, storage and treatment of agricultural effluents and waste (including safety fencing) and fixed disposal facilities for such effluents and waste; and (C) poultry manure stores (excluding those integral with the poultry-house, including fixed disposal facilities for agricultural effluents and waste and safety fencing). Rates of grant were 50 per cent whether within or outside the less favoured area. Grants have been available for very many years for fixed equipment including buildings, outside storage areas, concrete aprons, feedways and effluent storage installations. Such assistance has now ended, at least for the time being.

Air pollution falls under the Crop Residues (Restrictions on Burning) **2–18** Regulations (S.I. 1991 No. 1399) and the Crop Residues (Restrictions on Burning) (No. 2) Regulations (S.I. 1991 No. 1590) both of 1991. The very widespread burning of straw and other crop residues caused large numbers of complaints by virtue of the soot and smuts which covered surrounding properties. There were also cases where smoke drifted across highways and accidents were caused. As a result of the public outcry, these regulations were put in place. The Air Navigation Order (S.I. 1989 No. 2004) governs spraying from aircraft.

The Environmental Protection (Prescribed Processes and Substances) Regulations 1991 (S.I. 1991 No. 472) give effect to integrated pollution control (IPC) and for air pollution control by local authorities (LAAPC). The Environmental Protection (Applications, Appeals and Registers) Regulations 1991 (S.I. 1991 No. 507) provide procedures for licensing, variations of authorisation and appeals.

The Disposal of Controlled Waste (Exceptions) Regulations 1991 (S.I. 1991 No. 508) provide exemptions from COPA for certain controlled wastes where they are covered by IPC under Part I of the EPA. These include the use of untreated straw or poultry litter or used tyres as a fuel. Also depositing animal remains at the site of an incinerator for burning.

Government advice—Circulars and Planning Policy Guidance Notes

The government of the day issues guidance to regulatory authorities and to **2–19** the general public on how statutes and Regulations should be interpreted. It does so by means of Department of Environment (DoE) Circulars and Planning Policy Guidance Notes (PPGs) These provide authoritative advice but it is not statutory. It is often subject to scrutiny and revision. For example PPG 7 which gives advice on agriculture and the rural economy is, at the end of 1996, in process of its second revision in seven years. Other PPGs of relevance to agricultural planning, either in the wider sense or more specifically related to the environment, are PPG 1—General Policy and Principles. PPG4—Industrial and Commercial Development and Small Firms (which is relevant to diversified commercial and industrial enterprises on farm) and PPG 7—the Countryside—Environmental Quality and Economic Development. In the 1997 edition, Annex A covers development involving agricultural land in general terms. Importantly Annex B examines Planning Controls over agricultural development. It examines Part 6 of Schedule 2 to the GDO and in particular in paragraphs B2 to B4, deals with livestock units and slurry. This section is set out in full in Chapter 4.

PPG 9 is concerned with nature conservation and is only applicable in England. This is relevant in that it sets out the criteria to be examined when there is a proposal for development which may affect Sites of Special Scientific Interest (SSSIs), special areas of conservation, special protection areas under the Habitats Directive, and the Birds Directive and sites of international importance such as those under the Ramsar Convention.

PPG 18 provides a guide to the enforcement regime—enforcing planning control. This is important where farmers may have contravened planning regulations.

PPG 22 looks at renewable energy with annexes on energy produced by wind farms, waste combustion, water power, wood fuel, anaerobic digestion, landfill gas and solar energy. Not only are they on farm digesters but also commercial sized plants, such as those near the town of Eye in Suffolk. The original was designed for the reception of poultry manure to which it is brought over very long distances.

PPG 23—Planning and Pollution Control, is effective in England but not in Wales. It attempts to cover the difficult area of overlap between the two functions. Finally PPG 24 again applies only to England and advises local authorities on conditions which might be suitable to retain low ambient noise levels.

DoE Circulars

2–20 Circular 11/95 (WO 35/95) concerns the use of conditions in planning permissions and provides for model conditions to cover most eventualities. It details six tests for conditions which are that conditions should be:

(i) necessary;
(ii) relevant to planning;
(iii) relevant to the development to be permitted;
(iv) enforceable;
(v) precise; and
(vi) reasonable in all other aspects.

Circular 3/95 (WO 12/95)—Permitted Development and Environmental Assessment, covers the point where field drainage, which may affect a site of special scientific interest, a national nature reserve or a scheduled ancient monument, may require an EA. Land reclamation from the sea may require an EA, dependent upon its location. This is preceded by the Town and Country Planning (Assessment of Environmental Effects) Regulations 1988 (S.I. 1988 No. 1199). There are proposals to tighten up further on the requirement for an EA.

Circular 15/88 (WO 23/88) explains the requirements of the Town and Country Planning (Assessment of Environmental Effect) Regulations 1988. It indicates, in Appendix A, Schedule 2, projects which may be subject to control. New pig rearing installations for fewer than 400 sows or 5,000 fattening pigs are unlikely to need EA. New poultry housing developments of below 100,000 broilers or 50,000 layers, turkeys or other poultry are again unlikely to need EA. Additionally, salmon farming units which are designed to produce less than 100 tonnes of fish a year would not usually need EA.

Circular 8/93 (WO 29/93) deals with the award of costs incurred in planning and other (including compulsory purchase order) proceedings. The key test for the award of costs is "reasonableness". If either side has been unreasonable in its handing of a case, costs may be awarded in whole or in part.

Circular 24/91 (WO 68/91) covers private water supplies, and allows for sampling and analysis to ensure that the supplies are potable and wholesome.

Circular 11/94 (WO 26/94) provides guidance on Part II of the EPA 1990 concerning waste management licensing and the framework directive on waste. It confirms that agriculture waste is excluded from the definition of controlled wastes under section 75(7) of the EPA 1990. This includes faecal matter and other natural, non-dangerous substances used in farming. It does not exclude wastes such as oil, tyres, machinery, pesticides, solvents, etc.

Circular 17/89 (WO 38/89) covers development control relating to landfill sites and indicates concern where a site might be within 250 metres of other development.

Circular 19/91 (WO 63/91) describes the duty of care under section 34 **2–21**
of the EPA 1990. It provides advice for those persons in the waste chain who have a duty which is contained in a Code of Practice under section 34(7) of the Act.

Circular 14/92 (WO 30/92) advises on Parts II and IV of the EPA 1990 and the Controlled Waste Regulations 1992 (S.I. 1992 No. 588). It gives a detailed insight into a variety of wastes and explains that, by virtue of regulation 2(1) of the Sludge (Use in Agriculture) Regulations 1989 (S.I. 1989 No. 1263 as amended by S.I. 1990 No. 880) sludge for disposal on farmland is exempt. It highlights the exclusion of agricultural waste.

The section within the EPA 1990 which deals with contaminated land, sections 78A to 78YC, introduces both statutory regulations and mandatory guidelines. These have yet to be finalised but have currently reached the third draft stage. Mandatory guidelines are a novel concept.

Circular 13/85 (WO 36/85) provides guidance on public registers for discharges to the water environment. This includes such matters as applications for consents, the consents and their conditions, effluent samples, water samples and notices.

Codes of Good Agricultural Practice

2–22 MAFF have produced three "GAP" (Good Agricultural Practice) Codes. These are:

(a) The Code of Good Agricultural Practice for the Protection of Water. This statutory code under section 97 of the Water Resources Act 1991 provides no defence under Part 3 of that Act, nor does it indicate liability where the code is not followed.
(b) The Code of Good Agricultural Practice for the Protection of Air. This is a non-statutory code and again provides no statutory defence.
(c) The Code of Good Agricultural Practice for the Protection of Soil. Again, a non-statutory code which provides sound practical advice on this subject.

Adherence to the three codes, albeit providing no defence in the case of civil or criminal proceedings, is likely to aid any plea in mitigation. They are also available from the Welsh Office and they are free. Every farmer should have one of each. The Codes may be updated as required. Other types of guidance are available from the Environment Agency which publishes a list of documents available, normally from HMSO or its distributors. (The National Rivers Authorities R & D Programme, September 1989 to September 1995, provides a range of titles and explains whether these are available outside the NRA, now of course the EA). The Environmental Health Department of local authorities will also produce guidance notes which tend to be local to that authority rather than national in series.

The Code of Practice for Waste Management "the Duty of Care" was issued by the DoE under section 34 of the EPA 1990; see also the chapter on soil pollution and wastes. Guidance was also issued by the DoE and Welsh Office as "a practical guide on integrated pollution control.

The Regulators

2–23 The Environment Agency began life on April 1, 1996. It was formed from a number of previous bodies including the National Rivers Authority, the Waste Regulation Authorities, the Waste Disposal Authorities, the Alkali Inspectorate, responsibility for radioactive substances and control of improvement and prohibition notices under the Health and Safety at Work, etc. Act 1974. It broadly has powers and functions in all environmental spheres, that is to say air, land and water, with certain exceptions.

The Environmental Health Office of the local authority is responsible for statutory nuisances including noise and odours, contaminated land and the provision of private water supplies. Finally, local planning authorities have full responsibilities over planning matters with the ability of other national and regional bodies to be consulted. In almost every case the decisions of the bodies concerned are subject to a variety of appeals or judicial consideration.

Environment Agency

The areas of responsibility for pollution control are found in section 5 of the Environment Act 1995, and section 5(1) states "The Agency's pollution control powers shall be exercisable for the purpose of preventing or minimising, or remedying or mitigating the effects of, pollution of the environment". Its main areas cover integrated pollution control under Part I, waste on land under Part II and contaminated land under Part IIA of the EPA 1990. Chapter 3 of Part IV of the Water Industry Act 1991 deals with special category effluent: also Part II of the Water Resources Act 1991. It therefore controls all pollution emanating from agricultural land which may affect water, land, buildings or human health, and it is responsible for harm which may come to farmland, to water sources upon which farmers may rely (perhaps for drinking water, irrigation or the watering of livestock). **2–24**

Under section 6(1) of the EA 1995, "It shall be the duty of the Agency, to such extent as it considers desirable, generally to promote—

(a) the conservation and enhancement of the natural beauty and amenity of inland and coastal waters and of land associated with such waters;
(b) the conservation of flora and fauna which are dependent on an aquatic environment;
(c) the use of such waters and land for recreation purposes.

It has general environmental duties under section 7 and specific duties under section 8 regarding SSSIs. There is an advisory committee for Wales with environment protection advisory committees for both England and Wales throughout the regions.

The EA has published an Enforcement Code of Practice and it will take a tough and robust attitude to Category 1 offences, where it invariably prosecutes. It has not published its policy on prosecution but for minor offences or where there are clear mitigating circumstances, it may use other forms of action. One example is where a formal warning is given and accepted by an offender. This warning will prevent a prosecution but it will lie on the record and, should any offence occur in the future, it would be brought to the notice of the court should a prosecution ensue. It may also serve a variety of notices, in lieu of or as well as prosecution. There is a specific power to deal with the cause of imminent danger of serious pollution under section 109 of the EA 1995. Specific powers in related areas are dealt with in the chapters under soil and water pollution. There are substantial powers of entry under section 108 of the EA 1995 with **2–25** offences committed, under section 110, where there is deliberate obstruction of an authorised person. Evidence which is collected in pursuit of a prosecution may be inadmissible unless it complies with section 76 of the Police and Criminal Evidence Act 1984. The EA may issue licences and consents, and again there are appeal mechanisms available. When considering prosecution, it must apply itself to a cost/benefit approach and, in other respects, the way forward is one of sustainability, prevention and education. It may also seek, in immediate or persistent cases, an injunctive remedy. Where there is a likelihood of a recurrence of damage or pollution, then a mandatory or restraining injunction may be very swift and effective (See Appendix 5).

The EA has also produced a document entitled "The Environment Agency and Sustainable Development (1995)" which amplifies its statutory powers under section 7 of the EA 1995 concerning its general environmental, conservation and recreational duties.

Environmental Health Officers

2–26 EHOs have a general responsibility in relation to Part IIA of the EPA 1990 concerning any contaminated land in their area. Under this Part they must work closely with the EA. Under Part III their remit is the designated statutory nuisances, especially of odour pollution. (See Chapter 9). Noise problems are covered by Part III of the EPA 1990.

The local authority operates the LAAPC, or Local Authority Air Pollution Control, under Part I of the EPA. This covers all forms of air pollution except those which relate to prescribed processes under IPC, and integrated pollution control—see the chapter on air pollution. It has responsibility for dealing with statutory nuisances, which include smoke, fumes or gases and noise and vibration. It has power to serve an Abatement Notice, failure for compliance leading to prosecution. As a planning authority the LPA, rather than the Environmental Health Officers, supervise the planning system.

In all cases there are statutory appeals which may lead to decisions being taken in higher courts. Judicial review is gaining wide acceptance for checking the regulators. On the other hand even more stringent powers are available by means of High Court injunctions. These are rapidly available for instances where very swift action is required by the local authority.

2–27 The Environmental Health Officers are often called upon to give advice. The regulatory functions of the local authority must supervene. In the case of *Welton v. North Cornwall District Council* (1993) 93(34) L.S.G. 34 the Court of Appeal heard a claim in negligence against the local authority. By offering advice the officer had placed himself under a duty of care and the local authority's appeal failed. Damages of almost £40,000 were claimed and awarded.

The EHOs of the local authorities monitor and regulate air pollution, deal with statutory nuisances, hazardous wastes and contaminated land. They tend to take a less aggressive stance than the EA, unless there are obvious and perhaps wilful breaches. Their first line of approach is normally persuasion. So it is advisable to be persuaded to carry out certain preventative measures, provided that these are cost-efficient and would appear to provide a reasonable solution. This is not to say that the local authority will not prosecute where there is clear justification. It will.

Where the local planning authority acts as an enforcing agency against breaches of planning control, there is a slight change in emphasis. PPG 18 sets out the general approach to enforcement and indicates that, unless there is a wilful breach of planning law which requires immediate action, there is more discretion to take enforcement action as it is felt to be expedient. Indeed, it is proposed that formal enforcement action against a trivial or technical breach of control which causes no harm to the amenity in the locality of the area is normally inappropriate.

Criminal and statutory law

Procedures

This section concerns offences under relevant statutes. Not all statutory defences are "criminal" in nature. The distinction is often fine but, where a compensation order is sought in addition to a fine, it is not appropriate unless the offence is criminal.[3] Most offences are "summary", that is to say they are heard in the magistrates' court after an "information" has been laid by the prosecution. Section 127 of the Magistrates' Courts Act 1980 provides a six month time limit for the institution of summary proceedings, but section 101 of the Water Resources Act 1991 extends that to 12 months after the offence is committed. Magistrates normally operate on a scale of fine levels which, subject to updates, are laid down in section 17 of the Criminal Justice Act 1991: **2–28**

(a) Level 1 — £200
(b) Level 2 — £500
(c) Level 3 — £1,000
(d) Level 4 — £2,500
(e) Level 5 — £5,000

There are a range of environmental offences where the maximum fine has been raised to £20,000, to act as a strong deterrent—see WRA 1991, section 85, for example. Magistrates may also impose a term of imprisonment not exceeding three months, separately or in addition to the fine. The magistrates' court will award costs of the prosecution's case including the time spent on it and may award further costs related to clean up or remediation. It is rare that environmental offences come before the Crown Court but water pollution offences under section 85 of the WRA 1991 are "triable either way" This means that if the offence is considered sufficiently grave or wilful then the matter, if it proceeds to a conviction on

[3] *Botross v. Hammersmith & Fulham L.B.C.* (ELM, December 1994).

indictment, may result in imprisonment for up to two years, to a fine which is unlimited, or to both. There is no limitation period for offences which are triable either way.

Who is liable?

2–29 A whole range of "persons" may be charged with a statutory offence. A person is defined under the Interpretation Act 1889 to include a body of persons corporate or unincorporate. So in the case of *NRA v. Alfred MacAlpine Homes East Limited* 1994 (E.L.R.—QBD) the site manager accepted that he was responsible for an incident which caused pollution to a watercourse. The court found the defendant company to be vicariously liable for the acts of its employees which were undertaken during the course of their employment. There is also personal liability of individual employees or directors. In most environmental statutes, the common words are:

> "Where an offence committed by a body corporate is proved to have been committed with the consent or connivance of, or to be attributable to any neglect on the part of, any director, manager, secretary or other similar officer of the body corporate or any person who was purporting to act in such a capacity, he as well as the body corporate shall be guilty of that offence and shall be liable to be proceeded against and punished accordingly".

Subsequently there have been a number of cases where fines have been levied against individual directors; in some extreme cases there has been imprisonment, and in one case a director has been stripped of his directorship for two years.

Onus of proof

2–30 The onus is normally on the prosecution to prove their case beyond all reasonable doubt (Magistrates' Courts Act 1980, section 101). Where a defendant relies upon one of the few statutory defences available, for example sections 88 and 89 of the WRA 1991, the defendant must prove his case on the balance of probabilities. Where an offence is triable either way, the defendant has the right to advance information under the Magistrates' Courts (Advance Information) Rules 1985 (S.I. 1985 No. 603).

Cause or knowingly permit

2–31 A key phrase running through most environmental statutes is where "a person . . . causes or knowingly permits . . . any pollution to occur". A person should not be charged with both offences, either one or the other. Otherwise he is placed in a position of double jeopardy and the information or indictment will be duplicitous and is liable to be struck out. The key words have been tested on many occasions, the most notable of which are *Alphacell v. Woodward* [1972] 2 All E.R. 475, and *Impress v. Rees* [1971] 2

All E.R. 357. In the latter case the defendant was found not guilty because of a malicious vandalism by a nocturnal trespasser. The case was some 20 years before the WRA 1991. Where all precautions are taken to prevent an escape, say, of tractor fuel oil, by securing outlet pipes with padlocks, it is unlikely that a court would find a defendant guilty of an offence if a vandal had broken the lock or cut through it with bolt cutters or a hacksaw. To "cause" involves a positive act which results in pollution. "Knowingly permit" involves knowledge and failure to prevent pollution.

Mitigation

Where an offence is one of strict liability, then the defendant's advocate should plead in mitigation. There are many steps which a defendant could take, or might have taken, which will improve the persuasiveness of his plea. Where, for example, certain safeguards have been put in place to prevent pollution from a farmyard into a watercourse, and the staff have been advised what they should individually do, both in writing and orally, the approach will indicate the defendant's sympathetic aims with environmental security. Where he can be shown to have both had knowledge of, and followed, the Codes of Good Agriculture Practice, mitigation may be shown and where between the commission of the offence and the date of the hearing, preventative works have been put in place on a voluntary basis, rather than by adherence to orders from the regulators, the defendant may be shown to be taking prospective rather than merely reactive action. **2–32**

Costs

If a defendant is convicted of an offence, the prosecution may seek their own legal expenses, including the amount of time spent in preparation of the case: Prosecution of Offences Act 1985. In addition there is provision for the costs of remediation or clean-up to be made in addition. These extra costs may amount to more than the fine. Where, however, the prosecution fails to secure a conviction, perhaps by withdrawing from a case at the last minute, or on a successful appeal, the defendant may then seek an order for costs against them. **2–33**

Insurance

It is not in accordance with public policy for insurance cover to be provided against criminal liability. Insurance is normally available, however, against civil liability and third party claims and also the consequences of criminal behaviour by the insured or employees. Many policies do preclude such liability, and there may be own site exclusion and pollution exclusion within public liability policies. It is essential to check the exact wording of each policy. **2–34**

There is an important provision under section 137 of the Companies Act 1989. This permits companies to insure on behalf of their directors under dual policies. The first policy provides cover for directors and other officers where they are unable to claim indemnity from the company itself. The second policy provides indemnity to the company where it has provided the first indemnity to the directors. Unfortunately such policies tend to exclude environmental pollution.

Because of the substantial risks involved in the whole field of environmental pollution, insurers have, over recent years, become much more selective in providing cover. There are specialist insurers who will provide the necessary cover, but at a price.

Private prosecutions

2–35 Although relatively rare, there is, under some environmental statutes, the ability for individuals or persons with sufficient *locus standi* to prosecute. In other statutes, the consent of the Attorney-General is required before the prosecution may proceed. They are largely dependent on the availability of information from public registers. The other substantial deterrent is the legal cost involved and the possibility of failure with the costs of the defence to be added to the bill.

Appeals to higher courts

2–36 These are matters outside this book's remit but the usefulness of the judicial review system should not be overlooked. Challenges may be made to actions of regulators at various stages. Such appeals may be pursued in connection with planning decisions, sentencing and fines of magistrates' courts and verdicts from the Crown Court, for example. The key factor is to bear in mind that there is a very strict three month time-limit on seeking leave for judicial review. Advice should be taken at the earliest possible opportunity.

Civil remedies

2–37 Liability under common law is next examined. This will be necessarily brief because it is felt appropriate only to provide broad principles within the scope of this book. Where an environmental harm occurs to an individual, there may be a cause of action, or indeed more than one, which is appropriate for him to take against the polluter. But why should a person take such financial risk when the environmental regulators may be able to issue proceedings against the polluter under statute and to be awarded compensation which might include damage caused to that individual? There are several routes down which an individual may proceed and these are examined below, but it will be seen that public law is not always appropriate. Then there is the higher degree of proof to be shown by a prosecution rather than an individual under private law.

Increasingly, however, over recent years, there has been a drawing together of statute and common law relating to pollution offences. Section 73 (sub-sections 6 to 9) of the EPA 1990 deal with unlawfully depositing waste without a licence. A civil liability claim for damage may be made which not only includes injury to property, but personal injury as well. Under the Water Resources Act 1991, section 100, the provisions of the Act do not affect the use of civil law. There is a further point that precise standards and targets, for example for composition or quality of water under various circumstances, may provide a benchmark against which the viability of a civil claim may be judged.

Before turning to remedies, it is logical to look at preventative measures **2–38** or the use of the "precautionary" principles which may apply. Section 95 of the WRA 1991 allows farmers to enter voluntarily into management agreements relating to nitrate-sensitive areas. The controls which are imposed within that agreement on land use may generate compensation but the purpose is to prevent long term, diffuse pollution. Section 39 of the Wildlife & Countryside Act 1981 enables management agreements to be entered into by local planning authorities. These were previously restricted to sites of special scientific interest but are now extremely wide-ranging. The section gives LPAs the ability to impose controls over land use. There may be other contractual arrangements between individual parties which govern land use and would include the use of restrictive covenants. Additionally, planning conditions and planning obligations under section 106 of the Town and Country Planning Act 1990 may provide further safeguards against pollution.

Nuisance

Nuisance may be public or private. Public nuisance must affect a wide- **2–39** spread or range of persons and is rarely applicable. Private nuisance is where a person's right to the quiet enjoyment of his land or other proprietary rights suffers interference in some way. The harm caused must not be merely temporary but should extend over a reasonable length of time. Angling associations have tended to use the tort of nuisance successfully in claims where damage to fish stocks, breeding grounds or food sources have been caused.[4] There is a growing tendency for private prosecutions by clubs to take place under statute, where the regulators are unwilling or unable to proceed.

Negligence

To bring an action in negligence, the plaintiff must show fault on the part **2–40** of the defendant. There is no requirement upon him to demonstrate any proprietary interest. He must prove, again on the balance of probabilities, that the defendant has been negligent by some act or omission. So it is necessary to prove a fault by the defendant. This may be scientifically difficult. The plaintiff must be owed a duty of care by the defendant, who must have failed in that duty, and the resultant damage must have been

[4] *Pride of Derby and Derbyshire Angling Association v. British Celanese Limited* [1953] 1 All E.R. 179.

foreseeable. The claimant need not have any proprietary interest before he is able to make a claim. So the scope of persons able to claim is widened considerably.

Rylands v. Fletcher

2–41 The case of *Rylands v. Fletcher* (1868) L.R. 3 H.L. 330, effectively sets up a separate tort. In brief, the defendant employed contractors to build a reservoir. The contractors failed to seal some mine shafts. The mine which was owned by the plaintiff was flooded when the reservoir was filled. From the judgment, the principle emerged that "The person who for his own purposes brings on to his land and collects and keeps there anything likely to do mischief if it escapes must keep it at his peril and, if he does not do so, is prima facie answerable for all the damage which is the natural consequence of its escape". The courts appear to be reluctant to decide cases on this particular ground and there are many apparent restrictions upon its use. One of these is that there must be a non-natural user of land. In the original case the construction of the reservoir was not "natural".

However, in the case of *Leakey v. National Trust* [1980] 1 All E.R. 17, the owner of the land was held liable when naturally occurring substances, *e.g.* rocks, tree roots and soil, slid down a bank on to the neighbouring land. Again there was an element of foreseeability and a duty of care to prevent the land slide.

Riparian ownership

2–42 Rights in water have been determined, very broadly, in the definitive case of *John Young & Co. v. Bankier Distillery Co.* [1893] A.C. 691. It concerned the plaintiff distiller whose malting processes used soft water from the stream. The defendant (John Young & Co.) had changed the soft water into hard water by draining a mine into the stream. The key phrase from the judgment was "Every riparian owner is thus entitled to the water of his stream in its natural flow, without sensible diminution or increase, and without sensible alteration in its character or quality". This scope is very wide-ranging and it affects almost every situation to be found in the water environment with the exception of water flowing through undefined channels inland where it is not percolating through to any well or borehole. Any such change provides a remedy by way of a civil action but which could be, as in the *Cambridge Water* case below, taken under nuisance, negligence or the rule in *Rylands v. Fletcher.*

The Cambridge Water Case

2–43 The *Cambridge Water Company v. Eastern Counties Leather Plc* [1994] 1 All E.R. 53 was decided by the House of Lords. It found that the defendant (ECL) was not liable for losses caused by the plaintiff (CWC). A range of issues were dealt with by their Lordships and clarified. ECL stored and used toxic chemicals at its tannery. There had been repeated spillages of the chemical which had moved through the ground into a chalk aquifer. CWC had a borehole for drinking water abstraction but the chemical was not detected until 1983. They were unable to supply such water because of the intervening E.C. Drinking Water Directive 80/778. CWC showed costs of finding an alternative water source to be over £1,000,000.

There were several elements involved in the claim and on which decisions were made. First, the question of an owner to land to receive water, from whatever source, in an unaltered state. Secondly and crucially, would the operators of the tannery, *i.e.* the management and the persons in control of the storage and use of the chemcials, have reasonably foreseen the results of their actions, given the state of scientific knowledge and environmental awareness that then prevailed (in and around the 1960s)? The decision in this case fell in favour of the defendant, who it was decided could not reasonably have foreseen the consequence of the actions which took place. Thirdly, once the damage and its cause had been fully appreciated in the light of the Directive, what could the defendants have done about it? The judgment was that the chemicals has passed out of their control to such an extent that the chemical was "irretrievably lost". So far as the rule of *Rylands v. Fletcher* was concerned, the Court of Appeal found that the storage of the chemical was not a non-natural use. The House of Lords disagreed heartily. **2–44**

The case had been pursued in negligence, in nuisance and in *Rylands v. Fletcher*, with the decision giving clarity to the question of "non-natural" use of land in *Rylands v. Fletcher* and also the extremely important pre-emptive element of foreseeability which extends across any and all of these equitable remedies.

Trespass

A further action is available under the tort of trespass. There is no need to prove damage by the tortfeasor, merely that there has been direct interference with the plaintiff. So smoke or fumes blowing straight across a neighbour's property could be actionable *per se* without any damage being caused. The interference cannot extend to consequential or remote sources but must be direct. **2–45**

"Toxic torts"

So called toxic torts are an eponymous term for largescale chemical injuries, and is US in origin (Charles Pugh and Martin Day—*New Law Journal*, November 1991). The claims are taken under negligence, nuisance, *Rylands v. Fletcher* and also breach of statutory duty. Proving a continuing nexus within a line of causation when the issues may be extremely complex is often the weak link. There are likely to be large numbers of expert advisers required to establish that there is a fault, there was foreseeability and that a large number of plaintiffs to a multi-party action have all been affected. **2–46**

Summary

2–47 Good advice is essential for any person considering initiating one of the common law actions discussed above. So is a long pocket. By far the more usual route for the recipient of a tort is to complain to the relevant regulator. If he does so he must ensure that his own requirements are taken fully into account during the proceedings. If damages and costs are required then these should be included within the scope of the proceedings.

Chapter 3

Landlord and Tenant and Pollution

Background

Where, precisely, the onus for the renewal, repair or renovation of fixed equipment for pollution control may lie, between landlord and tenant, is often very unclear. Nevertheless it is necessary to analyse carefully the contractual and statutory position wherever possible, in three situations. These are, before the tenancy begins, during the course of the tenancy and at its termination. Within those three time zones there may be a statutory background, which must then be examined in the light of the powers of the regulators to anticipate pollution and also to deal with it after it has occurred. There are also statutory rules governing tenancies under the 1986 Agricultural Holdings Act (AHA), and the Agricultural Tenancies Act 1995 (ATA). Finally the common law rights of individuals must be examined. **3–01**

Types of tenancy

Agricultural Holdings Act 1986—tenancies

Any agricultural tenancy which came into existence before September 1, 1995 is governed by the AHA 1986. Any new tenancy, *i.e.* those which began on September 1, 1995 or after, falls under the Agricultural Tenancies Act 1995, with the exception of the carry over provisions from the AHA 1986. (The latter relate to succession cases, grant and re-grant of tenancies and certain statutory tenancies endorsed by the Agricultural Land Tribunal). **3–02**

Under the AHA 1986, it is necessary to look at the provision of the written contract in the first instance. Some of the earlier tenancies will specify, for example, that the holding should be managed as a "dairy farm". The underlying presumption here is that the fixed equipment available will be suitable for a herd of dairy cows. The agreement may indicate that there are no redundant buildings within the "Schedule of Redundant Buildings", and that the apportionment of repairs as between landlord and tenant is in accordance with the "model clauses": The Agricultural (Maintenance, Repair and Insurance of Fixed Equipment) Regulations (S.I. 1973 No. 1473), as amended by Agriculture (Maintenance, Repair and Insurance of Fixed Equipment) (Amendment) Regulations (S.I. 1988 No. 281). Where the written agreement is silent or if there is an oral agreement the model clauses come into effect. These broadly place the onus of replacement and renewal of structures and fixtures onto the landlord whereas internal fittings and fixtures, their maintenance, and repairs are matters which fall to the tenant. So, for example, the landlord must repair and replace various parts of farm buildings including water supply, pipes, wells, boreholes, reservoirs and sewerage disposal systems. The landlord must also insure farm buildings unless some of them are tenant's fixtures. The full text of the model clauses is found at Table I. Section 7(3) of the AHA 1986 states that "the model clauses shall be deemed to be incorporated in every contract of tenancy of an agricultural holding except in so far as they would impose on one of the parties to an agreement in writing a liability which under the agreement is imposed on the other". Therefore in the case of an oral tenancy, unless there is an oral agreement to differ from the terms of the model clauses, they will take effect. In the case of a written tenancy, the parties may agree to such different arrangements as they may choose.

3–03 A reference to arbitration may be served by either party where responsibilities are not properly met, and section 8 of the AHA 1986 provides for such arbitration where the written tenancy agreement is at variance with the model clauses. These allocate precise areas of repair and maintenance between the two parties. But, by writing into the agreement that the holding shall be managed as a dairy farm, the landlord has placed himself and the tenant in a position whereby they both have additional obligations and responsibilities. The landlord has a duty to ensure that worn out or obsolete items of fixed equipment, which are the responsibility of the tenant to maintain and repair, are replaced by appropriate new fixtures to ensure that the farm may continue as a dairy holding. The scope of such provision is clearly wide and covers not merely the provision for housing, handling and milking areas but also the relevant fixed equipment for effluent storage and handling. There will often be a fine line, sometimes almost invisible, where the responsibilities of landlord should end and tenant begin under such circumstances. So, should the tenant wish a higher standard of building or holding area than existed previously, then a higher specification may be reached by way of joint contributions. Alternatively the landlord may carry out the whole of the improvement, but charging an interest figure on the agreed balance over and above that which represented his own required contribution.

3–04 Later contracts may be for a full repairing and insuring lease (FRI) which places the responsibility for repairs and maintenance completely on the tenant. The tenant under these circumstances should ensure that, at the start of the lease, all the fixed equipment is in a good state of repair and maintenance. Anything which is obsolete or worn out should either be declared redundant or should be subject to an agreement with the landlord for it to be replaced by him at the end of its useful life. Such contracts need to be treated with great caution and full professional and legal advice should be sought. Clearly the rent payable should reflect the position of the tenant in regard to such onerous obligations.

Against that general background is a much more specific provision. Section 11 of the AHA 1986 states:

> "(1) Where, on an application by the tenant of an agricultural holding, the tribunal are satisfied that is reasonable having regard to the tenant's responsibilities to farm the holding in accordance with the rules of good

husbandry, that he should carry on on the holding an agricultural activity specified in the application to the extent and in the manner so specified and—

(a) that, unless fixed equipment is provided on the holding, the tenant, in carrying on that activity to the extent and in that manner, will contravene requirements imposed by or under any enactment or

(b) that it is reasonable that the tenant should use for purposes connected with that activity fixed equipment, already provided on the holding but that, unless that equipment is altered or repaired, the tenant in using the equipment for those purposes will contravene such requirements, the tribunal may direct the landlord to carry out, within a period specified in the Direction such work for the provision or, as the case maybe, the alteration or the repair of that fixed equipment as will enable the tenant to comply with the said requirements.

(2) Where it appears to the tribunal that an agricultural activity specified in the tenant's application has not been carried on on the holding continuously for a period for at least three years immediately preceding the making of the application, the tribunal shall not direct the landlord to carry out work in connection with that activity unless they are satisfied that the starting of the activity did not or, where the activity has not yet been started, will not constitute or form part of a substantial alteration of the type of farming carried on on the holding.

(3) The Tribunal shall not direct the landlord to carry out work under this section unless they are satisfied:

(a) That it is reasonable to do so having regard to the landlord's responsibilities to manage the land comprised in the holding in accordance with the rules of good estate management and also to the period for which the holding may be expected to remain a separate holding and to any other material consideration, and

(b) That the landlord has refused to carry out the work on being requested in writing to do so by the tenant who has not agreed to carry it out within a reasonable time after so being requested.

(4) The Tribunal shall not direct the landlord to carry out work under this section if he is under a duty to carry out the work in order to comply with the requirement imposed on him by or under any enactment or if provision is made by the contract of tenancy, or by any other agreement between the landlord and the tenant, for the carrying out of work by one of them.

(5) If the landlord fails to comply with a Direction under this section the tenant shall have the same remedies as if the contract of tenancy has contained an undertaking by the landlord to carry out the work required by this Direction within the period allowed by the Tribunal.

(6) Notwithstanding any term in the contract of tenancy restricting the carrying out by the tenant of alterations to the holding, the remedies referred to sub-section (5) above shall include the right of the tenant to carry out the work himself and recover the reasonable cost of the work from the landlord.

(7) The Tribunal, on application by the landlord, may extend or further extend the period specified in a direction under this section if it is shown to their satisfaction that the period so specified, or that period as previously extended under this sub-section as the case may be, will not allow sufficient time both for the completion for the preliminary arrangement necessary or desirable in connection with the work required by the Direction (including, in appropriate cases, the determination of an application by the landlord for a grant out of money provided by Parliament in respect of that work) and for the carrying out of the said work.

(8) The reference in sub-section (6) to the reasonable cost of work carried out by a tenant shall, where the tenant has received a grant in respect of the

> work out of money provided by Parliament, be construed as a reference to the reasonable costs reduced by the amount of the grant."

3–05 Under the circumstances of our example, that is to say where the holding was a "dairy farm" under the agreement, the provision of proper fixed equipment to meet statutory regulations is the responsibility of the landlord. Where there is no such provision within the agreement itself but the farm has been used as a dairy holding for at least three years, then it will still be necessary to conform to the Milk and Dairies (General) Regulations 1959 (S.I. 1959 No. 277) so the surfaces of the relevant buildings, mainly the milking parlour and the dairy, will need to be sufficiently hygienic and capable of maintenance as such. On larger holdings attention should also be paid to the Dairy Products (Hygiene) (Amendment) Regulations 1996 (S.I. 1996 No. 1699).

The Control of Pollution (Silage, Slurry and Agricultural Fuel Oil) Regulations 1991 (S.I. 1991 No. 324) (as amended) provide an area where there is likely to be most dissent between landlord and tenant. Where there is disagreement between parties, the Agricultural Land Tribunal (ALT) must determine the issue and it must have regard to whether the landlord has refused to carry out work on written request and it must also set the matter out against the rules of good estate management. It is the latter which may complicate the issue further.

3–06 The rules of good estate management are set out under the Agriculture Act 1947. The landlord, whilst complying with the rules, is entitled to look not only at the individual holding but at the wider interests of the estate and, within that wider sphere, to consider the prospects for the holding's long term viability. So he may be able to argue that amalgamation may be in the best interests of the estate. The average size of farm has grown steadily over the years and amalgamations are often the only way to maintain a viable structure within an estate. Where the holding is relatively small and is becoming unviable, the merger of its separate parts within the overall estate may be in the best interests of the estate. If the holding is likely to become unviable within a short time scale then expenditure on, for example, updating pollution control systems is likely to be uneconomic. The ALT would, of course, investigate any such claim diligently. It would be difficult for the tenant to pursue his claim under circumstances where the logical site for new farm buildings would be on the other holding. However, it also gives rise to considerations as to whether he might be the best tenant to take over the amalgamated holding. Again the Tribunal must consider these points at the same time.

One of the main difficulties under the AHA 1986 lies in the landlord and tenant relationship. This often, alas, carries feudal overtones where the landlord has the ability to offer additional land or buildings to a favoured tenant, if he considers him to be a good farmer and perhaps one who causes little trouble to the estate. On the other hand he might also seek higher rent revision where the tenant is "troublesome". There are few, therefore, who would challenge the landlord either by way of the service of the relevant notices, or by a hearing before the ALT. On a day to day basis, agreements are often made between landlord and tenant to cover the cost of essential improvements to systems in order to meet required standards on a shared basis. The share or split of costs should normally be based on the terms of the agreement, an equitable arrangement between the parties, and any other additional factors which may have a bearing. There is always a fear, real or imagined, that a reference to the ALT is likely to sour relations between landlord and tenant.

There is a further point which landlords need to consider with care. That is where there may be reservations out of the tenancy to the benefit of the landlord. If these may possibly impinge upon pollution factors, then the landlord may not be able to exonerate himself from involvement within costs or indeed any prosecution which may occur. The time to look at the clauses contained within a written tenancy agreement under the 1986 Act will have been prior to the agreement coming into force. Since no new 1986 AHA agreements may now be made, the point may be somewhat academic. During the course of the tenancy, and remembering that new tenancies created prior to July 12, 1984 may carry rights of two successions,[1] the terms of the agreement are most important, if and when it becomes necessary to rely upon them. **3–07**

Again, the only alteration which can be made, where the model clauses are not used, is by an arbitration under section 8 of the AHA 1986. At the end of the tenancy the tenant may have been able to leave the holding without complying with certain statutory requirements under section 11 of the AHA 1986. The landlord may only claim from the tenant, where there has been a contractual breach, the amount of damage actually suffered. Section 71 of the AHA gives general guidance as to the amount of compensation which the landlord may claim from a tenant at the end of the tenancy for contractual failures by the tenant. Essentially these are limited to the cost of putting those matters right but with an overall restriction which, under section 71(5), means that the maximum amount payable will be the diminution in the value of the landlord's reversion in the holding.

Summary

Clearly, under any particular set of circumstances, step by step analysis is required along the following lines: **3–08–3–09**

(i) Is the tenancy governed by the AHA 1986?
(ii) Is there an oral or written tenancy?
(iii) If the tenancy is oral then the model clauses will apply. In the absence of any other agreed clauses, whether oral (which would be unusual and certainly very difficult to prove) or written, then section 11 of the AHA 1986 takes effect.
(iv) If the tenancy is written, are there any other clauses which would be material? If so the impact of such clauses must be examined.

[1] AHA 1986, s.34.

(v) The circumstances of the tenancy should be examined against the provisions of section 11 of the AHA 1986.

(vi) Has the landlord or his agent taken an active part in the management of the farm? Has he a modern outlook and has a planned programme of modernisation and improvement taken place?

(vii) Are there any reservations to the landlord which may involve him in the operation of the farm?

(viii) Has the tenant suffered lack of investment by the landlord in silence? Or has he made requests, orally, and then in writing, for certain improvements?

(ix) Is the farm marginally viable and is it likely that, on a change of tenancy, it would be split up between other farms?

TABLE I

THE MODEL CLAUSES

RELATING TO 1986 AGRICULTURAL HOLDINGS ACT TFNANCIES FOR THE MAINTENANCE, REPAIR AND INSURANCE OF THE FIXED EQUIPMENT OF A HOLDING

Part I: Rights and Liabilities of the Landlord

3–10 1. (1) To execute all repairs and replacements to the under-mentioned parts of the farmhouse, cottages and farm buildings, namely: roofs, including chimney stacks, chimney pots, eaves-guttering and downpipes, main walls and exterior walls, howsoever constructed, including walls and fences of open and covered yards and garden walls, together with any interior repair or decoration made necessary as a result of structural defect to such roofs or walls, floors, floor joists, ceiling joists and timbers, the farmhouse and cottages, and doors, windows and skylights, including the frames of such doors, windows and skylights (but excepting the glass or glass substitute, sashcords, locks and fastenings): provided that in the case of repairs and replacements to floorboards, interior staircases and fixed ladders (including banisters or handrails), doors and windows and opening skylights (including frames), eaves-guttering and downpipes, the landlord may recover one-half of the reasonable cost thereof from the tenant.

(2) To execute all repairs and replacements to underground water supply pipes, wells, bore-holes and reservoirs and all underground installations connected therewith and to sewage disposal systems, including septic tanks, filtering media and cesspools (but excluding covers and tops).

(3) Except as provided by paragraph 8, to replace anything mentioned in paragraph 5(1) which has worn out or otherwise become incapable of further repair unless the tenant is himself liable to replace it under paragraph 6.

2. (1) (a) To keep the farmhouse, cottages and farm buildings insured to their full value against loss or damage by fire; and
(b) as often as the farmhouse, cottages and farm buildings or any, or any part, of them shall be destroyed or damaged by fire, to execute all works of repair or replacement thereto necessary to make good damage by fire and to cause all money received in respect of such destruction or damage by virtue of such insurance to be laid out in the execution of such works.
(2) The proviso to paragraph 1(1) shall not apply to works falling within sub-paragraph 1(b) of this paragraph.

3. (1) As often as may be necessary in order to prevent deterioration, and in any case at intervals of not more than five years, properly to paint with at least two coats of a suitable quality or properly and adequately to gas-tar, creosote or otherwise effectively treat with a preservative material all outside wood and ironwork of the farmhouse, cottages and farm buildings, the inside wood and ironwork of all external outward opening doors and windows of farm buildings (but not of the farmhouse or cottages), and the interior structural steelwork of open-sided farm buildings which have been previously painted, gas-tarred, creosoted or otherwise treated with preservative material or which it is necessary in order to prevent deterioration of the same so to paint, gas-tar, creosote or treat with preservative material: provided that in respect of doors, windows, eaves-guttering and downpipes the landlord may recover one-half of the reasonable cost of such work from the tenant, but if any such work to any of those items is completed before the commencement of the fifth year of the tenancy the sum which the landlord may so recover from the tenant shall be restricted to any amount equal to the aggregate of one-tenth part of such reasonable cost in respect of each year that has elapsed between the commencement of the tenancy and the completion of such work.
(2) In the last foregoing sub-paragraph "open-sided" means having the whole or the greater part of at least one side or end permanently open, apart from roof supports, if any.

4. (1) The landlord shall be under no liability: **3–11**
(a) to execute repairs or replacements or to insure buildings or fixtures which are the property of the tenant, or
(b) subject to paragraph 2(1)(b), to execute repairs or replacements rendered necessary by the wilful act or the negligence of the tenant or any members of his household or his employees;
(2) If the tenant does not start work on the repairs or replacements for which he is liable under paragraphs 5, 6, 7 and 8 within two months, or if he fails to complete them within three months of receiving from the landlord a written notice (not being a notice to remedy breach of tenancy agreement by doing work of repair, maintenance or replacement in a form prescribed under section

19(1) and (3) of the Agriculture (Miscellaneous Provisions) Act 1963) specifying the necessary repairs or replacements and calling on him to execute them the landlord may enter and execute such repairs or replacements and recover the reasonable cost from the tenant forthwith.

(3) (a) If the tenant wishes to contest his liability to execute any repairs or replacements specified in a notice served upon him by the landlord under the last foregoing sub-paragraph he shall within one month serve a counter-notice in writing upon the landlord specifying the grounds on which and the items of repair or replacement in respect of which he denies liability and requiring the question of liability in respect thereof to be determined by arbitration under the Act.

(b) Upon service of the counter-notice on the landlord, the operation of the notice (including the running of time thereunder) shall be suspended, in so far as it relates to the items specified in the counter-notice, until the termination of an arbitration determining the question of liability in respect of those items.

(c) In this sub-paragraph "termination" in relation to an arbitration, means the date on which the arbitrator's award is delivered to the tenant.

Part II: Rights and Liabilities of the Tenant

3–12 Except in so far as such liabilities fall to be undertaken by the landlord under Part I hereof:

5. (1) To repair and to keep and leave clean and in good tenantable repair, order and condition the farmhouse, cottages and farm buildings together with all fixtures and fittings, boilers, ranges and grates, drains, sewers, gulleys, grease-traps, manholes and inspection chambers, electrical supply systems and fittings, water supply systems and fittings in so far as they are situated above ground, including pipes, tanks, cisterns and sanitary fittings, drinking troughs and pumping equipment, hydraulic rams (whether situated above or below ground), fences, hedges, field walls, stiles, gates and posts, cattle grids, bridges, culverts, ponds, watercourses, sluices, ditches, roads and yards in and upon the holding, or which during the tenancy may be erected or provided thereon.

(2) To repair or replace all removable covers to manholes, to inspection chambers and to sewage disposal systems.

(3) To keep clean and in good working order all roof valleys, eaves-guttering and downpipes, wells, septic tanks, cesspools and sewage disposal systems.

(4) To use carefully so as to protect from wilful, reckless or negligent damage all items for the repair or replacement of which the landlord is responsible under paragraph 1; and also to report in writing immediately to the landlord any damage, however caused,

to items for the repair or replacement of which the landlord is responsible.

6. Subject to paragraph 2(1)(b):
   (1) To replace or repair and, upon replacement or repair, adequately to paint, gar-tar, creosote or otherwise treat with effective preservative material as may be proper, all items of fixed equipment, and to do any work, where such replacement, repair or work is rendered necessary by the wilful act or negligence of the tenant or any members of his household or his employees; and
   (2) To replace anything mentioned in paragraph 5(1) which has worn out or otherwise become incapable of repair if its condition has been brought about by or is substantially due to the tenant's failure to repair it.

7. As often as may be necessary, and in any case at intervals of not more than seven years, properly to clean, colour, whiten, paper, paint, limewash or otherwise treat with materials of suitable quality the inside of the farmhouse, cottages and farm buildings, including the interior of outward opening doors and windows of the farmhouse and cottages, which have been previously so treated and in the last year of the tenancy to limewash the inside of all buildings which previously have been limewashed. **3–13**

8. (1) Notwithstanding the general liability of the landlord for repairs and replacements, to renew all broken or cracked tiles or slates and to replace all slipped tiles or slates from time to time as the damage occurs, but so that the cost shall not exceed £100 in any one year of the tenancy.
   (2) This paragraph shall not have effect so as to render a tenant liable for the cost of any renewals or replacement of tiles in excess of £25, which have been carried out by the landlord prior to 24th March 1988.

9. To cut, trim or lay a proper proportion of the hedges in each year of the tenancy so as to maintain them in good and sound condition.

10. To dig out, scour and cleanse all ponds, watercourses, ditches and grips, as may be necessary to maintain them at sufficient width and depth, and to keep clear from obstruction all field drains and their outlets.

11. (1) If the last year of the tenancy is not a year in which such cleaning, colouring, whitening, papering, painting, limewashing or other treatment as is mentioned in paragraph 7 is due to be carried out, the tenant shall pay to the landlord at the end of such last year either the estimated reasonable cost thereof or a sum equal to the aggregate of one-seventh of that cost in respect of each year that has elapsed since such last cleaning, colouring, whitening, papering, painting, limewashing or other treatment as aforesaid, was completed, whichever is the less.
   (2) If the last year of the tenancy is not a year in which the landlord is liable, under paragraph 3, to paint, gas-tar, creosote or otherwise treat the doors, windows, eaves-guttering and downpipes of buildings, the tenant shall pay to the landlord at the end

of such last year either one-half of the estimated reasonable cost thereof or a sum equal to the aggregate of one-tenth part of that cost in respect of each year that has elapsed since such last painting, gas-tarring, creosoting or other treatment as aforesaid, was completed, whichever is the less.

(3) In the assessment of any compensation payable by the tenant on the termination of the tenancy in respect of dilapidation, any accrued liability under the two preceding sub-paragraphs shall be taken into account.

3–14 12. (1) If the landlord fails to execute repairs other than repairs to an underground waterpipe which are his liability within the three months of receiving from the tenant a written notice specifying the necessary repairs and calling on him to execute them, the tenant may execute such repairs and, except to the extent to which under the terms of Part I hereof the tenant is liable to bear the cost, recover (subject to the landlord's right to require arbitration under sub-paragraph (5) below) the reasonable cost from the landlord forthwith.

(2) If the landlord fails to execute any repairs which are his liability to an underground waterpipe within one week of receiving from the tenant a written notice specifying the necessary repairs and calling on him to execute them, the tenant may execute such repairs and, except to the extent to which under the terms of Part I hereof the tenant is liable to bear the cost, recover (subject to the landlord's right to require arbitration under sub-paragraph (5) below) the reasonable cost from the landlord upon the expiry of a period of one month from the execution of the repairs.

(3) Subject to sub-paragraph (4) below, if the landlord fails to execute any replacements which are his liability with three months of receiving from the tenant a written notice specifying the necessary replacements and, except to the extent to which under the terms of Part I hereof the tenant is liable to bear the cost, recover (subject to the landlord's right to require arbitration under sub-paragraph (5) below) the reasonable cost from the landlord forthwith.

(4) The tenant shall not be entitled to recover, in respect of the aggregate of the replacements executed by him after being specified in a notice given in pursuance of sub-paragraph (3) above, in any year of the tenancy any sum in excess of whichever of the following sums is hereinafter specified in relation to the replacements so executed, that is to say—

(a) in relation to replacements executed in any year of the tenancy terminating on or before March 24, 1988, a sum equal to the rent of the holding for that year or £500, whichever is the smaller, or

(b) in relation to replacements executed in any year of the tenancy terminating after March 24, 1988, a sum equal to the rent of the holding for that year or £2,000, whichever is the smaller, or

(5) (a) If the landlord wishes to contest his liability to execute any repairs or replacements specified in a notice served upon him by the tenant under sub-paragraph (1), (2) or (3) above he shall within one month of the service of that notice serve a counter-notice in writing upon the tenant specifying the grounds on which and the items of repair or replacement in respect of which he denies liability and requiring the question of liability in respect thereof to be determined by arbitration under the Act.

(b) Upon service of a counter-notice on the tenant which relates to a notice served on the landlord under sub-paragraph (1) or (3) above, the operation of the notice so served under sub-paragraph (1) or (3) (including the running of time thereunder) shall be suspended, in so far as it relates to the items specified in the counter-notice, until the termination of an arbitration determining the question of liability in respect of those items.

(c) Upon service of a counter-notice on the tenant which relates to a notice served on the landlord under sub-paragrpah (2) above, the tenant's right under that sub-paragraph to recover the reasonable cost of the repairs specified in the counter-notice shall not arise unless the question of liability to execute those repairs is first determined by arbitration in favour of the tenant, and shall thereupon arise from the termination of the arbitration.

(d) In this sub-paragraph "termination" in relation to an arbitration means the date on which the arbitrator's award is delivered to the landlord.

Part III: General Provisions

13. (1) If at any time and from time to time the landlord or the tenant shall be of opinion that any item of fixed equipment is, or before the same was damaged or destroyed by fire was, redundant to the farming of the holding, the landlord or the tenant may by giving two months' notice in writing to the other of them require that the question whether such item of fixed equipment is, or before such damage or destruction was, so redundant shall be determined, in default of agreement, by arbitration under the Act, and if the arbitrator shall award that the said item of fixed equipment is, or before such damage or destruction by fire was, redundant to the farming of the holding then, as from the date of such an award, paragraph 14(1) shall apply to that item and both the landlord and the tenant shall be relieved from all liability in respect of any antecedent breach of any obligation to maintain, repair or replace the item of fixed equipment so awarded to be redundant and the landlord shall be entitled to demolish and remove such item of fixed equipment and to enter upon the holding for these purposes. **3–15**

(2) In any arbitration to which sub-paragraph (1) of this paragraph applies, no item of fixed equipment shall be determined to be, or have been before damage or destruction by fire, as the case may be, redundant to the farming of the holding, unless the arbitrator shall be satisfied that the repair or replacement of such item is or, as the case may be, was not reasonably required having regard to—

(a) (i) the landlord's responsibilities to manage the holding in accordance with the rules of good estate management; and

(ii) the period for which the holding may reasonably be expected to remain a separate holding; and

(b) the character and situation of the holding and the average requirements of a tenant reasonably skilled in husbandry.

14. Nothing contained in Part I or Part II hereof shall create any liability on the part of either landlord or tenant:

(1) to maintain, repair, replace or insure any item of fixed equipment which the landlord and the tenant agree in writing to be obsolete or redundant to the farming of the holding or which in the event of any dispute between them as to whether it is, or before the same was damaged or destroyed by fire was, redundant to the farming of the holding, shall be awarded to be so redundant by an arbitrator in an arbitration as mentioned in paragraph 13; or

(2) to execute any work if and so far as the execution of such work is rendered impossible (except at prohibitive or unreasonable expense) by reason of subsidence of any land or the blocking of outfalls which are not under the control of either the landlord or the tenant.

15. If any claim, question or difference shall arise between the landlord and the tenant under the foregoing provisions hereof, not being a matter which, otherwise than under the provisions of this paragraph, is required by or by virtue of the Act or section 19 of the Agriculture (Miscellaneous Provisions) Act 1963 (notice to remedy breach of tenancy agreement) or regulations or orders made thereunder or the foregoing provisions hereof to be determined by arbitration under the Act, such claim, question or difference shall be determined, in default of agreement, by arbitration under the Act.

1995 Agricultural Tenancies Act

3–16 The Act permits complete freedom of negotiation and agreement on all the relevant points. If the agreement is silent on any matter, there is no equivalent position to section 11 of the AHA 1986. However, covenants may be implied and may be enforceable under case law or common law. Contracts will be written anew between the parties, so appropriate clauses should be written into the agreement. The Act itself permits free negotiation on all aspects of contractual liability, responsibility and reservation but with certain fall back provisions. Where there are no such provisions then nothing is implicit. Disputes are either referred to arbitration or the parties decide upon other means of determining disputes under arrangements contained within the body of the agreement. These for example may be the use of mediation or alternative dispute resolution (ADR).

Drafting such agreements should take account of appropriate clauses and covenants and should also refer where necessary to planning and environmental legislation which may impose further obligations and constraints. To save problems occurring during, or at the end of, the tenancy, the farm business tenancy (FBT) should cover as may aspects as possible.

It is a matter for the parties to create their own written tenancy agreements. There are some useful precedents which have been drawn up by various bodies including the Law Society, the Royal Institution of Chartered Surveyors, and some individual firms of solicitors. An oral agreement is still a binding contract but its existence may be hard to prove in retrospect. This is especially so when one or both parties to the agreement have died. However, the much-feared security of tenure, which could be claimed under the AHA 1986, forms no part of any arrangements under the ATA 1995.

Buildings, structures fixed equipment, lagoons and pits, channels and slurry systems

Any agreement made under the ATA 1995 may be oral or in writing. If it is **3–17**
oral, with no other agreement than the amount of land and buildings to be farmed in exchange for a rental consideration, there are only a few statutory clauses which then become mandatory and these will apply and override any conditions to the contrary in a written tenancy agreement. On repairs, the parties may negotiate freely and, in the absence of any clause(s), there is no right to arbitration on the matter under section 28. So, if the agreement is silent then there is a common law presumption that the tenant will farm the land and occupy and use the buildings and other equipment in a fair and proper manner. And, unless there is an appropriate clause to ensure that one or other party must renew or replace worn out equipment and buildings, then there is no obligation on either party to do so. So, at the start of the tenancy, the tenant should satisfy himself that, under those circumstances, the fixtures are not likely to be worn out prior to the end of his term of tenancy. It is therefore clearly preferable to identify areas of responsibility as specifically as possible within the terms of the tenancy agreement.

The same provisions affect insurance requirements which, again, are freely negotiable. Should the agreement be silent on the issue, the recourse to arbitration is then not available.

Anti-pollution measures

In the absence of any clause to the contrary, liability for any pollution **3–18**
incident or breach of any environmental regulations will rest with the party or parties concerned. It is therefore recommended that the tenant should be required to fulfil all obligations under statute and regulation not to

cause pollution to air, water and to soil. To strengthen such obligations, the agreement could specify that the tenant should conform to the Codes of Good Agricultural Practice relating to air, soil and water.

At the end of the tenancy, unless there is specific provision within the agreement, there is no provision for a landlord's claim for dilapidations. This would leave the landlord with the only option of seeking damages on the diminution in the landlord's reversion following the tort of waste. It emphasises the importance of taking a "record of condition" at the start of the tenancy or a "marching-in state".

Where a tenant takes over fixtures from an outgoing tenant, and pays the outgoer directly, then it is reasonable to assume that the landlord has no responsibility for the repair and condition of those items of fixed equipment. Where, however, the landlord includes landlord's buildings within the agreement, unless the liability for their maintenance and state of compliance with statute and regulation is firmly placed with the tenant at the start of the tenancy, the landlord must assume some statutory liability should problems arise therefrom.

Landlord/Tenant system

3–19 The regulatory authorities may enter the frame at a number of points. First they may be brought in to consider a planning application. Secondly, as part of their general duties or by way of a complaint, they may visit premises with a view to inspection. Thirdly, they may order action to be taken if they feel that pollution may arise, or they may carry out works themselves (before or after pollution has occurred) and recover their reasonable costs. Finally, they may issue warnings, serve a variety of notices, and prosecute on the commission of offences.

The local authorities deal with the statutory nuisance position (see Chapter 10). The Environment Agency will normally take proceedings under the Water Resources Act 1991 (WRA 1991) providing that it can be shown that the defendant has caused, or knowingly permitted the pollution to take place. This gives rise to consideration of the chain of causation and the essential nexus between links in that chain. In the case of the *National Rivers Authority v. Welsh Development Agency* [1993] E.C.G.S. 160, the WDA as landlord let some industrial units on land where a drainage system was already in place. The tenant polluted a water course via this drainage system. It was found that, whilst the WDA had constructed the system, they had not caused the pollution. It was the use or abuse of the drainage system by the tenant which caused the pollution to occur. The WDA were exonerated. This concurred with the common sense view that where a drainage system is provided by the landlord and is capable of working properly but is misused by the tenant, the landlord should not be held to account.

The reverse may occur where a tenant operates fixtures in a reasonable and acceptable manner, but pollution does occur by reason of some fault in the design or construction of the fixture itself. There it is likely that the landlord will carry some responsibility. (Other cases of note are *Alpacell* and *Impress*). As farmers are better trained, become more environmentally aware, and are conscientiously updated in changes in the law by the farming press, it becomes more difficult for them to avoid the full impact of the law. There is a corresponding and heightened awareness of environmental issues amongst the population at large and, in tune with that, come fines of increasing magnitude.

Common Law and Torts

3–20 The usual remedies by way of injunctions and damages in cases of nuisance, negligence or *Rylands v. Fletcher* will again seek out the personal persons responsible. For example in *R. v. Shorrock* (*The Times*, March 11, 1993) Mr Shorrock hired out a field for an "acid house party" this generated much noise and he was convicted of public nuisance. In this case it was the person hiring out the land who was liable and it would not therefore matter whether it was landlord or tenant. However, if the tenant had hired the field with permission in writing from the landlord for that specific purposes, that is to say the landlord was in a position to foresee what might be the result, then some degree of liability would undoubtedly fall on both parties.

In the case of a tort under the rule of *Rylands v. Fletcher*, strict liability for damage caused by a non-natural user of land and an subsequent escape of some material, provides strict liability. What is essential, as shown in the case of *Cambridge Water Company v. Eastern Counties Leather*, there must be foreseeability, and there must be an unbroken chain of causation. Dependent upon the circumstances, the landlord or the tenant or both may have some joint or several liability. So if the container or fixture provided by the landlord bursts and the material which it contains escapes, then some liability may attach to the landlord under *Rylands v. Fletcher*. The main question might be whether the use of a lagoon or weeping wall silo, for example, was a "non-natural use" of land.

Conclusion

3–21 It will be seen that most operational problems are caused by the farmer who is working the farm. In the case of an agricultural holding this is likely to be the tenant or owner occupier. However, since there may be some liability attaching to the landlord, he would be imprudent if he left the tenant and all the landlords fixtures alone for long periods. The landlord's agents should be instructed to make regular inspections of all the equipment on the farm, including that belonging to the tenant, to see if there is any cause for concern. Once a pollution incident has occurred, it is far too late and there is no doubt that the EA will continue the robust campaign against polluters which was previously followed by the NRA. Indeed, the Control of Pollution (Silage, Slurry and Agricultural Fuel Oil) Regulations 1991 (S.I. 1991, No. 324) as amended contain a provision under regulation 9 whereby a Works Notice may be served on the person "having custody or control of the relevant substance" to carry out certain works and, under regulation 4, that person shall only store slurry where they are satisfied the requirements of Schedule 2 are satisfied (or it is an exempt structure). The same applies in relation to fuel oil and silage so that, at all times through the 20-year life of the installation, the person using it must be satisfied that it will not cause pollution. The landlord cannot absolve himself from such contributory responsibility except by contracting out.

Chapter 4
Introduction to the Planning Process

The planning system is very complex. The increasing weight of environmental regulation is having additional affect. In this chapter we try to provide a wide canvas against which to assess individual problems or development proposals. But every case is different and more detailed analysis is often essential. These should be pursued either by direct discussion with the LPA (local planning authority) or through the retention of a planning consultant. **4–01**

Development

The definition of development is set out in section 55(1) of the TCPA 1990 (Town and Country Planning Act 1990): "The carrying out of building, engineering, mining, or other operations in, on, over or under land, or the making of any material change in the use of any buildings or other land". Under those circumstances, there is an initial presumption that planning consent will be required for any such development. **4–02**

There are, however, two important exceptions for agriculture. The first is contained in section 55(2)(e) of the TCPA 1990 which indicates that "the **use** of any land for the purposes of agriculture or forestry (including afforestation) and the **use** for any of those purposes of any building occupied together with land so used" is not development. So, the **use** of any land or buildings for agriculture does not require planning consent. Whereas a change of use from agricultural land or buildings to a different use will always require planning permission (unless it is not material, *i.e.* it is *de minimis* or it is ancillary to the agricultural use), the reverse (a change of use to agriculture) does not require planning permission. However, under the Agricultural Land (Removal of Surface Soil) Act 1953, the removal of more than 5 cubic yards of top soil from farm land in any three-month period requires planning consent, unless it is necessary for cutting peat or turf.

The second part of the planning equation relates to operational development. This is concerned with the construction of buildings, excavation and engineering operations, the creation of roads and accesses, and the installation of pollution control systems. Unless these are covered by the exemptions set out below, that is to say they are permitted development and have a deemed planning consent, they are subject to the requirements to obtain a planning consent.

Permitted Development

Permitted Development (PD) rights have been reined in since the original Order and they are now contained in the Town and Country Planning (General Permitted Development) Order 1995 (S.I. 1995 No. 418) (GPDO **4–03**

1995). Certain PD rights are conditional, some unconditional. Where there are conditions these will relate to the need for prior notification. The full text of the statutory instrument is annexed but the chart which follows is an endeavour to simplify a complicated set of rules. Part 6 of Schedule 2 provides for a number of exemptions whereby farmers do not need to apply for planning consent. They are granted a "deemed planning permission" by virtue of the Order. Nevertheless the LPA must be notified in advance of certain works proceeding, under a prior notification scheme. The LPA may grant consent under this procedure or it may seek certain amendments. The LPA also has the ability to require a full application to be made in order to determine matters such as design and siting. However, and most importantly, provided that the agricultural qualifications are met, then the LPA may not question the agricultural need. Where substantial modifications are not made to suit the views of the planners, then the application is likely to be refused. The applicant must then decide whether to abandon the scheme, whether to substitute a modified scheme, or whether to take the matter to appeal.

The main areas covered are found in Part 6 of Schedule 2 of the order. Its provisions are complicated. Farms are divided into smaller areas of up to five hectares and larger areas of five hectares and over. The latter fall into Class A.

Development on farms which comprise less than five hectares but above 0.4 hectares have their own rules relating to permitted development rights which fall under Class B. These are set out in the table found at page 74. They are simplified but it will be seen that their scope is more limited (see below).

4–04 Class C, where minerals are worked for agricultural purposes, states the "the winning and working on land held or occupied with land used for the purposes of agriculture or any minerals reasonably necessary for agricultural purposes within the agricultural unit of which it forms part" is permitted subject to two conditions. First, if any excavation would be made within 25 metres of a metalled part of a trunk or classified road. Secondly, the minerals may not be moved on to other land which does not form part of the same agricultural unit.

Class A deals with the larger developments and grants PD rights to the carrying out on agricultural land comprised in an agricultural unit of five hectares or more in area of—

(a) Works for the erection, extension or alteration of a building: or
(b) Any excavation or engineering operations, which are reasonably necessary for the purposes of agriculture within that unit.

The full schedule is found at pages 74 but below is a summary. The Schedule in the GPDO has been expanded so far as the Conservation (Natural Habitats, etc.) Regulations 1994 are concerned and also to include environmental assessment where necessary.

PERMITTED DEVELOPMENT

Applications

Building work and excavation or engineering operations "which are reasonably necessary for the purposes of agriculture within that unit." **4–05**

Class A

Data

1. Minimum size of unit 5 ha.
2. Minimum size of parcel 1 ha.
3. Maximum ground area (calculated as para. d.2) 465m^2.
4. Maximum height within 3 km of perimeter of an aerodrome 3m.
5. Maximum height elsewhere 12m.
6. Minimum distance from metalled part of classified road 25m.
7. Minimum distance from prtoected building (for livestock, slurry or sewage sludge, see "emergencies" below) 400m.

Exclusions

1. Fish farming developments on article 1(6) land.
2. Dwellings or parts thereof.
3. Developments not designed for agricultural purposes.
4. Land subject to an article 4 direction.
5. Land subject to an SSSI.
6. Demolition of farm buildings, which are listed or within a conservation area; any dwelling.
7. Any development requiring an environmental assessment.
8. Total area exceeds 465m^2 (by calculation).

Conditions

1. Prior notification to LPA in case of:
    1. Any "significant" erection, extension or alteration of a building.
    2. Any extension or alteration of a building on article 1(6) land (National Parks and certain designated Parishes).
    3. Formation or alteration of a private way.
    4. Areas of excavation or waste deposits over 0.5 ha (aggregated).
    5. Tanks, cages, structures for fish farming.
    6. Development to be carried out within five years of approval (or notification) where approval is unnecessary.
    7. Development with a significant effect on land covered by the Conservation (Natural Habitats, etc.) Regulations 1994 (S.I. 1994 No. 2716). (European Site).

2. Any minerals extracted not to be moved off the farm.

3. Waste materials (*e.g.* hard core) to be incorporated immediately.

Emergencies

A building erected within 400 metres of protected building must not be used for housing livestock unless:

1. There is no other appropriate building 400 metres or more from the protected building AND EITHER
   (i) The building is required for quarantine purposes or other buildings have been destroyed by fire or flood.

OR

   (ii) Outdoor animals need shelter temporarily for sickness, parturition or incase of severe weather.

Applications

Certain developments which are reasonably necessary for the purposes of agriculture within the unit.

Class B

Data

1.	Minimum Size of Unit	0.4 ha.
2.	Minimum distance from metal part of classified road	25m.
3.	Minimum distance from protected building (for livestock, slurry or sewage sludge)	400m.
4.	Maximum size of Unit	5 ha.
5.	Maximum ground areas (calculated at paragraph D.2	65m^2.
6.	Maximum height within 3 kilometres of perimeter of an aerodrome	3m.
7.	maximum height elsewhere	12m.
8.	Maximum increase on cubic content of original building	10%
9.	Maximum height of any building, plant or machinery	as original

Exclusions

1. Alterations to external appearance of premises.
2. No extension is permitted where any part of the building would be more than 30 metres from the original building.
3. No development within 5 metres of any boundary or the agricultural unit.
4. Any work to a building for slurry or sewage sludge storage or for livestock accommodation if the building is within 400 metres within a protected building. See "emergencies" below.
5. The placing or assembly of a tank or construction of a pond for fish farming.
6. Developments not designed for agricultural purposes.

7. A loan subject to an article 4 direction.
8. Land subject to SSS1.
9. Demolition of Farm Buildings, listed or within a conservation area; any dwelling.
10. Total area exceeds 465m^2 (by calculation)

Condition

1. Prior notification is required for
   (a) significant buildings
   (b) "habitats directive" land
2. Waste materials, *e.g.* (hard core) to be incorporated immediately.
3. No land raise.
4. Prior notification to LPA in case of an extension or alteration of a building, provision, rearrangement or replacement of a private way on article 1(6) land.
5. Areas of excavation or waste deposit over 0.5 ha. (aggregated).

Emergencies

A building erected within 400 metres of protected building must not be used for housing livestock unless:

1. There is no other appropriate building 400 metres or more from the protected building AND EITHER
   (i) The building is required for quarantine purposes or other buildings have been destroyed by fire or flood.

OR

   (ii) Outdoor animals need shelter temporarily for sickness, parturition or in case of severe weather.
2. Any land designated under the Conservation (Natural Habitats, etc.) Regulations 1994.

The prior notification procedure is set out in the conditions to Class A.2(2) to (4) of Part 6.

Notes on permitted development rights

"Protected building" under B1 of the GPDO 1995, Schedule 2, Part 6 means "any permanent building which is normally occupied by people or would be so occupied, if it were in use for purposes for which it is apt: but does not include: **4–06**

(i) a building within the Agricultural units: or
(ii) a dwelling or other building on another agricultural unit which is used for or in connection with agriculture."

The definition of "protected building" relates to the building itself but such protection extends to its curtilage. The way to test whether a proposed livestock building or slurry store will be within 400 metres is to measure by scale rule or compass, from the nearest edge of the proposed development to the nearest edge of the curtilage of the building which may be protected. It should be remembered that 400 metres in any direction covers a considerable area. But with the wide spread use of scale farm plans and OS 1–2500 plans for IACS and the use of a scale rule, the exercise should not be too difficult. It should be remembered, however, that if there are buildings on a neighbouring agricultural unit which are let for holiday purposes or which may be building conversions to residential use that are not associated in any way with the farm, then these will be "protected". PPG 7 (Annex B2–B6) tries to minimise the potential for future conflict between farmers and adjoining land owners. Its suggests to planners that they should be very careful before allowing new dwelling or other protected buildings within the 400 metre cordon sanitaire around established livestock units.

Other permitted development

4–07 There is a range of development which does not require planning permission by virtue of the General Permitted Development Order 1995. Much of this has no direct relevance to this book, such as development within the curtilage of a dwellinghouse and the Schedule to Part 1, minor operations under Part 2 and temporary buildings under Class A of Part 4. However Class B of Part 4 provides for "the use of any land for any purpose for not more than 28 days in total in any calendar year, of which not more than 14 days in total may be for the purposes referred to in paragraph B2 and the provision on the land of any moveable structure for the purposes of the permitted use". B2 refers to the holding of a market and motor car and motor cycle racing. There are specific exclusions where there is a building or the land is within the curtilage of a building, for a caravan site, where the land is within a site of special scientific interest, or for clay pigeon shooting, war games or motor sports, but clearly many of these activities can be deemed to be antisocial by reason of the detrimental effects on the amenity of the area and the local population. Hence the relevant restrictions.

So far as caravans are concerned, Part 5 of Schedule 2 of the GPDO does grant certain rights. Caravans do, however, impact on the landscape by virtue of their size and colour. Permanent sites are controlled by the requirement for planning consent. Environmental health issues are dealt with by a site licence which is again through the Environmental Health Officer of the local council. Planning restrictions may permit caravans to be on site for only the summer months, for example. Thus when the leaves have fallen the caravans are not on site to be visible through ineffective tree screens.

There are exemptions which are set out in Part 5 of Schedule 2 of the GPDO and which are specified under Schedule 1 of the Caravan Sites and Control of Development Act 1960. The more important agricultural exemptions are:

(1) Use within the curtilage of a dwellinghouse: provided the use is ancillary or incidental to the enjoyment of the dwelling, the caravan does not require a separate consent.
(2) Five-acre holdings: provided there is a minimum holding of five acres, then three caravans are allowed without a site licence for up to 28 days in any year.
(3) Certificated sites: organisations such as the Caravan Club and the Caravan and Camping Club may certificate the use of a site for up to five caravans without either a planning permission or a site licence.
(4) The use of a caravan on farmland for agricultural purposes again is not development. It may not be used as a permanent residence.

Livestock and slurry

The exemption takes particular notice of the environmental effects of odours produced by livestock buildings and also from slurry and sewage sludge containment areas. So, if there is a protected building within 400 metres of a proposed development of that type, then planning permission is required, Class A or Class B. Annex C of PPG 7 gives guidance to LPA in this regard. Providing that all the requirements under the GPDO are met, then the LPA should not consider the principle of the development at all, they should only look at siting and design. It is only where the proposal may have a substantial impact on its surroundings that the LPA should require formal submission of details for approval. The LPA should be required to take fully into account the circulation of people, live and dead stock in and around buildings. It is no use having a development which may be more aesthetically pleasing but which is faulty in operation or design. **4–08**

Annex B of PPG 7 explains that a protected building includes most residential and other permanent buildings such as schools, hospitals and offices normally occupied by people. Excluded from this definition is any building on the same agricultural unit, any farm dwelling or other farm building on another agricultural unit and any building used for special industrial purposes which are covered by the Town and Country Planning (Use Classes) Order (S.I. 1987 No. 764), Class B3. Also, the 400 metres is normally to be measured from the boundary of the land on which the protected building stands, for example the end of the garden of a house.

B3 goes on to say that the LPA should take special care where they have to consider a planning application for a house or any new "protected" building within 400 metres of an established livestock unit.

The emergency use of buildings which are not normally permitted to be used for housing livestock does provide welcome relief on occasion. Nevertheless it should only be in the case of a true emergency.

Where an Article 4 direction is in place, all permitted development rights are withdrawn. This applies to all PD rights under the GPDO and requires a developer to seek planning permission, even for the smallest building. Under certain circumstances, compensation may be payable.

Diversification

4–09 A modern problem lies with the definition of "agriculture", which in our view, is over due for some expansion. There is an economic imperative on many farm businesses to diversify activities away from mainstream farming. This has been actively encouraged by government, particularly in their planning advice note PPG 7.

At the same time there has been no change in the definition of agriculture from section 336 of the TCPA 1990 which states that "agriculture" includes "horticulture, fruit growing, seed growing, dairy farming, the breeding and keeping of livestock including any creature kept for the production of food, wool, skins or fur or for the purpose of its use in the farming of land, the use of land as grazing land, meadow land, osier land, market gardens and nursery grounds and the use of land for woodlands where that use is ancillary to the farming of land for other agricultural purposes, and 'agricultural' shall be construed accordingly". No mention is made of diverse activities. In addition, the interpretation of relatively straight forward definitions of farming activities still provide many grey areas. Take for example farm shops, where these may sell unprocessed produce which comes directly from the farm unit without the need for planning consent. It is an activity which is ancillary to the main business of agriculture (see *Williams v. Minister of Housing and Local Government*, 18 P. & C.R. 514). However, if in excess of about 5 per cent of produce (using the *de minimis* rule) is bought in, then planning consent is likely to be required. The 5 per cent is not prescriptive (see *Allen v. SSE and Reigate and Banstead Borough Council* (1990) J.P.L. 340) and, providing that the sales are ancillary to the main business, then all the produce of the farm could be sold in that manner. If produce is processed, it may become a stage removed from agricultural production and so may then not benefit from the exemption.

There is also the problem of "planning units". A planning unit may differ from an agricultural unit. In the case of *Fuller v. The SSE* (1987) 283 E.G. 847), grain silos on two farms were used as intervention stores. The court found in favour of the inspector who decided that, on the facts as presented, the two farms did represent two separate planning units even though grain came in from a wide number of other farms and was dealt with as if it were one agricultural unit. This concept of planning units is complex, but it is again a matter of fact and degree. The term "fact and degree" permeates the consideration of difficult matters within the planning system. In other words it is usually a matter of judgment for the decision-maker based on the particular facts and the degree to which those facts are more or less important.

4–10 There are occasions when the need to make a planning application is uncertain. An application may then be made for a CLOPUD or a certificate of proposed operational use and development, under section 24 of the Town and Country Planning (General Development Procedure) Order 1995 (S.I. 1995 No. 419). This is a formal application to the LPA for them to determine whether a full planning application is required or not. It follows that any material operational development or change of use which lies outside the permitted development (PD) rights granted under the GPDO, or which are not a change of use to "agriculture", will require a planning application to be made.

Furthermore, if development or a change of use has already taken place and no planning permission was granted at the time, it is possible to apply for a permission retrospectively. If this is refused and no appeal is made, or if an appeal is lost, then the LPA is likely to take enforcement action. Where operational development has taken place over four years before the LPA take formal action, or where there has been a residential use of a building, or in any other case a change of use had occurred ten years before that time, then the use or development becomes technically immune from enforcement action. The applicant should apply for a certificate of lawful use or development (CLEUD). Under those circumstances, the onus lies on the applicant to prove his case "on the balance of probabilities". He may do this with the help of statutory declarations, documentary, photographic and other evidence. The lawful use certificate (LUC) not only provides immunity from enforcement action but it grants a deemed planning permission. It is often more valuable than a planning permission since the LPA should impose no new conditions upon it.

The Planning Process

The decision makers (planning officers, planning committees, or in the case of an appeal the inspector, or ultimately the Secretary of State) are guided by section 54A of the TCPA 1990 in the process of coming to a conclusion, as follows: "where, in making any determination under the Planning Acts regard is to be had for the development plan, the determination shall be made in accordance with the plan unless material considerations indicate otherwise." Section 70(2) of the TCPA 1990 puts this in slightly different language: "in dealing with such an application the authority shall have regard to the provisions of the development plan, so far as material to the application, and to any other material considerations." **4–11**

Broadly, the "development plan" usually consists of the County Structure Plan (or Unitary Plan) the District or Borough Wide Local Plan and where relevant, the County Minerals Plan. In most cases some reasonable allowances are made within development plans for necessary agricultural development. But where there are areas of particular concern, such as national parks, SSSI's A's–ONB, special areas of conservation, and specially protected areas, together with certain local designations such as special landscape areas or areas of local landscape significance, then policy tends to be much more restrictive.

Farmers should be very aware of the local plan process. It is important to consider potential future uses of ones own land and equally to keep a weather eye on proposals for development nearby. There are reviews of the local plan from time to time and amendments which may be proposed by the LPA. For example, a neighbouring landfill site proposal or the erection of a chemical plan both have a detrimental impact on the area generally and on the farm in particular. During the review or amendment process there may be opportunities which should be grasped. It is also worth considering joint ventures with others where the use of two adjoining pieces of land may produce an interesting marriage value.

4–12 Background guidance is provided by Planning Policy Guidance Notes (PPG's), (together with Development Control Notes (DCN's)) (now largely obsolete), and Department of Environment (DoE) circulars, which generally give guidance to LPA's and developers. They also give expression to government's intentions on how national planning policy should be interpreted. Also, there are ministerial statements, government white papers and responses to parliamentary questions, which are material planning considerations. Judge-made law from the higher courts provides judicial interpretation. We are currently living in a period of intense change, not merely in the statute itself and policy guidance, but in the decisions handed down by the courts. The interplay between all these is vitally important for the LPA's, planning advisors and developers.

The importance of the development plan must not be underrated although other material planning considerations may be equally or more important. Financial considerations may be material and are often of considerable help to farmers attempting to process applications through the LPA. Further, and largely as a result of the government white paper "This Common Inheritance", (published September 1990—Cm. 1200), is the issue of sustainability. This tenet permeates the whole of both government and LPA thinking on development and is being incorporated into new structure and local plans. It is the subject of government guidance and policy. It is difficult conceptually to define, but broadly means that the effects of development should have no long-term damaging environmental consequences.

Sometimes environmental assessments or statements are required. The requirements are set out in the Town and Country Planning (Assessment of Environmental Effects) Regulations 1988 (S.I. 1988 No. 1199) and the amendment Regulations 1994 (S.I. 1994 No. 677). Applications for Schedule 1 Developments must be accompanied by an environmental assessment. A Schedule 2 Development may require environmental impact assessment (EIA) since it is likely to have significant effects on the environment "by virtue of factors such as its nature, size or location". The LPA will decide whether or not an EIA is required and other regulations enable prospective developers to seek an opinion from the LPA as to whether their proposals would fall within Schedule 1 or 2. This ability is found under the Town and Country Planning (Environmental Assessment and Permitted Development) Regulations 1995 (S.I. 1995 No. 417). These include under regulation 1—agriculture:

(a) Water management for agriculture;
(b) Poultry rearing;
(c) Pig rearing;
(d) A salmon hatchery;

(e) An installation for the rearing of salmon;
(f) The reclamation of land from the sea.

Under regulation 2 come "an installation for hydro electric energy production and wind generators". Also in regulation 11 it includes a waste water treatment plant and a site for depositing sludge.

Schedule 3 sets out in some detail of what an environmental statement should comprise. DoE Circular 15/88 advises on the Regulations and sets out as its starting point, that the best environmental policy consists in preventing the creation of pollution or nuisances at source, rather than subsequently trying to counteract their affects. Clearly, where the project is of wider importance than its immediate locality, or where it is sited in a sensitive location, or where there are potentially wide adverse effects, then an environmental statement is likely to be required.

Types of Application

There are four separate types of application. These are an outline application, a full application, an application for reserved matters (technically not a planning application), and notification under the GPDO. The purpose of an outline application is normally to establish the principle that development of a certain type may be permitted without going to the expense of producing very detailed plans and designs at an early stage. An outline application for a new farm dwelling is usual. Once an outline permission is achieved then the LPA may not refuse a reasonable scheme which is submitted by way of a reserved-matters application. Nor may it apply excessive conditions. Any doubt the LPA has had in the first instance should be covered by conditions relating to the outline permission. A reserved-matters application should be submitted within three years of the grant of an outline consent. Any plans submitted with an outline application are considered to be included within that application, unless they are marked "informational", or in some way described so as to identify that they do not form part of the outline application itself. Alterations at a later stage may be difficult to achieve. Justification for a farm dwelling must be provided by satisfying both the functional and financial tests set out in Annex E of PPG7. The site should be agreed with the LPA at a pre-application stage. Then, once the outline application is permitted, detailed drawings may be submitted. **4–13**

Time scales should be watched closely. An outline consent lasts for five years. An application for reserved matters must be submitted before the expiration of three years following the grant of the outline consent. Renewal applications should always be made within the time scale of the original. Farmers and others should always diarise consents so that critical dates, *i.e.* when operational developments should be begun or when various applications need to be made, should be firmly on the calendar.

Once an application is received by the LPA it is checked to see if it is correct and, if so, it is then registered. If the application is not determined by the LPA within two months from the date of registration, it may be appealed. This is on grounds of non-determination within the specified period. This course of action is not normally recommended where there is a reasonable likelihood of a decision being reached by negotiation. The appeal process is likely to take between eight to 12 months and so delays may be substantial.

In cases where an application is likely to be contentious, the twin track or duplicate application approach may be appropriate. For example, where a proposed pig or poultry unit is to be sited fairly close to a settlement. It is not usually considered favourably by the LPA but nevertheless it is a legitimate device. Two identical applications are submitted. One can be negotiated with LPA and the other left. If the one being negotiated is not agreed within the two-month period, then the other application can be appealed. This does put pressure on the LPA to reach some decision. If after say a further month the matter is resolved amicably then the first application appeal may be withdrawn. Whilst it does have the effects of pressurising the LPA, the reaction to such pressure may of course be adverse. Also there are now two full application fees.

Consultations

4–14 Once the application is registered, then letters are sent automatically to all the relevant statutory consultees, as set out in Article 10 of the GDPO 1995 and also non-statutory consultees as set out in Appendix C to DoE Circular 9/95. In addition there may be other interested organisations, bodies, quangos and certainly neighbours, all of whom should receive notification of the application. When all the comments are received, the planning officer puts all the various factors into the balance and reaches a conclusion. This is contained normally within a recommendation for the consideration of the planning committee, but in some cases he is able to issue a decision under delegated powers. That is to say he does not need to use the full committee structure to indorse his recommendation. On other occasions he may require further consent of the chairman and possibly one or two others of the committee as an intermediate step. Most LPA's have their own ground rules.

Planning Conditions

4–15 A planning permission may be given with or without conditions. Since *every* operational development or a change of use has the potential to contain some environmental impact, the use of conditions is nearly always appropriate. There are six tests for conditions which are found in DoE Circular 11/95: they must be necessary, relevant to planning, relevant to the development to be permitted, enforceable, precise, and reasonable. If they are found to be too onerous or incorrectly or needlessly applied, then they may be subject to appeal within a six-month period. Alternatively, an application may be made outside that period, for the retention of the remainder of the consent without complying with one or more conditions. The procedure here is found under section 73 of the TCPA 1990. This enables only the condition(s) to be considered on an application or appeal so that the remainder of the position is not put in jeopardy. If the application is refused, the refusal may then be appealed.

Understanding the mind of the planner

The importance of informal negotiations cannot be over-emphasised. These should certainly take place with the LPA officer so that any application is presented in a form which is likely to be acceptable and thus recommended for approval. Usually there are two main stumbling blocks to a planning application. One of these may be any planning consideration including the impact of the development on the amenity of the area itself. The other may be its effect on the road system and traffic generation. Also, in the case of pollution control systems, the LPA will want to ensure that the risk of potential nuisance, particularly from odours, is minimised. Here the importance of a proper farm waste plan is critical and may help to persuade the LPA that any proposal is acceptable. This is because it deals with the issues in their widest sense. It is not enough, nowadays, to consider merely whether a storage area for slurry from a livestock unit is adequate in itself. The Environment Agency (EA), as consultee, will want to know about the storage and disposal of all the related liquids as well as the solids and semi solids which are produced; whether storage is to be adequate and whether spreading areas are also adequate, bearing in mind ground porosity and proximity to water courses and underlying aquifers, particularly if these are sources of drinking water. Environmental issues are varied and their interaction within the scope of a planning application are likely to be wide. So decisions to proceed with a development should be taken long in advance. They should be planned rather as a military operation to ensure that all the logistics are in place. There should be allowance made for the possibility of refusal and appeals or revised applications, and finance should be organised appropriately. For example, an application for a new silage clamp and liquor store should not be left till spring with the hope of filling the clamp at the end of May in the same year! Long lead times are required for proper planning, allied to much patience and a good, tactical, approach. **4–16**

Lobbying

It is quite legitimate to speak with one or more members of a planning committee. One is normally sufficient, provided he is someone with good knowledge of agricultural practice. The purpose should be to give to the committee, through that member, a better grasp of certain salient facts which may not have been included within the planning officer's recommendation. The written recommendation amongst the committee papers is available to the public three working days before a committee meeting, so it is advisable to call at the council offices and obtain the report. After lobbying, the member should be able to consider the officer's recommendation in the light of better background knowledge, although attempts to **4–17** influence his mind positively are not to be recommended. The case must speak for itself.

If the recommendation is for refusal it may sometimes be prudent to withdraw the application. This must be done in writing. Some LPAs may agree to defer the application to a future committee, and to allow modifications to be submitted and agreed in the meantime. Other LPAs may be unwilling to defer applications. If an application is refused, or if a revised application is substantially the same as that refused, it may be resubmitted within 12 months at no additional fee.

Section 106 agreements

4–18 PPG 7 (Annex G) recommends that legal agreements, known as planning obligations, be used to tie farm buildings with a new dwelling. So where a new farm dwelling is agreed, the house will often be tied to the farm buildings and also to farm land so that one part cannot be sold off without the rest. This is so that a "viable" unit will remain. An alternative may be a unilateral planning obligation, again under Section 106 of the TCPA 1990. This allows the applicant to bind himself and his successors in title to certain covenants expressed in that agreement, normally made subject to the granting of a planning consent. This may be a useful device where a decision is likely to be borderline. A further practical problem is that the agricultural occupancy condition, which is normally applied as a matter of course, is likely to be placed not merely on the application dwelling, but on the original dwelling as well, if it was free of such condition. Whilst this is good planning and retains the "viable" unit, it affects substantially the value of the original dwelling. It is likely to suffer a reduction of between 20 and 50 per cent of its open market value as a result.

Appeals

4–19 If a refusal is issued or a consent granted on conditions which are unsatisfactory or unacceptable, then an appeal may be made within six calendar months of the date of the refusal or onerous conditions being received. There are normally three methods of appeal:

(i) Written representations.
(ii) An informal hearing,
(iii) Public inquiry.

Individual circumstances of each case should dictate which route is preferable and under all circumstances competent professional advice should be sought. At present costs may not be awarded in the case of written representations except for enforcement appeals but they are available in the case of hearings and public inquiries. A guide to the award of costs is found in DoE Circular 8/93. The question to be determined in seeking costs is whether one party or the other has been "unreasonable", at any stage during the course of appeal.

Enforcement

The enforcement regime, which was strengthened considerably in the TCPA 1990 and its subsequent amendments under the Planning and Compensation Act 1991, has provided new and stronger weapons to the armoury of the LPA. PPG 18—"Enforcing Control"—(1992) still advocates initial discussion with a view to the use of persuasion. Only if that fails should the tougher remedies available be used, unless immediate steps are necessary. An LPA is able to take enforcement action against a developer where the development is unauthorised, in whole or in part. If the development continues after an enforcement notice becomes effective then criminal proceedings may follow. **4–20**

The normal prelude to enforcement is the service of a planning contravention notice (PCN). This information-seeking questionnaire, which collects data on ownership, occupation, lessees, licensees, provides the legal basis on which formal proceedings may be started. The LPA may serve an enforcement notice requiring certain actions to be taken within a time period. Unless the notice is appealed within *one month*, it becomes operative. If it is appealed it does not become operative until the inspector's decision letter indicates when the time should start, if the appeal is lost. Once the notice comes into force, either by virtue of a lost appeal or no appeal, the notice lies with the land and is recorded on the Land Charges Register. It can be removed only with the agreement of the local authority or by a supervening planning consent.

In more serious cases the LPA may consider the use of an injunction or a stop notice. Injunctions can be sought now in the county court rather than in the High Court and the procedure is swifter and cheaper for the LPA. A stop notice may take immediate effect and is usually served together with an enforcement notice specifying the steps to be taken. However, if the stop notice is challenged at appeal and found to be have been wrongly administered, then the LPA lays itself open to a compensation claim. **4–21**

If the LPA begin enforcement proceedings, it will be only after the sanction of the planning committee. This is an important event both tactically and psychologically. Any enforcement notice which is associated with an area of land tarnishes that land, not only by being included within the Land Charges Register, if the notice succeeds, but it also effects the minds of both planners and the planning committee members. However hard they try to disassociate themselves with it, it is almost inevitable, human nature being what it is, for this to occur. So farmers, through the good advice and work of their agents, should use their best endeavours to stay away from such trouble. Where a planning condition has not been complied with, the LPA may issue a breach of condition notice (BCN). This gives 28 days, or other agreed time scale, for the work to be carried out. Failure to do so will lead to an immediate prosecution. There is no appeal to the Secretary of Sate. This is a swift and effective measure for the LPA.

Where an enforcement appeal is wholly or partly successful, it will mean a grant of a planning permission. The Town and Country Planning (Environmental Assessment and Unauthorised Development) Regulations

1995 (S.I. 1995 No. 2258) ensure that if a development was one which would have normally required an environment assessment, the LPA must serve a "Regulation 4 Notice" alongside the enforcement notice. This requires an environmental assessment to be provided.

On Farm Development

4–22 Some types of development are likely to have significant environmental impact. These may be "agricultural" in nature or they may be diversifications away from main-stream farming. They can be considered under various headings and are merely examples. The list is by no means exhaustive.

Noise
Trail riding, moto-cross, clay-pigeon shooting, rock concerts, raves, acid house parties, wind turbines, grain dryers, milking machine motors, bird scarers.

Intrusion
Land fill and land raise, mineral extraction, caravan sites, the physical presence of buildings, certain commercial and industrial uses of buildings.

Odours
Pig and poultry units with associated transport movements; calf rearing; cattle housing; the handling, storage and spreading of slurries, farm-yard manures and silage liquor; run off from brewer grains, silage odours.

Dust
Pig and Poultry units, mill and mix units, grain dryers.

Highway aspects
Traffic generation causing congestion and danger on narrow rural lanes from car boot sales, Sunday markets, haulage depots.

Burning of waste products
Farmers who wish to burn crop residues should have a good working knowledge of the "Crop Residues (Restrictions on Burning) (No. 2) Regulations 1991 (S.I. 1991 No. 1590). These were brought in under section 152 of the EPA 1990 as a direct result of numerous complaints against strawburning. The result had been soot and smut effecting property including washing on outside lines, hedgerows being burnt out accidently, and thick smoke across major roads causing traffic accidents. The Regulations are annexed in full. It will be seen that the restrictions on burning crop residues either as straw or stubble are now very significant. Failure to comply may result in substantial fines or imprisonment.

The creation of power stations to generate electricity from the combustion of a wide range of waste materials is becoming popular. They may use materials such as straw, poultry litter and scrap tyres.

PPG 22 also deals with the planning implications. Other types of power generation may come from the industrial use of sewage sludges and farm slurries.

In many of these areas the potential for environmental harm is substantial. A constructive approach is required both in terms of any planning application and resolution with planning officers. In some cases LPA's are likely to be hostile to any application say, for car-boot sales. Use must then be made of the 14-day exemption under the GPDO, as with clay-pigeon shoots.

Waste disposal

Provisions for landfill sites are becoming very restricted, given the government's concern for the minimisation of waste, reuse and recycling programmes and a punitive land-fill tax. Such sites are hard to come by except perhaps in terms of borrow pits or completed quarry workings. Planning consent is often given to such an area where the land concerned is required for construction of say a new road. Gravel may be extracted for construction purposes and the resulting holes are either back filled with inert fill, sub-soil or builders rubble, or sometimes left open to become ponds or lakes. Suitable and stringent landscaping conditions are imposed along with the planning consent. **4–23**

Landfill sites for domestic waste may give rise to pollution problems. Methane and other gases are produced by the degradation of the fill. However, some large sites have been successfully linked to bio-gas convertors for electricity production. At the same time leachate production from such sites may give rise to later contamination of nearby waters with a result that the site will be declared contaminated.

Renewable energy

To try to meet new and cleaner environmental targets for energy generation, the government has given encouragement over recent years to developers to find cleaner ways of electricity production using non-fossil fuels. The Non-Fossil Fuel Obligation (NoFFO) in its various rounds, has given encouragement to wind farms, bio-gas and water turbines, straw and bio-mass burning power stations. The use of wave power and solar energy, including photo voltaic cells have all been examined. Wind turbines have met particularly strong criticism because of the obvious requirement that they should be sited on exposed hill tops or up slopes where wind tends to be strongest. They are therefore very visible and have been examined in great detail particularly in Wales. PPG 22 on renewable energy has an Annex on wind energy. **4–24**

Rental of land to generators by farmers can become lucrative in the same way as for radio masts and transmitters. Nevertheless the turbines, because of their size, are highly visible and the moving blades create distractions in the landscape. In addition, given the right type of conditions, the noise from the turbines together with the blades can be substantial. On occasions, particularly in summer, noise can filter down from the hill tops into the valleys by a process known as the "sleepy hollow syndrome". Carcful siting and design of the turbines is critical.

Areas of conservation interest

4–25 There may be particular problems for farmers who wish to develop land which has a particular designation such as an SSSI. With such designation comes a schedule of operations which are restrictive and so any development proposals are likely to be examined very carefully. There may be areas with international designations such as wetlands under the RAMSAR Convention or Special Areas of Conservation. There may be site designations under the Conservation (Natural Habitats etc.) Regulations 1994 (S.I. 1994 No. 2716) and under the Wildlife and Countryside Act 1981.

In addition some councils have produced their own registers of land with biological or other ecological interest with various grades. Furthermore local councils in their development plans, create other areas, for example open space land, natural zones, etc. All these present problems for would be developers.

Planning fees

4–26 The payment of fees is governed by the Town and Country Planning (Fees for Applications and Deemed Applications) Regulations 1989 (S.I. 1989 No. 193) with various updates, the latest of which came into effect on January 3, 1995. Since fees are subject to periodic changes, it is prudent to check with the LPA the relevant fee for the application. There are special rates relating to prior notification applications under Part 6 of the GPDO. There are also certain exempt classes such as a reapplication of a substantially similar type within a 12-month period.

Planning and pollution

4–27 The inter-relationship between development control under the TCPA 1990, and pollution control under other legislation, is complex. The Guidance Note PPG 23 entitled "Planning and Pollution" attempts clarity but broadly fails. It states that planning and pollution control systems are separate but complementary, and that the planning system should not be operated so as to duplicate controls which are the statutory responsibility of other bodies, for example environmental health officers or officers from the Environment Agency (including local authorities in their non-planning functions). However, LPA's should consult pollution control authorities so that they can "take account of the scope and requirements of relevant pollution control". In practice many of these controls are safe guarded by means of planning conditions so there is inevitably an element of duplication. Where, for example, an intensive pig or poultry unit is likely to cause environmental problems through the production of dust or odours, planning conditions may detail the use of certain types of control equipment within the building and may also require that these are kept in good working order. If a problem arises the Environmental Health Department of the local authority may still proceed under the Environmental Protection Act by serving an abatement notice on the grounds that the result of the pollution is a statutory nuisance.

When a planning application is made that relates to development or change of use, either of which may give rise to pollution, planning factors themselves should be weighed up, not only by the LPA, but by the developer. PPG 23 details some of these. Paragraphs 3.2 and 3.3 are listed below because of their importance.

> "Material considerations may include:
> (i) The availability of land for potentially polluting development, taking into account its proximity to other development or land use, which may be affected.
> (ii) The sensitivity of the area, in particular as reflected in landscape, agricultural land quality, nature conservation or archaeological designations, if evidence suggests that there is a risk of such features being affected by pollution.
> (iii) The loss of amenity which the pollution would cause.
> (iv) Any particular environmental benefits, such as the regeneration of derelict land, or transport improvements.
> (v) The design of the site and the visual impact of the development, including, for example, transport mode and the impact on the road network and on the surrounding environment.
> (vi) The condition of the site itself, where it is known to be or likely to be contaminated, and any potential remediation.
> (vii) The proposed after use of the site, and feasibility of achieving restoration to the required standard where its intended use has limited duration.
> (viii) The potential use of mineral working sites for landfill.
> (ix) The hours of operation required by the development where these may have an impact on neighbouring land use.
> (x) The possibility of nuisance being caused, for example by the release of smoke, fumes, gases, dust, steam, smell or noise, where not controlled under Part one of the EPA 1990, or, in the case of waste facilities by birds, vermin or over-blown litter.
> (xi) Transport requirements arising from the need to transport polluting substances or waste, including the scope for transport by rail or water.
> (xii) The possibility of land contamination arising from the proposed development and protection and remediation measures as appropriate.
> (xiii) The impact of any discharge of effluent or leachate which may pose a threat to current and future surface or underground water resources or to adjacent areas.
> (xiv) The risk of toxic releases, whether on site or on access roads.
> (xv) The waste generated by the development including that arising from the preparation and construction phases and proposed arrangements for storage, treatment and disposal."

There is something in most of these paragraphs with which to concern any farmer developer. It is important to attempt to assess the weight which should be given to such considerations. There may also be countervailing benefits. to be borne in mind. These may include the economic benefits of a proposal, social benefits and the possibility of additional employment generation perhaps through recycling processes. As an example of the latter, the use of a separator for slurry, to remove liquids from solid 4–28 fractions, could result in a composted material which might be bagged and sold for garden fertilizer. This recycling benefit is enhanced by the creation of additional jobs. As discussed elsewhere, separation of solids and liquids is an important and indeed key element in dealing with slurries and farm manures. With an eye to the possibilities of processing waste, the wider strategy of the E.U. and the government includes waste minimisation, recycling and reuse of materials. As indicated in the previous chapter, every planning application will have an environmental dimension, because it in some way affects air and water and the general ambience of an area. However, the importance and degree to which necessary consideration is given to various facets of that environmental impact will depend upon the perception of those concerned including the statutory consultees and other representations which may be made.

Contaminated land

4–29 Part 2A of the EPA 1990 contains 28 clauses dealing with contaminated land (by virtue of section 57 of the Environment Act 1995). Contaminated land is defined at section 78A(2) as "any land which appears to the local Authority . . . to be in such a condition, by reason of substances in, on or under the land, that:—

(a) Significant harm is being caused or there is a significant possibility of such harm being caused; or
(b) Pollution of controlled waters is being, or is likely to be, caused. . . ."

This is an extremely wide-ranging definition. The methods of dealing with such land are currently being set out by the Department of Environment in regulations and statutory codes of practice under the Act. The essential principles are that the polluter should pay for the clean-up costs, or remediation. If he cannot be found then the owner or possibly the occupier is held liable. In some cases there may be several persons concerned. (Two volumes of draft statutory guidance on contaminated land have been produced by the DoE and Welsh Office. Annex A contains draft statutory guidance. This indicates that the primary regulatory role stays with local authorities, corresponds with statutory nuisance procedures and is complimentary to their role as planning authorities. Contaminated land is assessed on the basis of risk. The statutory guidance provides the details of the new regime and in particular the apportionment of liability. The regulations set out detailed technical procedures or working methods).

This approach can have alarming consequences for farmers who take on land which has already been contaminated. Problem areas are landfill sites which have been completed and restored to agriculture. There is often a danger of leachate appearing from these sites and getting into watercourses or indeed into underground aquifers. (Where there is a water pollution problem liability rests on those persons who caused the pollution or, under some circumstances, who now own the land, in accordance with the provisions of the Water Resources Act 1991). Costs of clean up can be very substantial, in fact much more than the ordinary value of the land itself. Farmers are urged to carry out proper evironmental checks before completion of a purchase of such land. Where land is bought in that condition it should be done so with eyes open and fully cognisant of the underlying risks. There is a test within the statutory guidelines relating to land which is "sold with information". Because this is so important, the text of the draft is set out below.

Test 3—"Sold with Information" **4–30**

58. The purpose of this test is to exclude from liability anyone who has knowingly caused or permitted the presence of significant pollutants and who has sold the land, or let it on a long lease, and has ensured that the purchaser or lessee had information as to the presence of those pollutants and thus had the opportunity to take that into account.

59. In applying this test, the authority should consider whether all the following circumstances exist:
   (a) one of the members of the liability group has sold the freehold interest and (or, in Scotland, an interest in the *dominium utile*) in the land in question to a person who is now another member of the liability group;
   (b) the sale took place at arms' length (that is, on terms which could be expected in a sale on the open market between a willing seller and a willing purchaser);
   (c) before the sale became binding, the purchaser had information that would reasonably allow that particular purchaser to be aware of the presence on the land of the pollutant identified in the significant pollutant linkage in question, and the broad measure of that presence; in transactions since 1990 between large commercial organisations, permission from the seller for the purchaser to carry out his own survey should normally be taken as sufficient indication that the purchaser had the necessary information;
   (d) the seller has done nothing material to the purchaser's decision to purchase to misrepresent the implications of that presence to the purchaser;
   (e) the seller had no further connection with the land after the date of the sale.

60. This test also applies in the equivalent circumstances in relation to a long lease rather than a sale of the freehold interest (or, in Scotland, a sale of an interest in the *dominium utile*). A "long lease" is a lease granted for a fixed period of more than 21 (or, in Scotland, 20) years under which the lessee satisfies the definition of "owner" in section 78A. In considering paragraph 59(e), holding the reversion under a long lease which had not taken effect by the date at which the authority first served a

notice under section 78(B)(3) in respect of land, significant pollutant linkage should not be regarded as a connection with the land.

61. If the circumstances in paragraph 59 apply, the authority should exclude the seller or lessor.
62. Where the application of this test results in the exclusion of any person, the subsequent tests should be applied as if:
    (a) the purchaser (or lessee) and the seller (or lessor) were a single person, and
    (b) the purchaser (or lessee) were that person.

    (In other words, the purchaser or lessee "steps into the shoes" of the seller or lessor with respect to liabilities relating to the significant pollutant linkage in question, and any liability thus incurred by the purchaser or lessee is in addition to any other liability he may incur in his own right).

4–31 There are a number of other tests, exclusions, reservations and clauses for deciding where responsibility and the cost of remediation should lie. Once the guidelines and regulations are formally published, they will become mandatory.

Another example of contaminated land likely to be found on the farm are burial sites for diseased cattle and dedicated sewage sludge disposal areas. Despite the strict controls on the disposal of sewage sludge under the Sludge (Use in Agriculture) Regulations 1989 (S.I. 1989 No. 1263 as amended by S.I. 1990 No. 880) there is a risk of build up of heavy metals.

A further cause for concern is that of neighbouring or nearby land from which pollution may escape and affect land belonging to the farmer. It is possible for contaminants by way of leachates, pollutants or toxic matter in above or underground waters to percolate great distances. Methane from landfill sites may also be trapped and find its way through strata to affect land outside the area of the site itself.

It should be noted that the problems of contaminated land relate directly to the existing use of that land. The land must be "fit for the purpose" for which it is currently being used. If there is a proposed use which requires tighter standards than can be met by the land in its present form, that is a matter for the planning system to deal with. In many cases, therefore, the land may continue to be safe for use for growing crops or grazing animals. The risk is more often from the percolation of leachate, or perhaps the emission of dangerous gases near to residential areas.

Planning checklist

4–32 1. Is planning permission required.
2. Is the proposed use agricultural and so exempt from the need to apply for planning permission under section 55E of the TCPA 1990?
3. Does the proposal benefit from permitted development rights under the GPDO?

4. Are the PD rights subject to prior notification?
5. Do you require an architect or agent?
6. Carry out informal consultations with LPA.
7. Have you diarised important time limits? If not, do it **now**!

Extract from Annex B of PPG 7: the Countryside and the Rural Economy—1992[1]

Livestock units and slurry

B3.1. Permitted development rights under Part 6 of the GDO do not extend to buildings to be used for the accommodation of livestock, or to associated structures such as slurry tanks and lagoons, when these are to be built within 400 metres of the curtilage of a "protected building". This applies to new buildings and structures, to ones created by the conversion of other farm buildings and structures erected under Part 6 since January 2, 1992 and to ones extended or altered under Class B. These may however be used for livestock in special circumstances (as defined in paragraph D.3 of Part 6 of the GDO). A full planning application is required for the livestock use of buildings and structures erected within the 400 metre cordon under Part 6 between 1988 and January 1, 1992, unless they were completed more than five years ago. **4–33**

B3.2. The term "protected building" includes most residential and other permanent buildings such as schools, hospitals and offices that are normally occupied by people. It excludes any building on the same agricultural unit, any farm dwelling or other farm building on another agricultural unit, and any building used for the special industrial uses covered by Classes B3–B7 of the Town and Country Planning (Use Classes) Order 1987 (S.I. 1987 No. 764). The 400 metres will usually be measured from the boundary of the land on which the "protected building" stands—for example, from the end of the garden of a house.

B3.3. To minimise the potential for future conflict between neighbouring land uses, local planning authorities should exercise particular care when considering planning applications for houses or other new "protected" buildings within 400 metres of established livestock units. By requiring planning permission for livestock units within the 400 metre cordon, the Government has recognised the potential risk of nuisance. This recognition should similarly apply to applications for new protected buildings. It is important also to have regard to the advice on not siting incompatible development close to animal waste processing factories in DoE Circular 43/76 (Welsh Office 17/76, MAFF 76/CSAWP/1), *Control of smells from the animal waste processing industry*.

B3.4. The spreading of slurry from livestock units for the purposes of agriculture is not subject to planning control. It remains important, however, to minimise the risk that such activities may cause nuisance from

[1] In course of revision.

noise or smell. Accordingly, those responsible for the operation of livestock units should follow the advice given in the new code of good agricultural practice for the protection of water published by the Ministry of Agriculture, Fisheries and Food and the Welsh Office Agriculture Department codes relating to the protection of air and soil which should be published in 1992.

B3.5. The Control of Pollution (Silage, Slurry and Agricultural Fuel Oil) Regulations 1991 (S.I. 1991 No. 324) set minimum standards for new, substantially reconstructed or enlarged silage, slurry or fuel oil facilities. The Regulations also empower the National Rivers Authority to serve notice requiring action to improve existing installations when they consider that there is a significant risk of pollution. Further guidance on these regulations is contained in "The Control of Pollution (Silage, Slurry and Agricultural Fuel Oil) Regulations 1991; Guidance Notes for Farmers" prepared by the Department of the Environment and the Welsh Office. The Regulations form an important part of the Government's commitment to reduce agricultural pollution of rivers. Local planning authorities are therefore encouraged to consider sympathetically development proposals aimed at meeting the requirements of these Regulations.

B3.6. Local planning authorities should in general adopt a positive approach towards development proposals which are designed, or are necessary, to achieve compliance with new environmental, hygiene and welfare legislation. For example, the Welfare of Pigs Regulations 1991 (S.I. 1991 No. 1477) prohibit the installation of stall and tether systems from October 1, 1991 and ban the use of these systems altogether from January 1, 1999. Currently, up to 70 per cent of sows in the United Kingdom are housed in stall and tether systems. Farmers using these close confinement systems are likely to need to double the space allocation for sows and provide extra storage space for bedding straw and solid manure. Planning applications for associated building development may therefore be necessary.

Extract from The Town & Country Planning General Development Order 1988—Part 6

AGRICULTURAL BUILDINGS AND OPERATIONS

4–34 Class A Development on units of 5 hectares or more

Permitted development

A. The carrying out on agricultural land comprised in an agricultural unit of 5 hectares or more in an area of—

(a) works for the erection, extension or alteration of a building; or

(b) any excavation or engineering operations,

which are reasonably necessary for the purposes of agriculture within that unit.

Development not permitted

A.1 Development is not permitted by Class A if—

(a) the development would be carried out on a separate parcel of land forming part of the unit which is less than 1 hectare in area;

(b) it would consist of, or include, the erection, extension or alteration of a dwelling;

(c) it would involve the provision of a building, structure or works not designed for agricultural purposes;

(d) the ground area which would be covered by—

(i) any works or structure (other than a fence) for accommodating livestock or any plant or machinery arising from engineering operations; or

(ii) any building erected or extended or altered by virtue of this Class,

would exceed 465 square metres, calculated as described in paragraph D.2;

(e) the height of any part of any building, structure or works within 3 kilometres of the perimeter of an aerodrome would exceed 3 metres;

(f) the height of any part of any building, structure or works not within 3 kilometres of the perimeter of an aerodrome would exceed 12 metres;

(g) any part of the development would be within 25 metres of a metalled part of a trunk or classified road;

(h) it would consist of, or include, the erection or construction of, or the carrying out of any works to, a building, structure or an excavation used or to be used for the accommodation of livestock or for the storage of slurry or sewage sludge where the building, structure or excavation is, or would be, within 400 metres of the curtilage of a protected building; or

(i) it would involve excavations or engineering operations or over article 1(6) land which are connected with fish farming.

Conditions

A.2(1) Development is permitted by Class A subject to the following conditions—

(a) where development is carried out within 400 metres of the curtilage of a protected building, any building, structure, excavation or works resulting from the development shall not be used for the accommodation of livestock except in the circumstances described in paragraph D.3 or for the storage of slurry or sewage sludge;

(b) where the development involves—
  (i) the extraction of any mineral from the land (including removal from any disused railway embankment); or
  (ii) the removal of any mineral from a mineral-working deposit, the mineral shall not be moved off the unit;

(c) waste materials shall not be brought on to the land from elsewhere for deposit except for use in works described in Class A(a) or in the creation of a hard surface and any materials so brought shall be incorporated forthwith into the building or works in question.

(2) Subject to paragraph (3), development consisting of—
  (i) the erection, extension or alteration of a building;
  (ii) the formation or alteration of a private way;
  (iii) the carrying out of excavations or the deposit of waste material (where the relevant area, as defined in paragraph D.4 below exceeds 0.5 hectare); or
  (iv) the placing or assembly of a tank in any waters,

is permitted by Class A subject to the following conditions—

(a) the developer shall, before beginning the development apply to the local planning authority for a determination as to whether the prior approval of the authority will be required to the siting, design and external appearance of the building, the siting and means of construction of the private way, the siting of the excavation or deposit of the siting and appearance of the tank, as the case may be;

(b) the application shall be accompanied by a written description of the proposed development and of the materials to be used and a plan indicating the site together with any fee required to be paid;

(c) the development shall not be begun before the occurrence of one of the following—
  (i) the receipt by the applicant from the local planning authority notice of a written notice of their determination that such prior approval is not required;
  (ii) where the local planning authority gives the applicant notice within 28 days following the date of receiving his application of their determination that such prior approval is required, the giving of such approval; or

(iii) the expiry of 28 days following the date on which the application was received by the local planning authority without the local planning authority making any determination as to whether such approval is required or notifying the applicant of their determination;

[(cc) (i) where the local planning authority gives the applicant notice that such prior approval is required the applicant shall display a site notice by site display on or near the land on which the proposed development is to be carried out, leaving the notice in position for not less than 21 days in the period of 28 days from the date on which the local planning authority gave the notice to the applicant;

(ii) the applicant shall not be treated as not having complied with the requirements of sub-paragraph (i) if the site notice is, without any fault or intention of his, removed, obscured or defaced before the period of 21 days referred to in that sub-paragraph has elapsed, if he has taken reasonable steps for its protection and, if need be, replacement;]

(d) the development shall, except to the extent that the local planning authority otherwise agree in writing, be carried out—

(i) where prior approval is required in accordance with the details approved;

(ii) where prior approval is not required, in accordance with the details submitted with the application; and

(e) the development shall be carried out—

(i) where approval has been given by the local planning authority, within a period of five years from the date on which approval was given;

(ii) in any other case, within a period of five years from the date on which the local planning authority were given the information referred to in sub-paragraph (b)

(3) The conditions in paragraph (2) do not apply to the extension or alteration of a building if the building is not on article 1(6) land except in the case of significant alteration or a significant extension.

(4) Development consisting of the significant extension or the significant alteration of a building may only be carried out once by virtue of Class A(a).

4–35 Class B development on units of less than 5 hectares

Permitted development

B. The carrying out on agricultural land comprised in an agricultural unit of not less than 0.4 but less than 5 hectares in area of development consisting of—
(a) the extension or alteration of an agricultural building;
(b) the installation of additional or replacement plant or machinery;
(c) the provision, rearrangement or replacement of a sewer, main, pipe, cable or other apparatus;
(d) the provision, rearrangement or replacement of a private way;
(e) the creation of a hard surface;
(f) the deposit of waste; or
(g) the carrying out of any of the following operations in connection with fish farming, namely, repairing ponds and raceways; the installation of grading machinery, aeration equipment or flow meters and any associated channel; the dredging of ponds; and the replacement of tanks and nets,
where the development is reasonably necessary for the purposes of agriculture within the unit.

Development not permitted

B.1 Development is not permitted by Class B if—
(a) the development would be carried out on a separate parcel of land forming part of the unit which is less than 0.4 hectare in area;
(b) the external appearance of the premises would be materially affected;
(c) any part of the development would be within 25 metres of a metalled part of a trunk or classified road;
(d) it would consist of, or involve, the carrying out of any works to a building or structure used or to be used for the accommodation of livestock or the storage of slurry or sewage sludge where the building or structure is within 400 metres of the curtilage of a protected building; or
(e) it would relate to fish farming and would involve the placing or assembly of a tank on land or in any waters or the construction of a pond in which fish may be kept or an increase (otherwise than by the removal of silt) in the size of any tank or pond in which fish may be kept.

B.2 Development is not permitted by Class B(a) if—

(a) the height of any building would be increased;
(b) the cubic content of the original building would be increased by more than 10 per cent;
(c) any part of any new building would be more than 30 metres from the original building;
(d) the development would involve the extension, alteration or provision of a dwelling;
(e) any part of the development would be carried out within 5 metres of any boundary of the unit; or
(f) the ground area of any building extended by virtue of this Class would exceed 465 square metres.

B.3 Development is not permitted by Class B(b) if—
(a) the height of any additional plant or machinery within 3 kilometres of the perimeter of an aerodrome would exceed 3 metres;
(b) the height of any additional plant or machinery not within 13 kilometres of the perimeter of an aerodrome would exceed 12 metres;
(c) the height of any replacement plant or machinery would exceed that of the plant or machinery being replaced; or
(d) the area to be covered by the development would exceed 465 square metres calculated as described in paragraph D.2 below.

B.4 Development is not permitted by Class B(e) if the area to be covered by the development would exceed 465 square metres calculated as described in paragraph D.2 below.

Conditions

B.5 Development permitted by Class B and carried out within 400 metres of the curtilage or a protected building is subject to the condition that any building which is extended or altered, or any works resulting from the development, shall not be used for the accommodation of livestock except in the circumstances described in paragraph D.3 or for the storage of slurry or sewage sludge.

B.6 Development consisting of the extension or alteration of a building situated on article 1(6) land or the provision, rearrangement or replacement of a private way on such land is permitted subject to—
(a) the condition that the developer shall, before beginning the development, apply to the local planning authority for a determination as to whether the prior approval of the authority will be required to the siting, design and external

appearance of the building as extended or altered or the siting and means of construction of the private way; and

(b) the conditions set out in paragraphs A.2(2)(b) to (e) above.

B.7 Development is permitted by Class B(f) subject to the following conditions—

(a) that waste materials are not brought on to the land from elsewhere for deposit unless they are for use in works described in Class B(a), (d) or (e) and are incorporated forthwith into the building or works in question; and

(b) that the height of the surface of the land will not be materially increased by the deposit.

4–36 Class C mineral working for agricultural purposes

Permitted development

C. The winning and working on land held or occupied with land used for the purposes of agriculture of any mineral reasonably necessary for agricultural purposes within the agricultural unit of which it forms part.

Development not permitted

C.1 Development is not permitted by Class C if any excavation would be made within 25 metres of a metalled part of a trunk or classified road.

Condition

C.2 Development is permitted by Class C subject to the condition that no mineral extracted during the course of the operation shall be moved to any place outside the land from which it was extracted, except to land which is held or occupied with that land and is used for the purposes of agriculture.

4–37 **Interpretation of Part 6**

D.1 For the purposes of Part 6—

"agricultural land" means land which, before development permitted by this Part is carried out, is land in use for agriculture and which is so used for the purposes of a trade or business, and excludes any dwellinghouse or garden;

"agricultural unit" means agricultural land which is occupied as a unit for the purposes of agriculture, including—

(a) any dwelling or other building on that land occupied for the purposes of farming the land by the person who occupies the unit, or

(b) any dwelling on that land occupied by a farmworker;

"building" does not include anything resulting from engineering operations;

"fish farming" means the breeding, rearing or keeping of fish or shellfish (which includes any kind of crustacean and mollusc);

"livestock" includes fish or shellfish which are farmed;

"protected building" means any permanent building which is normally occupied by people or would be so occupied, if it were in use for purposes for which it is apt; but does not include—

- (i) a building within the agricultural unit;
- (ii) a building used for a purpose referred to in Classes B3 to B7 (special industrial uses) of the Schedule to the Use Class Order, or
- (iii) a dwelling or other building on another agricultural unit which is used for or in connection with agriculture;

"significant extension" and **"significant alteration"** mean any extension or alteration of the building where the cubic content of the original building would be exceeded or altered would exceed the height of the original building; and

"tank" includes any cage and any other structure for use in fish farming.

D.2 For the purposes of this Part—

- (a) an area calculated as described in this paragraph comprises the ground which would be covered by the proposed development, together with the ground area of any building (other than a dwelling), or any structure, works, plant, machinery or ponds or tanks within the same unit which are being provided or have been provided within the preceding two years and any part of which would be within 90 metres of the proposed development;
- (b) 400 metres is to be measured along the ground.

D.3 The circumstances referred to in paragraphs A2(1)(a) and B.5 are that no other suitable building or structure, 400 metres or more from the curtilage of a protected building, is available to accommodate the livestock; and

- (a) that the need to accommodate it arises from—
  - (i) quarantine requirements;
  - (ii) an emergency due to another building or structure in which the livestock could otherwise be accommodated being unavailable because it has been damaged or destroyed by fire, flood or storm; or

(b) in the case of animals normally kept out of doors they require temporary accommodation in a building or other structure—
   (i) because they are sick or giving birth or newly born; or
   (ii) to provide shelter against extreme weather conditions.

D.4 For the purposes of paragraph A.2(2)(iii) the relevant area is the area of the proposed excavation or the area on which it is proposed to deposit waste together with the aggregate of the areas of all other excavations within the unit which have not been filled and of all other parts of the unit on or under which waste has been deposited and has not been removed.

[D.4A In paragraph A.2(2)(cc) **"site notice"** means a notice containing—
(a) the name of the applicant,
(b) the address or location of the proposed development,
(c) a description of the proposed development and of the materials to be used,
(d) a statement that the prior approval of the authority will be required to the siting, design and external appearance of the building, the siting and means of construction of the private way, the siting of the excavation or deposit or the siting and appearance of the tank, as the case may be,
(e) the name and address of the local planning authority,

and which is signed and dated by or on behalf of the applicant.]

D.5 For the purposes of Class B—
(a) the erection of any additional building within the curtilage of another building is to be treated as the extension of that building and the additional building is not to be treated as an original building;
(b) where two or more original buildings are within the same curtilage and are used for the same undertaking they are to be treated as a single original building in making any measurement in connection with the extension or alteration of either of them.

D.6 In Class C, **"the purposes of agriculture"** includes fertilising land used for the purposes of agriculture and the maintenance, improvement or alteration of any buildings, structures or works occupied or used for such purposes on land so used.

Chapter 5

Water Pollution from Diffuse Sources —Nutrients and Pesticides

Introduction

5–01 Water pollution is most often thought of as relating to spillages of toxic materials which are often associated with catastrophic consequences for water quality and aquatic life such as fish. There is another more insidious process whereby small quantities of a potential pollutant seep into water over a wide area. This is described as pollution from diffuse sources. Often there is no dramatic consequence, but simply a presence in water of a substance somewhat above the normally accepted concentration. This is a problem which is particularly likely to occur with agriculture because of its ubiquitous presence in the catchments of almost all water sources, and because of the integration of farming activities into the environment. The materials involved are plant nutrients and plant health products (pesticides) and although as yet there is relatively little specific legislation addressing this type of pollution, it seems inevitable that more will be introduced in due course.

This chapter describes the background and problems arising from diffuse pollution in agriculture. What legislation there is largely relates to nitrate pollution and we describe the legislation currently in force or in the process of implementation in this area. We also discuss in some depth the development of the United Kingdom's approach to the nitrate issue, the different control systems and how they may affect farmers, and the administrative procedure by which areas for control have been defined and designated. The experience with nitrates may assume particular significance in the future were controls to be extended to other agricultural pollutants from diffuse sources.

Nutrients

5–02 Nutrients are essential for plant growth. They are the elements which are used to build the more complex chemicals and proteins comprising plant tissue and which animals use as food. The main ones are nitrogen, phosphorus and potassium, although of these nitrogen is the most important. A variety of trace nutrients, for example zinc, are also required in smaller quantities.

It may seem strange that pollution can occur from materials which are nutrients and therefore beneficial for plants. But nutrients are not toxic in the normal sense and the problem is, as we have said, rather one arising from excessive concentrations. This can occur when nutrients escape into environments for which they were not intended, particularly the water environment. Agriculture, moreover, is not the only source of nutrients in the environment. Nitrogen compounds, for example, arise from combustion in vehicle engines and from electricity generation in particular. They are also by-products of human biological processes (sewage), of natural decomposition and of electrical storms in the atmosphere. The routes by which such substances reach the water environment are often the normal pathways of atmospheric dispersion and deposition, rainfall, and eventually, water flow from the soil via watercourses and groundwater to the sea.

A particular feature of nitrogen, and to a lesser extent phosphorus, is that it is soluble in water, which makes it particularly mobile. This, combined with the fact that most farming activities take place on the many thousands of acres in the environment, means that this pollution cannot be regulated by those procedures designed to control discharges from specified points or pipes, such as when emerging from factories. Diffuse pollution by nutrients can therefore be difficult to control. It requires much broader measures of a pre-emptive nature which aim at restricting those types of operations at risk of causing pollution.

Since the problems occur largely in the water environment, nutrient pollution has been addressed mainly through water legislation. Much of this has emanated from Europe, and is likely to expand further. Not all of the E.U. legislation agreed to date has yet been fully incorporated in United Kingdom law due to implementation timetables, but there is little doubt that the United Kingdom will comply with its obligations to introduce all of the appropriate legislation in due course.

Nitrate

Description

Nitrate is a compound of nitrogen which itself is an abundant element making up about 80 per cent of the atmosphere, and which is crucial for all forms of life. Yet, in spite of its abundance, nitrogen is frequently the element in shortest supply for plant growth. This is because animals and most plants cannot extract "pure" nitrogen directly from the atmosphere, but can only absorb it in compound form. In the case of plants, this is mainly in the form of nitrate from the soil. **5–03**

Most nitrate in the soil is produced and released naturally as dead plant and animal tissues are broken down by micro-organisms. However, this naturally-occurring nitrate is in relatively short supply in most natural ecosystems and is not usually sufficient on its own to allow most plants—at least commercial ones—to achieve their potential growth. Yields of most farm crops are increased by providing additional supplies of nitrogen compounds to the soil in the form of animal manures or manufactured fertiliser containing nitrogen. Wheat yields, for example, can be doubled or trebled by supplying additional nitrogen. One plant family, known as legumes, does not require the addition of nitrogen fertiliser. These crops, which include peas and beans are able to obtain nitrogen from the air through micro-organisms sheltering in the nodules on their roots.

Despite any drawbacks, nitrogen fertilisers today are an essential part of the agricultural technology which has enabled the high yield potential of modern agricultural crop varieties to be exploited. Great increases in crop production worldwide have played a major part in transforming scarcity into relative plenty in many countries during recent decades, and given the rapidly growing world population and likely increasing influence of climate change, the role of nitrogen fertilisers in securing adequate food supplies seems set to continue.

Hazards

5–04 Once in the wider environment in areas where it is not required, excessive quantities of nitrate can be harmful to human health and to sea life. The following section briefly describes these health and ecological hazards.

(a) Health

5–05 Health hazards largely relate to methaemoglobinaemia, or "blue baby syndrome", and to possible links to gastric cancer. Methaemoglobinaemia is a condition which can occur in young, bottle-fed infants when bacterial contamination of water occurs together with high nitrate levels. Treatment is simple and recovery complete once the condition has been identified, allowing the withdrawal of the contaminated water. Unfortunately, if the condition is not identified, it can be fatal.

The combination of bacterial contamination and high nitrate levels are typical of waters polluted with sewage or farmyard waste. But in the United Kingdom, where more than 99 per cent of the population is connected to public water supplies, only about a dozen cases have ever been suspected, one of which was fatal. The last suspected case was in 1972. In the view of the World Health Organisation, methaemoglobinaemia had ceased to occur in Western Europe by 1989 and this is certainly the case in the United Kingdom on the basis of the above information.

A link has also been suggested between nitrate levels and gastric cancer. Epidemiological and other work has not supported this, since there is a tendency for high nitrate levels to occur in parts of the country where gastric cancer incidence is lowest, and vice versa. Although it is almost impossible to entirely disprove the suggested link, the Government's Chief Medical Officer has concluded that the evidence as a whole gives no support to the suggestion of a link between nitrate and cancer of the stomach, or indeed of any other organ letter from Sir Donald Acheson to Department of the Environment, August 26, 1988. There is even some recent work suggesting that nitrate may in fact be beneficial for health. (*Benjamin*, 1994)

There is little doubt that a standard is needed to ensure that human health is not subject to a significant risk. However, the rigour appropriate to such a standard is the subject of differing approaches. The World Health

Organisation recommends a guideline figure of 50 mg/l applied as an average, whereas the E.U. enforces the same figure but as a maximum never to be exceeded.

(b) Ecological

In the environment, high levels of nitrate in water can cause excessive growth of some plants, especially algae. This is known as eutrophication, which is defined in the Code of Good Agricultural Practice for Soil as "the enrichment of water by nitrogen or phosphorus, causing algae and higher forms of plant life to grow too fast which disturbs the balance of organisms present in the water and the quality of the water concerned". It can have devastating effects on aquatic life, as well as causing scums and deposits which humans find unpleasant, for example on holiday beaches. Fresh waters are usually less vulnerable to nitrate-induced eutrophication problems since plant and algal growth is normally constrained by phosphorus being in relatively short supply. In marine and estuarine waters, where phosphorus is more abundant, the level of nitrate becomes the determining factor for the amount of algal growth and where this is also high then the waters are liable to become eutrophic. 5–06

Eutrophication problems tend to occur in coastal areas where the waters are shallow, or where there is limited tidal movement, both of which tend to reduce the dispersion and dilution which normally occurs where rivers enter the sea. The Baltic, the eastern North Sea and the northern Adriatic Sea are examples of areas in the E.U. which experience such conditions and eutrophication of these waters is a recognised problem.

Little nitrate-limited eutrophication has been identified in the United Kingdom. Coasts here have strong tidal movements and waters tend to be deeper. The nitrate load of rivers in the United Kingdom is also much less than that of the larger Continental rivers, which often flow through a number of countries collecting nitrate along their paths. Nevertheless work is in progress around the United Kingdom coast to monitor conditions to determine whether waters should be regarded as eutrophic. Should eutrophication be identified, the catchments of rivers draining into these waters are likely to be affected by European legislation requiring them to be designated as Nitrate Vulnerable Zones (NVZs).

Sources of nitrate

Agriculture is an important source of nitrate entering the environment, but so are sewage and atmospheric deposition, while in certain situations airfield de-icers may be important. Lightning can also make a contribution. Atmospheric deposition arises largely from vehicles, the electricity supply industry and from ammonia emissions from agricultural livestock. Some nitrates from these other sources find their way either directly into watercourses (for example sewage and industrial effluents) or indirectly, via the land, as in the case of atmospheric deposition. 5–07

(a) Agriculture

Agriculture is generally the best-known source of nitrate entering water supplies, and it is commonly assumed that nitrogen fertilisers cause nitrate levels in drainage water from agricultural land to increase. The truth is 5–08 rather more complex. The beginnings of "the nitrate problem" in the United Kingdom in fact occurred during the Second World War and continued in subsequent years when extensive areas of grassland were ploughed for conversion to arable cropping in the push to raise national self-sufficiency in food production. Little use of nitrogen fertilisers was made at that time, but it is now known that ploughing long-established grassland releases much larger quantities of nitrate from the accumulated organic matter of the pasture than can be utilised by any succeeding crop. This release process led to high levels of nitrate leaching which continued, albeit on a declining trend, for many years. The natural process of nitrate release from the breakdown of the very large reserves of organic matter in the soil, particularly under the warm, damp conditions in the autumn, is also a particular feature of arable cropping. Crops have little opportunity to take up this nitrate before the onset of water passing through the soil from winter rains and this process constitutes one of the main sources of nitrate escape, known as leaching.

Although the general principles and the importance of soil organic matter in nitrate leaching are now well understood, the system is so complex and variable, particularly on account of the weather, that accurate predictions of nitrate release are still not a realistic prospect. Nevertheless, correct management of the soil is vital to minimising leaching and it is in the farmer's best interests to try and bear these things in mind when deciding on farming practices on economic grounds and to avoid future controls.

Animal manures are another important source of nitrate, and, as in the case of soil organic matter, the rate of release is rather difficult to predict. Again, careful management of the timing and rate of manure applications to land are needed to minimise leaching. Similarly, the residues of pea and bean plants remaining after harvest are an important source of nitrate, and leaching from these crops tends to be greater than from cereals and sugar beet, despite not receiving nitrogen fertilisers.

5–09 These examples illustrate that nitrogen fertilisers are not the proximate cause of a great deal of nitrate leaching. In fact, fertiliser nitrate has the great advantage of being released into the soil more quickly and more predictably than naturally occurring sources, thus enabling nitrate to be provided to the crop when it is needed, and in the quantities which are required. Research findings have demonstrated that accurate applications leave very little unused fertiliser to be leached after the crop has ceased to take it up, as occurs with manures and other organic sources of nitrate.

But predicting fertiliser requirements is not an exact science. It is influenced by factors outside man's control such as the weather, which affect crop growth and yield after fertiliser has been applied. This means that, for example, in the case of drought-affected crops, nutrients may at times be in excess and liable to escape when sufficient rainfall does occur. Also like any other source of nitrate, fertiliser nitrogen which has been taken up by the crop but remains in the field in the form of roots, stubble or other crop residues enters the "pool" of organic nitrogen and becomes difficult to control. To the extent that nitrogen fertilisers increase the amouunt of nitrogen circulating through the "pool", they do inevitably play a part in the leaching which accompanies modern agriculture.

In the case of land draining directly to river systems, nitrate released from the soil and not taken up by crops will mainly find its way to the sea in the same winter that it is washed out of the soil by rainfall. But on areas of "light" soils, where the land drains to underground aquifers contained in porous rocks such as sandstone, limestone or chalk, the nitrate will gradually percolate downwards to the water table before it is pumped out for human use, or emerges as springs. In some situations this may take 40 years. In southern and eastern England, extensive outcrops of chalk provide the catchments for a major aquifer which forms an important part of the public water supplies and large numbers of water company boreholes utilising this source are distributed over the aquifer. The catchments of these boreholes are predominantly agricultural land. High concentrations of nitrate, and the consequent breaching of the drinking water standard of 50 mg/l, is a feature of low-rainfall areas such as eastern England, where there is insufficient water to dilute concentrations of nitrate to acceptable levels during the winter months when drainage from such land takes place.

(b) Sewage

Each of us excretes about 5 kg N/year, and sewage is a major source of nitrogen entering the environment. For the most part, it is gathered together at sewage treatment works, and the nitrogen remaining after the process is then partly released into rivers and streams in their discharges, constituting potential point source pollution. It is also contained in the sludge which is removed from the works. About half of such sludge is spread on agricultural land, sometimes at rates which exceed the ability of crops to absorb it. The discharges to water are licenced by the Environment Agency, and the effluent from smaller works can contain 200 mg nitrate/l or more. Larger works are regulated by the Urban Waste Water Treatment Directive and have more sophisticated treatment to reduce nitrate to lower concentrations. In summer, when there is little or no water draining from farmland, sewage effluent is often the major source of nitrate in rivers. Some rivers such as the River Lea in Hertfordshire, have been particularly heavily influenced by sewage discharges. Quantities of sewage sludge applied to agricultural land are increasing as other disposal routes, such as dumping at sea, are closed, and as more sewage is treated to higher standards. **5–10**

The effect of sewage on groundwater is not well documented. Considerable numbers of small sewage works and septic tanks discharge to soakaways of one sort or another—sometimes watercourses which are dry for much of the year—and the effluent can percolate down to the groundwater. In addition, much of the sewage sludge which is disposed of to agricultural land is applied on light soils which drain to groundwaters. There are a number of examples where, in the past, sewage undertakers applied excessive quantities and caused or contributed substantially to nitrate pollution of groundwaters.

(c) De-icers

5–11 While salt is the de-icer of choice on most roads on grounds of cost, there are some situations where its corrosive properties are unacceptable. These include airfields and elevated sections of motorways. The principal alternative to salt has often been industrial urea, a chemical containing about 46 per cent nitrogen (as compared to 34 per cent in ammonium nitrate, the commonest nitrogen fertiliser in the United Kingdom). All-weather airfields may use very substantial quantities of urea in a severe winter, and much of the nitrogen will drain into rivers or groundwater. These have the potential to have a significant local impact on water sources from rivers or aquifers.

(d) Lightning

5–12 The fixation of nitrogen by lightning is very similar to a commercial process of fertiliser manufacture by means of an electric arc. Globally, the amounts fixed by lightning represent a significant addition to the nitrogen available for plant growth. But in the developed world where agriculture utilises relatively high fertiliser applications, lightning is of minor importance as a nitrogen source and it is not considered to be important in nitrate leaching. Inevitably though, it provides unplanned additions of nitrogen and it is likely that much of the input from lightning will contribute to leaching in these circumstances.

(e) Atmospheric deposition

5–13 Atmospheric deposition involves nitrogen compounds which find their way into the atmosphere from a variety of sources and recent research has shown these to contribute very significant quantities of nitrogen to land over wide areas of the country. These nitrogen compounds arise predominantly from man-made processes and in particular from high temperature combustion in vehicle engines and power stations. Ammonia from livestock, particularly cattle, is also believed to make a significant contribution. Ammonia tends to be deposited closer to its sources than the other important compounds and is probably less significant than its total emissions would suggest since the dairy and beef industries are predominantly in the wetter west where nitrate is less of a problem. Ammonia emissions may be addressed by measures proposed for certain larger intensive livestock units under the draft European Union Directive on Integrated Pollution Prevention and Control (see Chapter 8).

Nitrogen deposited on agricultural land during the growing period will be taken up by crops as part of their nutrient requirement. This nitrogen therefore probably makes little impact on nitrate pollution, since recommended fertiliser application rates are calculated from field trials, which themselves will receive atmospheric deposition and automatically take account of that part of the deposited nitrogen which is utilised by the crop. However, nitrogen deposited at times of the year when the nitrate formed from it is not taken up by the crop will be leached from the soil and so does contribute to pollution. The extent of this pollution is difficult to measure, but recent work carried out by Rothamsted Research Station estimates that atmospheric deposition contributed 29 per cent of nitrate leached (*Powlson and Goulding*, 1995). The contribution may be more or less in other areas, but this result is very significant in the light of the legislation being imposed on agriculture to control the nitrate problem.

Control techniques

In the mid 1980s, during the implementation of the 1980 Drinking Water Directive, the government began to address the question of controlling nitrate levels in water. There are two main approaches to complying with nitrate standards for drinking water—"prevention" and "cure". The "cure" option involves the water industry treating water to remove nitrate, or in blending high nitrate water with water from lower nitrate sources. About a dozen such nitrate removal plants have now been installed, mainly operated by Anglian Water Services plc. Most other water companies have opted for blending, but in the Anglian area supplies of low nitrate water for blending are not always available. **5–14**

The "prevention" option involves reductions of nitrate at source. This is being addressed mainly through agriculture and is being effected through two main routes in the United Kingdom. The first is to encourage farmers to follow "Good Agricultural Practice" (GAP) and a Code of Good Agricultural Practice has been in existence since 1985, when it was introduced in accordance with section 31 of the Control of Pollution Act 1974. The original version of the Code was superceded by separate Codes for the Protection of Water, Air and Soil, published in 1991–1993.[1] The current Water Code, which is statutory in the sense that it is referred to in the Water Resources Act 1991, includes a section dealing with means of reducing nitrate leaching. This approach is also the main thrust of measures currently proposed under the E.U. Nitrates Directive.

It is important to recognise that the benefits to be obtained from the good practice approach are limited. Nitrate leaching from productive agriculture is unavoidable, and where this occurs with either sandy/shallow soils or low rainfall, the most careful and conscientious farmer may have difficulty in complying with the standard. A second main route for controlling nitrate goes beyond good practice measures and involves modifying or restricting agriculture. This approach is the main thrust of the United Kingdom Nitrate Sensitive Areas (NSA) scheme introduced in 1990, but it is also implicit in the Nitrate Directive to some extent, such as where restrictions on manure application go beyond GAP. Some non-agricultural sources are also being addressed but in many instances rather less formally and less directly. Emissions from electricity generation are being reduced by the installation of "low-NOx" burners in certain power stations. In transport, whilst the progressive introduction of three-way catalytic converters on petrol-engined vehicles can substantially reduce emissions of nitrogen compounds, rapid growth of traffic will tend to offset this. For airfields, some encouragement is being given to airfield operators to switch

[1] Available free of charge from MAFF Publications, London SE99 7TP.

from urea to glycols for use as de-icers. This is despite the suspicion that glycols may be more harmful to the environment than urea. In respect of sewage, action is in hand under the Urban Waste Water Treatment Directive to reduce nitrogen in effluents but only from the larger sewage treatment plants. In NVZs, rates of application of sewage sludge to farmland will be subject to similar limits to animal manures.

5–15 The voluntary Code of Good Agricultural Practice for the protection of Water (CGAP 1991) was intended to raise general awareness of the importance of following good practice and to give general guidance on such practices. The main elements are as follows:

Fertiliser — ensure fertiliser rates are correctly calculated;
— ensure the timing of fertiliser applications are correct;
— ensure the fertiliser spreader is properly calibrated.

Manure — apply no more than 250 kg nitrogen/ha in organic manure;
— do not apply more available nitrogen in manure than the crop can utilise.

General — do not apply fertiliser or manure when the risk of run off is high;
— establish the following crop as soon as possible after grassland is ploughed.

These measures are intended to avoid excess nitrogen being applied, and to maximise the chances of the nitrate which is present being utilised by the crop. It is intended only to avoid excess applications in the case of fertiliser and as such it should not impose net costs on farmers, and may in fact offer savings. The optimum rate of fertiliser application is that beyond which the value of any extra crop yield obtained is offset by the cost of the additional fertiliser. It is therefore lower than the rate which will achieve the maximum yield, but it is the most profitable rate to use. In the case of manures, costs may be involved if a farmer is currently applying manures in such a way as to cause serious leaching losses. This is wasteful of the nutrients within the manures, and farmers should ensure that they take account of the fertiliser value. The principle is for manure spreading arrangements to both fit in with the farm system and to observe the maximum levels of application, while utilising as much as possible the nutrients contained within the manure for crop growth.

When further nitrate reductions beyond those which can be achieved by good agricultural practice are required, the necessary action must involve some modification in agricultural practice, by reducing the intensity, changing the type of farming practised or even ceasing farming some of the land. Useful reductions in leaching can be achieved by relatively minor modifications, for example by growing cover crops on land that would otherwise be bare soil over the winter, prior to the establishment of spring sown crops. In other situations the changes required are more dramatic, particularly where crops are grown that are prone to high levels of nitrate leaching. These include brassicas grown as vegetables (cabbage, cauliflower, sprouts), potatoes, peas, beans and oilseed rape, and it is for this reason that potatoes and vegetable brassicas are severely restricted on land in the NSA scheme.

The disposal of manure from keeping of livestock under intensive systems is an important cause of nitrate leaching problems. The manure needs to be spread with care, and at controlled rates, and in the case of broiler manure the requirements of the Nitrate Directive dictate that it be spread at lower rates than many machines are capable of applying. The requirement to spread manure more thinly means that additional land will also be required for spreading, and where there are closed periods for spreading manure, additional storage may be needed. Outdoor intensive livestock are a particular problem because there is no opportunity to distribute manure thinly. High levels of leaching from this activity are inevitable and the areas where the soil type is most suitable for outdoor pigs are also the areas which tend to be the catchments of boreholes used for public water supplies. At present there is no proposal to prevent or control the keeping of outdoor intensive livestock in such areas, other than the overall limit on stocking density over the farm. Farmers should however be aware that such activity will inevitably result in significant leaching and increase the likelihood of the nitrate standard being exceeded. **5–16**

Changes in commodity support policy at E.U. level also have implications for nitrate leaching. These arise from the introduction of setaside policy under the Integrated Administration and Control System (IACS) set up to control production of cereals, oilseeds and proteins. This requires that a specified percentage of arable land is left uncropped each year. Monitoring in the NSAs has confirmed the potential impact of nitrate leaching of the E.U.'s setaside policy. This indicates that non-rotational setaside, involving grassing down part of the farm for a number of years, would result in minimal leaching until it was ploughed. However, rotational setaside, where land is uncropped only for one year, is shown to have exceptionally high levels of nitrate leaching, far in excess of the crops it has replaced. It therefore appears that E.U. policies for controlling the supply of agricultural commodities may be increasing leaching substantially, especially where rotational setaside is concerned. The leaching implications of this policy are partially recognised in the management provisions for setaside land contained in the IACS scheme, under which green cover is required to be maintained for a specified period. Compliance with these provisions is policed through the system's enforcement procedures.

Legislation

The various methods of control have been addressed in legislation at both United Kingdom and European level, although in the case of nitrate pollution it is a European initative which has provided the driving force. Article 130(r) of the Treaty of Rome provides for the incorporation of both the "Polluter Pays Principle" and the "Precautionary Principle" into environmental legislation. It states: **5–17**

"Community policy on the environment shall aim at a high level of protection . . . it shall be based on the precautionary principle and on the principles that preventive action should be taken, that environmental damage should as a priority be rectified at source and that the polluter should pay. Environmental protection requirements must be integrated into the definition and implementation of other Community policies."

The Polluter Pays Principle requires that the cost of avoiding or remedying pollution be borne by the polluter, who is ultimately the consumer, while the latter envisages the extension of controls to cover all possible risks where there is insufficient information to exclude them. The Precautionary Principle tends to vary according to the viewpoint. At its most conservative, as in the 1992 Rio Convention, it means that an absence of complete scientific proof cannot be used to resist prudent action. Even the more radical interpretations of the principle envisage that there must be some reason to presuppose a problem exists before the principle can be invoked. Some balance to the use of the Precautionary Principle is provided by Article 130r(3) which requires the preparation of a "Cost Compliance Assessment" before environmental legislation is adopted, thereby enabling the likely costs to be appreciated before final decisions on E.U. Directives are taken. In view of the virtual irreversibility of such decisions, this is an important provision.

While point source discharges of pollution into the environment have been the focus of legislation in the past, emphasis is increasingly shifting to diffuse sources. In the case of drinking water, the trend is to shift the burden of meeting standards established for water at the tap back to the point of abstraction, resulting in pressure being exerted on agriculture in a similar way as point source discharges have been addressed in the past. However, in the case of diffuse sources of pollution, it is very difficult to identify polluters individually, or to set standards for their "discharges". The approach adopted has therefore been to identify broad groups of businesses as a proxy for the individual polluters, and to impose standardised controls on a range of agricultural operations with a view to reducing emissions. The inevitable consequence of this is that costs will be borne by some farmers who are not actually polluting.

5–18 Increasingly the tendency is for E.U. legislation to provide a framework, including the objectives, and for Member States to be allowed considerable flexibility in the way they choose to implement Directives in order to achieve their objectives. This is embodied in Article 189 of the Treaty of Rome, which states that:

"A Directive shall be binding, as to the result to be achieved . . . but shall leave to the national authorities the choice of form and methods."

This permits the prescribed objectives to be achieved in ways appropriate to the circumstances of each country.

Legislation may restrict the type of control techniques which are to be followed. Under the Drinking Water Directive, the standard is set for water at the consumer's tap and so control can in principle be applied anywhere along the pathway from source to the tap. However, under the Nitrates

Directive the standard is applied at the point of abstraction. This prevents any process carried out by a water supply company affecting the measure of water quality and only measures at the source, or between the source and the point of abstraction, can achieve the objectives of this Directive.

(a) E.U. Drinking Water Directive 1980 (80/778)

This Directive is intended to standardise drinking water quality standards throughout the E.U. It is very prescriptive and sets precise maximum standards for many parameters in drinking water covering both aesthetic and health concerns, including nitrate. Provisions exist allowing Member States to permit exceptions (derogations) from the standards, such as where the problem arises from natural conditions and there is no risk to health. The United Kingdom government made a number of such derogations for nitrate under these provisions in 1985, but under pressure from the European Commission, it obtained legal advice and subsequently withdrew these in 1988. It has now moved towards full compliance with the nitrate standard on all public supplies. **5–19**

Article 7 of this Directive fixed the maximum acceptable concentration of nitrate in drinking water at 50 mg/l for the whole of the European Union. No account of the costs and benefits of this measure was taken, and it has already required the expenditure of about £150 million in the United Kingdom to move towards compliance. The scientific and medical merits of this nitrate standard have been questioned by institutions such as the Royal Commission on Environmental Pollution in its 16th Report, and it has been assessed as extremely cost ineffective by the Parliamentary Office of Science and Technology. Indeed, the strictness of the standard contrasts with the approach adopted by the World Health Organisation (WHO). The United Kingdom government has partially taken on board this advice and now favours an average, as opposed to a maximum, of 50 mg/l. It pressed for this view to be adopted in the 1993 European Commission Conference reviewing the Directive's standards, but has not been able to secure any progress towards a more scientific or objective view at European level. The standard of 50 mg/l nitrate as a maximum was accepted by the United Kingdom government when it signed the Directive in 1980, although the inflexibility of the standard was perhaps not appreciated at the time, and, despite the government's current reservations, it has a legal obligation to enforce it.

The standards imposed by the Drinking Water Directive were formally transposed into United Kingdom law by the Water Quality Regulations 1989 (S.I. 1989 No. 1147, as amended). Responsibility for compliance with these standards at the consumer's tap rests with the company providing public water supplies. Where the quality of water abstracted from a source does not meet the standards, the water supply company will have to take the necessary steps to ensure compliance is achieved. Indeed, this is the normal approach for a number of parameters, such as bacteriological quality, particularly for surface water. This action will usually be closing the source, blending with low-nitrate water, or treatment to remove nitrate.

(b) E.U. Nitrate Directive 1991 (91/676)—Nitrate Vulnerable Zones

5–20 Rather than curing it once it has occurred, this Directive is aimed at reducing and preventing water pollution caused or induced by nitrate from agricultural sources (Article 1). It comes into play when nitrate interferes with any legitimate use of water. In the case of water for human consumption, it effectively takes the nitrate standard set for water at the tap in the Drinking Water Directive and applies it at the point of abstraction. The basis for triggering the Directive may not only involve the exceedence of a particular standard. Other criteria may be involved, such as the existence of an unwelcome state of affairs in the water body in question.

The Directive requires those drinking water sources exceeding or likely to exceed 50 mg/l nitrate to be classed as "polluted waters", and their catchments to be designated as "Nitrate Vulnerable Zones". Action programmes must be brought into effect to reduce nitrate levels, and to avoid further such pollution and these will have a direct impact on farmers through restrictions on farming practices. The action programme *must* include certain controls, such as limits on the timing and rate of application of fertilisers and manures, but Member States *may* add to these, and the Directive makes reference to certain identified options (Articles 4 and 5, and Annexes 2 and 3). Farmers will be required to keep records of all manure and fertiliser application.

Article 6 of the Directive required Member States to monitor waters at appropriate points over a period of 12 months within two years of adoption of the Nitrate Directive in December 1991. Article 6.1(b) requires that monitoring must be repeated at least every four years, except where nitrate levels are low and are not expected to rise, where the interval may be extended to eight years. The monitoring points are defined in Annex 1 as including points identified for the purposes of the Surfacewater Abstraction Directive (75/440). Pollution is defined at Article 2(j) as the discharge of nitrogen compounds from agricultural sources (see p. 93), etc., and Article 3(1) states that waters affected by pollution must be identified in accordance with criteria in Annex 1. Where land is within the catchments of these waters and contributes to pollution it must be designated as a Nitrate Vulnerable Zone (NVZ). The Directive required these designations to be made within two years of the Directive's adoption. Monitoring must be repeated and designations reviewed at least every four years.

The Member State's action programme setting out the measures to be followed by farmers in NVZs must be settled within four years of the Directive's adoption in December 1991 (see p. 96), and this action programme must be brought into force within the subsequent four years (*i.e.* by December 1999). It must address matters identified in Annex III (Article 5). The measures proposed by the government, together with the requirements of Annex III, are in Appendix 7.

Article 4 requires Member States, by December 1993, to adopt a voluntary Code of Good Agriculture Practice (CGAP) to be followed on a voluntary basis by farmers outside the NVZs. The Code must include provisions addressing various matters which are specified at Annex IIA, and may also address further matters specified at Annex IIB.

The United Kingdom has not complied with the Directive's timetable for designation or setting up action programmes. However, it is still the intention to implement the action programmes within the prescribed period of December 1995 to December 1999.

Definitions

The Directive includes the following defintions; **5–21**

> "nitrogen compound" means any nitrogen containing substance except for gaseous nitrogen;
> "livestock" means all animals kept for use or profit;
> "livestock manure" means waste products excreted by livestock, or a mixture of litter and waste products excreted by livestock, even in processed form;
> "eutrophication" means the enrichment of water by nitrogen compounds, causing an accelerated growth of algae and higher forms of plant life to produce an undesirable disturbance to the balance of organisms present in the water and to the quality of the water concerned;
> "pollution" means the discharge, directly or indirectly, of nitrogen compounds from agricultural sources into the aquatic environment, the results of which are such as to cause hazards to human health, harm to living resources and to aquatic ecosystems, damage to amenities or interference with other legitimate uses of water.

Implementation in the United Kingdom

Member States have flexibility regarding implementation of the Directive. **5–22** They may designate either their entire national territories, or the parts of catchments contributing to polluted sources. The United Kingdom chose the latter route, and in 1996 the government designated 66 NVZs in England and 2 in Wales, totalling 600,000 ha (1.5 million acres) and one further small NVZ in Scotland. This is in contrast to many other European countries, where much larger areas have been designated. Denmark, the Netherlands and Germany have all designated their entire territories, while a large proportion of Belgium and about 40 per cent of the agricultural area of France are also designated. These areas mainly have problems arising from high concentrations of livestock, which are manifested as eutrophication as well as in difficulty in complying with the drinking water standard. In the United Kingdom, there are no such large concentrations of livestock other than in Humberside where the livestock areas are relatively lightly used as drinking water catchments. No nitrate-limited eutrophication has been linked to agriculture by the United Kingdom government.

The United Kingdom designations were based on nitrate levels in 1992, and the first review will take place after the 1996 monitoring results are available. In future it is possible that additional areas will be designated where nitrate levels in previously undesignated catchments exceed or seem likely to exceed the 50 mg/l threshold.

In implementing this Directive, the Government has made use of the facility at Article 3.1 allowing areas within catchments of polluted waters, but which are not contributing to pollution, not to be designated. The procedure adopted was to examine nitrate levels from long-established monitoring points upstream of surfacewater abstraction points to ascertain whether or not the upstream monitoring points showed a 95 per cent probability of complying with the Directive standard of 50 mg/l nitrate. Any areas upstream of a monitoring point achieving compliance were excluded from the designation, despite being within the overall catchment. In groundwater catchments, however, the government has made less use of the provision to exclude land draining to waters not exceeding, or likely to exceed, the 50 mg/l standard and several designations include the entire catchments of low nitrate boreholes as well as larger areas which do not drain to drinking water sources or any polluted water at all.

Administrative procedure in the United Kingdom

5–23 While the procedure adopted for the first round of designations may be viewed as a precedent for the future, it cannot be assumed that the process will necessarily be the same. However, there have been lessons which may be of value in dealing with future designations.

In 1992 the United Kingdom government embarked upon a long consultation process to implement the Directive. This was an exercise of administrative discretion rather than a legal obligation. The procedure included the following:

- — a government consultation document issued in 1992 on the methodology to be adopted for identifying "polluted waters" whose catchments were to be designated;
- — a further consultation in 1993 on the methodolgy for defining the catchments of polluted waters;
- — a third consultation in 1994 inviting comments on the existence and boundaries of the NVZs then proposed on the basis of monitoring carried out in 1992;
- — a "response document" in May 1995 which summarised the government's responses to individual representations about the proposed NVZs and which also set out the arrangements for the last stage in the procedure, namely an Independent Review Panel (IRP) to consider appeals against the government's decisions;
- — the report of the Panel published in October 1995, containing recommendations to government;
- — the government's designation of NVZs in March 1996, together with an explanation of the action it had taken on the Panel's report.

Individual farmers became involved in the process in 1994, when commenting on the proposals for the individual zones. The government had established a set of rules for converting hydrological catchment boundaries into workable zone demarcations such as field boundaries and roads. The detailed local knowledge about both water movement and local topography which farmers were able to bring into the process revealed many errors, the majority of which were corrected swiftly during the consultation period itself.

A few such boundary issues were not resolved, and neither were the majority of more fundamental issues, such as the source of the nitrate in question. This resulted in over 500 representations on the proposed NVZs being submitted to the government in 1994, mainly from individual farmers or representatives of groups of farmers, challenging the inclusion of the farms in question and raising a wide variety of technical points and matters of principle. The government response dismissed the majority of these, but allowed "appeals" to the Panel over certain technical matters, but not over matters of principle or policy.

The Panel consisted of a Queen's Counsel as Chairman, a hydrogeologist as the technical member and a former civil servant as the lay member. It conducted no hearings and considered the 87 written objections, which were submitted, behind closed doors between August and October 1995. Its findings were published at the end of that October, and the government, while not committing itself to accepting all of its recommendations, did nevertheless announce that it intended to be guided by them. The government made the order designating the NVZs, taking account of the Panel's clear recommendations, in March 1996 (S.I. 1996 No. 888). **5–24**

The operation of the Panel has raised a number of questions. In 1989 the government had indicated to Parliament that compulsory designations would be accompanied by public inquiries where new matters of policy arose (*Hansard*, H.L., June 13, 1989, col. 1315). However, the government decided not to hold public inquiries, and instead constituted the Independent Review Panel. The terms of reference of the Panel fixed by the government specifically excluded all matters of policy and, even on some technical matters, the Panel found itself unable to reach conclusions without the facility to hear expert evidence and cross-examination which a public inquiry would have provided. In consequence of the restricted terms of reference, many representations made to the Panel were dismissed as outside its remit. Most of the remaining representations were not accepted for a variety of reasons, one of the most frequent being that the standard of proof required by the Panel had not been satisfied. This was that the objector was required to show that the government's proposal was "manifestly unreasonable". This imposes a high burden of proof on the objector, greater than that required in the civil courts (balance of probability), and moreover seems to assume that the alleged polluter is guilty unless he can provide evidence to the standard required that he is not a polluter. The standard of proof was not included in the terms of reference, and was unknown to objectors until the Panel's report was published.

The Panel made a number of recommendations which have attracted criticism from farmers and their representatives. These included the decision not to discount nitrate originating from non-agricultural sources, despite the definition of pollution provided in the Directive itself at Article 2(j) which does not include nitrate of non-agricultural origin. The Panel, however, applied the definition selectively and not in crucial parts relating to designations. For example, concern was expressed that the siting of those monitoring points only short distances downstream of non-agricultural nitrate sources was not necessarily representative of agricultural nitrate leaching as the point sources in question had a major impact on the monitoring point. However, such arguments were not accepted. It was deemed sufficient that agriculture could be assumed to make a contribution to overall nitrate levels.

5–25 The transposition of the Nitrate Directive into United Kingdom law has been substantially achieved with the Designation Regulations (S.I. 1996 No. 888) of March 1996, made under the European Communities Act 1972. The Directive requires the action programme to be in effect by December 1999 and it is likely to be an offence not to comply with the requirements of the action programme. The restrictions on farming activities comprising the action programme were proposed by the government in its November 1995 consultation document. These will be introduced by further regulations, probably during 1998, and are also expected to include provisions dealing with enforcement and penalties.

The action programme

5–26 The action programme is essentially based on Good Agricultural Practice, but the Directive's requirements exceed the provisions of the government's 1991 CGAP in two important respects which particularly affect livestock farmers. These are a reduction in the amount of manure which can be applied involving a mandatory ceiling on manure application rates, and a prohibition on spreading manures under certain circumstances. While the current CGAP permits manure containing 250 kg N/ha to be applied, in addition to manure deposited by grazing animals (which can amount to up to c. 100 kg N in the case of dairy cows), it is proposed to impose the following limits to total manure (deposited and applied):

Arable — 170 kg N/ha, with 210 kg N/ha permitted for the first four years.
Non-arable — 250 kg N/ha.

The Directive also requires a closed period for spreading manures to be introduced.

The contents of the United Kingdom's proposed action programme are shown at Appendix 7. It will be noted that manure applications on grassland would be permitted up to 250 kg N/ha. This proposal reflects an exception provided for in the Directive for manure levels to be increased above the prescribed figures, but these must be justified and must not prejudice the attainment of the Directive's objectives (Annex III.2(b)).

The main costs of the proposed action programme will fall on livestock farmers, with arable agriculture being more lightly affected. However, the Directive requires Member States to take such additional measures or reinforced actions as they consider necessary to achieve the objectives if it becomes apparent that the initial action programme will be insufficient

(Articles 5.5). In determining these measures, Member States shall take into account their effectiveness and their cost relative to other preventive measures, and action programmes generally are required to take account of the respective contributions of agricultural and other sources (Articles 5.5 and 5.3). It is clear therefore that more restrictive action programmes are a possibility in the future.

Costs of compliance

In the November 1995 consultation document in which the government published the proposed action programme, it also included a cost compliance assessment. This estimates the cost of the 1996 designations as £10 million capital cost, and £3 million annually. However, many farmers believe these figures underestimate the true costs. What is certain is that the costs of the measures for individual farmers will be very variable according to particular circumstances but will prove very expensive for those worst affected. Many farmers may face bills in excess of the average annual cost on the basis of the government's figures, which amount to, for example, about £50 per dairy cow and £1 per pig place per annum. The measures which give rise to greatest cost are those which go beyond the requirements of the Code of Good Agricultural Practice. These are the reduction in the amount of manure which can be spread (currently 250 kg N/ha, *excluding* manure deposited while grazing), and also the prohibition on spreading slurry and poultry manure on sandy or shallow soils for periods in the autumn, thus requiring the construction of storage in many cases. 5–27

Grants and free advice

The government has honoured a commitment, given at the time when general grant aid for the construction of farm waste facilities was withdrawn, to re-introduce similar provisions in NVZs. With effect from April 1996, grant aid of 25 per cent of the total eligible cost is available towards new and replacement capital works for manure storage and handling. There is a limit on eligible expenditure of £85,000 for each business, and while the works need not be located within the NVZ itself, for example if the farmstead is outside the boundary, there must be a benefit to the NVZ. The government has indicated that it expects that these grants will remain available for seven years, which coincides approximately with the likely introduction of the 170 kg N/ha manure application restriction on arable land. However, potential applicants will need to ensure they are able to comply with the detailed requirements of the scheme and that sufficient funds will be available since the budget provided initially is limited. 5–28

(c) Water Act 1989/Water Resources Act 1991 (WRA 1991)—Nitrate Sensitive Areas (NSAs)

Legislation providing for Nitrate Sensitive Areas was first introduced in the Water Act 1989, although in the subsequent reorganisation of water legislation the provisions were consolidated, without amendment, into the 5–29

Water Resources Act 1991. This legislation was the logical extension of a variety of initiatives, including the government's Nitrate Co-ordination Group, which took stock of knowledge relating to the nitrate problem in the mid 1980s, and the subsequent economic appraisal of the various options for action published by the government in "The Nitrate Issue" in 1988.

Section 94 of the Act empowers the government to designate areas in which nitrate from agricultural sources can be addressed by measures which may be compulsory or voluntary, and with or without compensation. These powers were first used in 1990, as section 112 of the Water Act 1989, to designate 10 pilot Nitrate Sensitive Areas, under which farmers are invited to accept restrictions on their farming practices in return for annual payments. In 1994 these powers were used again, this time as section 94 of the WRA 1991, to designate a further 22 NSAs, and in 1995 to re-designate the 10 pilot areas on the expiry of their initial five-year term and to align their conditions of operation with those of the 1994 areas. A total area of about 35,000 ha (86,000 acres) of eligible agricultural land is covered by these designations. These powers could also have been used to designate the NVZs, where participation is compulsory and no compensation is to be paid, rather than under the European Communities Act.

Although the pilot NSA designations were made solely under United Kingdom law, the subsequent designations have been made under the E.U. Agri-Environment Regulation (S.I. 2078 No. 92) which attracts a 25 per cent funding contribution from the E.U. budget. The NSAs are therefore recognised by Brussels as a legitimate and effective tool for addressing nitrate leaching. However, the Agricultural Directorate sponsors the Agri-Environment Regulation, while the Nitrate Directive and hence NVZs come within the remit of the Environment Directorate.

The Statutory Instruments establishing the NSAs (S.I. 1994 No. 1729) as amended and (S.I. 1995 No. 2095) do not provide for enforcement penalties or offences. Farmers only enter the scheme where they choose to sign a contract or undertaking with the Minister of Agriculture, and enforcement of the obligation of the contract is through contract law.

Comparison of NSAs and NVZs

5–30 NSAs and NVZs are often confused, but there are important distinctions between the two schemes. Not least is the fact that participation in NSAs is voluntary, and that participating farmers receive payments, whereas NVZ restrictions are mandatory and attract no payments, although capital grants towards the cost of manure storage and handling facilities were introduced in April 1996.

NSAs tend to be smaller than NVZs and there are, proportionately, far fewer NSAs in areas such as East Anglia, where low rainfall and slow-response chalk aquifers make the nitrate problem more intractable and less amenable to resolution through agricultural action. In some such cases, for example, the timetable for achieving results is expected to be 40 years, or more, on account of the time taken for water to percolate down to the aquifer, and in some cases reducing levels below the figure of 50 mg/l would require the effective abandonment of arable agriculture over significant parts of the catchments.

Within the NSAs, the current scheme offers payments to farmers who adopt restrictions on their farming operations which go substantially beyond good agricultural practice. There are two levels at which farmers can join, and which attract different levels of payment. At the basic level, participants can opt to continue their existing system of farming, while making adjustments to, for example, fertiliser application rates and planting cover crops on bare land over winter. Alternatively, they can agree to make more drastic changes by converting arable land to low-intensity or ungrazed grass and intensively grazed grass to low-intensity grass.

The level of payment per hectare reflects the severity of the restrictions selected and also the profitability of farming in the various NSAs. Standard payments will inevitably tend not be attractive to the highest performing farms, and these are unlikely to join the scheme. It is for every farmer to assess the impact of the scheme in the light of his own circumstances before deciding whether it is advisable for him to enter the scheme. A farmer also has to take a view on the wisdom of committing himself for five years on the basis of fixed payments which are only reviewed at three-yearly intervals. There has been a provision allowing farmers to withdraw before expiry of the contract if payments are revised downwards, but there is no such option where farming profitability rises and payments are not increased to reflect this.

All of the NSAs are included within the designated NVZs, and farmers **5–31**
within the areas will also be subject to the binding but generally less rigorous NVZ restrictions when these are introduced, regardless of whether they participate in the NSA scheme. Those farmers not participating in the NSA scheme will therefore suffer some restrictions without payment, in common with farmers within NVZs but outside NSA areas. The judgment to be made about the merits of entering the NSA scheme may well change according to the impact of the NVZ restrictions in individual circumstances.

NSA designations, and agreements, are made for five years with no guarantee of renewal. This is a fact for a farmer to bear in mind if he is considering major changes to his business involving fixed cost adjustments. The government has nevertheless renewed the 10 pilot areas for a second five-year term and there would also seem to be little point in establishing what are essentially long-term projects in terms of the time taken to influence water quality at the borehole unless it was envisaged that they would continue in the longer term.

The acceptability of NSAs to the farming community is demonstrated by the high level of participation, with 87 per cent of the eligible land entered into the pilot scheme. In contrast there is considerable concern on the part of farmers who find their land has been placed in an NVZ. Whereas NSAs are carefully selected areas where it is considered that compensation payments for agricultural action can play a cost-effective role in maintaining nitrate levels in drinking water below 50 mg/l, NVZs are much more broad-brush and of uncertain and perhaps dubious efficacy. There are a number of areas of particular concern, in particular the lack of compensation for restrictions which go beyond good agricultural practice. Livestock farmers are most affected, but while the current measures will have only a minor impact on most arable farmers, there is concern that further restrictions might be introduced in the future. This has lead to fears that land in NVZs may be devalued relative to similar but non-NVZ land where only the voluntary code of good agricultural practice applies and where there are no controls on manure.

5–32 The United Kingdom government rationale for not providing compensation is based on the Polluter Pays Principle. However, many farmers believe that they are taking all steps which can reasonably be expected in complying with the good practice measures previously specified by the government. The development of the particular types of agriculture now practiced, and which in many areas is the fundamental reason for the levels of nitrate which leach from agricultural land, is in no small measure the result of government polices for increasing agricultural production since the Second World War. It has been argued that it is unreasonable for the government to invoke the Polluter Pays Principle in relation to farming systems and practices which it directly encouraged and supported through its past advice, policy and grants. Whilst a grant has been made available to contribute 25 per cent of the cost of capital facilities for manure handling and storage within the NVZs, there remain major costs to be borne by some farmers.

It has also been questioned whether the approach genuinely reflects the Polluter Pays Principle, which envisages that costs are passed on to the ultimate consumer and that choices are made between alternative products by society through the market place. However, the structure of markets for most major agricultural commodities, where there is a large number of relatively small producers, means that farms are "price takers" rather than "price makers" and it is not possible for them to pass additional costs to consumers. The outcome is that the costs of NVZ designations are borne directly by farmers in these areas. Since the designations have not been restricted to areas where pollution problems exist, non-polluters within the zones bear the costs equally with polluters. Such an approach does not seem to accord with the Polluter Pays Principle on which the government has sought to justify it.

The NVZ issue would appear to have been exacerbated further by the United Kingdom government's approach. Initially two million hectares was thought likely to be designated but the government adopted a minimalist approach and in the event only 600,000 ha was designated. This more closely targeted approach may have implications for land values as the designated areas may be more easily avoided by purchasers. Concern over the effect of the Directive's implementation on land values has led some farmers to scrutinise and question the adequacy of the evidence on which designations have been based. As already described, a few challenges have been successful, but considerable concern remains about the soundness and fairness of the designation process. Legal proceedings to test some of the points at issue are in progress at the time of writing.

A farmer within an area proposed for designation has the opportunity to prepare a case, perhaps in conjunction with others, if he feels the proposal is flawed. In doing this, he can expect to have access to the monitoring data and other supporting evidence from the Environment Agency, which advises the government. However, since the burden of proof has been placed on the objector and has been set at a very high standard in circumstances where knowledge is limited, the scales would appear to be tilted against the objector. This is evidenced by the very low success rate for objections and appeals in the past, in striking contrast to the planning system where the success rate of appeals is very respectable. It may therefore be in farmers' interests to take pre-emptive action. Even where there is no proposal for designation, it will be helpful to follow good agricultural practice, and to encourage others to do likewise. Since nitrate from non-agricultural sources was in practice included when the first round of NVZ designations were made, it would also be prudent to ask the Environment Agency about such sources and the measures it is taking to control nitrogen discharges from them. **5–33**

Conclusion

Nitrate levels in water have increased as agriculture has intensified over the past 50 years, partly as a result of wartime policies. The standard which has been introduced for nitrate in drinking water appears to be unnecessarily rigorous in medical and scientific terms, and the resources which have been and continue to be devoted to achieving it are yielding little public benefit. However, there seems little prospect of a reappraisal of the standard on objective grounds. **5–34**

While agriculture has tended to be blamed for nitrate leaching, it is now becoming clear that there are very significant non-agricultural sources. A particular impact is the contribution of atmospheric deposition to leaching from agricultural land, estimated at 29 per cent. Such factors do not appear to have been taken into account in current nitrate policy.

A particular failing of the existing policy is the narrowness of the approach. Little or no attempt has been made to integrate the desirability of limiting nitrate leaching with other objectives coherently. Examples are the increase in nitrate leaching caused by rotational setaside, the impact of outdoor intensive livestock, and the possible consequences of farmers attempts to reduce the nitrogen content of manures, which may increase ammonia emissions. There is a need for the "Best Practicable Environmental Option" approach long advocated by the Royal Commission for Environmental Pollution to be put into effect.

The essential point to emerge from the nitrate issue is that in some areas modern agriculture is incompatible with a standard of 50 mg/l. If the objectives of the Directive were to be pursued to the extent of achieving compliance with this standard for drinking water at the source, this could require significant alterations to farming practices in some catchments. The burden on agriculture will be correspondingly heavier if non-agricultural contibutions are not reduced. The alterations necessary may require land being converted to low-intensity grassland, or removed from agriculture entirely. Questions would inevitably arise as to whether the implications of such changes for food production for the local and regional economies were acceptable.

E.U. policy is having an increasing influence on environmental legislation and the impact of this is probably greatest in water quality issues. It has brought about substantial change in approach in the United Kingdom, with detailed legal regulations replacing administrative directions. This trend is likely to continue and there is the potential for further effects on agriculture as phosphorus and pesticides are addressed. These are dealt with in the following sections of this chapter.

Phosphate

Description

5–35 Phosphorus, like nitrogen, is an essential element for life. Pure phosphorus is highly reactive and is not found in nature but it occurs in a variety of compounds in all living organisms, in soils, in water and in rocks. Together with nitrogen and potassium ("potash"), it has been found to be one of the major crop nutrients which farmers need to ensure is available for their crops to achieve good yields. The principal sources for farms are in animal manures and in artificial fertiliser manufactured from phosphate rock.

Hazards

5–36 The main threat posed by phosphorus is that of eutrophication of freshwaters. Phosphate is usually the nutrient in shortest supply, and this constrains the growth of plants and algae. When phosphate levels in freshwaters increase, growth of some plants and algae may become excessive, to the detriment of the system as a whole.

Sources

5–37 The principal source of phosphorus in freshwater is sewage, both from detergents and from human wastes. Pollution from manures is also a source. Until recently it had been believed that only small quantities of phosphorus were lost from agricultural soils, mainly attached to soil particles which are lost by erosion. However, work recently reported by Rothamsted Experimental Station in Hertfordshire has shown that for some soil types at least significant quantities can be leached out once phosphorus levels reach a certain threshold. This can then contribute to freshwater eutrophication. There does in fact appear to be a fundamental problem in that greater quantities of phosphate are imported into agriculture than are exported from it, leading to increasing amounts in soil and a greater risk of leaching into water. The risk of agricultural phosphate causing ecological problems in water is exacerbated by the small quantities which cause such problems, relative to the very much greater quantities which circulate in agricultural systems. The more these increase, the greater is the risk that sufficient phosphate to trigger water quality problems will escape (Foy and Withers; Fert Soc Proceedings No. 365).

Phosphate inputs to agriculture are fertiliser, imported feedstuffs and materials such as sewage sludge applied to land, while exports are crops and animal products. Since there are no major routes by which phosphate is lost to air or water, the potential exists in principle to match the phosphorus contained in fertiliser with the net exports of phosphorus in products sold of the farm, after imported feed inputs have been deducted. Mixed farms are best placed to do this since the arable and livestock enterprises can balance each other with the phosphate contained in imported feeds supplying the needs, at least in part, of the arable crops and thereby reducing the need to buy in phosphate fertiliser. The phosphate used by the arable crop will then be partly exported from the farm, and in an ideal system would balance the phosphate imported. While animals may be fed on imported feeds, at least in part, the extra phosphorus in the manure can be applied to the arable crops and help to reduce or avoid the need for purchased phosphate fertiliser. Arable farms may simply be able to balance the fertiliser imported against the crop exported, but the position can be more difficult for specialised livestock farms. These cannot hope to export in animal products the amount of phosphorus contained in imported feeds. If such farms utilise their own manures, they will therefore accumulate increasing quantities of phosphate in the soil, and consequently be at risk of contributing to water quality problems.

Legislation

No legislation has been introduced specifically to address phosphorus levels in freshwater. A limit of 0.4 mg/l has been set for drinking water in the E.U. Drinking Water Directive, but compliance with this standard does not present practical problems. Where sewage discharges have been found to cause eutrophication, water service companies have sometimes installed phosphate removal equipment. A proposed European Directive on the Ecological Quality of Water (COM 680/93 final) would provide a legislative vehicle which the European Commission intended should be used to address phosphate levels, but the proposal has not been agreed, having aroused serious concerns amongst all member countries. It now appears likely that this proposal will not proceed, and that instead scope for requiring control of phosphorus will be included in the new Framework Directive for Water which is expected shortly. **5–38**

Control Techniques

Sewage effluent

Phosphate removal equipment can be installed at sewage works where phosphate is found to be causing eutrophication. Examples are some of the sewage works which drain into the Norfolk Broads. **5–39**

Sewage sludge

5–40 The guidance contained in the Department of the Environment's Code of Practice for the Agricultural Use of Sewage Sludge and the Water Code provides that application rates should not exceed the fertiliser requirements of crops, or alternatively of the crops in the rotation, considered together.

Fertilisers and manures

5–41 Previously it was believed that extra phosphorus applied to the land over and above crop requirements would be retained in the soil, and farmers have been advised accordingly. It now appears that above ADAS phosphorus soil index 4 (46–70 mg phosphorus/l), leaching is a risk. Once Index 3 or 4 has been reached, only sufficient phosphorus to meet crop requirements should be added.

Potassium

5–42 Potassium is a common element, and is the third of the major crop nutrients. Unlike nitrogen and phosphorus, it is not known to cause significant pollution problems in water. Heavy applications of livestock manures to organic and light soils may lead to leaching of potassium, and groundwater in certain regions of the Netherlands now contains levels in excess of that specified in the Drinking Water Directive (12 mg/l). However, these are of no concern for human health as the Directive standard was chosen as an indicator of possible sewage pollution rather than for an intrinsic health concern. For comparison, cow's milk contains 1400 mg/l potassium. (*Bøchman*, 1990)

Pesticides

5–43 The problem experienced with pesticide levels in drinking water sources is that the concentration of pesticides exceeds that permitted under the E.U.'s Drinking Water Directive, namely 0.1 μg/l for single pesticides and 0.5 μg/l for all pesticides. However, the standard is not health-related, but was chosen as the limit of detection at the time. It was set on the basis that it was as close to zero as could be measured. More recently, the World Health Organisation (WHO) has published health-related standards for 34 pesticides, based on acceptable daily intakes. These are almost all less stringent than the E.U. figure, in some cases by a factor of 100.

One consequence of the strict E.U. standard is that substantial expenditure has been incurred by water companies in ensuring that the standard is met. There is some debate within the E.U., in the course of a review of the Drinking Water Directive, as to how pesticide levels ought to be addressed. A number of Member States are believed to be strongly opposed to any relaxation of the current standard, regardless of the WHO recommendations.

The question of possible damage to the environment from pesticide levels in water also arises. While local problems have arisen from acute pollution incidents, dealt with at Chapter 6, there is little evidence of significant problems arising from diffuse pollution.

Pesticides are not used in agriculture alone. They are also widely used by local authorities and utilities such as railways for keeping areas free of plant growth, by the carpet industry for mothproofing, in forestry and for timber preservation. It has been found that, while the majority of pesticides are used in agriculture, the major contributors to diffuse pollution are non-agricultural users. This does not mean that agriculture does not play a part in the problem; indeed, some of the major problem chemicals, such as isoproturon, are predominently or exclusively in agricultural use.

An assessment of the incidence of the principle pesticides found in water is set out at Tables 1 and 2 on pp. 107–108. This shows the frequency with which pesticides are detected and the proportion of samples which exceed the E.U. limit. Particularly noticeable are the triazine compounds—simazine and atrazine—the incidence of which have fallen in recent years following a ban on their use in non-agricultural applications. The prevalence of isoproturon in the figures is also striking. This is a very widely used and effective herbicide for controlling the most serious weeds in cereal crops—the most widely grown crop in the United Kingdom.

There are a range of factors which influence the behaviour of pesticides **5–44**
in the soil and determine whether they are likely to cause a problem in water. Clearly, one is the scale on which they are used, while the other is the physical and chemical properties of the particular product itself. Materials which are highly soluble in water are most likely to be washed out of the soil into water supplies, although this is not in itself a problem if they break down sufficiently rapidly into harmless compounds. Identification of the critical properties of pesticides will usually allow those at most risk of posing problems for water supplies to be identified and appropriate precautions selected.

The question of how to control the amounts of pesticides entering water has yet to be resolved. The first line of defence is the approval process. Before a pesticide can be used, it must be approved by the Pesticides Safety Directorate, which advises the government, or by comparable bodies in Europe. Obtaining such approval involves the submission of a comprehensive dossier of data and studies, including those relating to the environmental effects of the product in question. If an unacceptable hazard is thought to exist, an application for approval can be refused, or granted subject to restricted conditions of use. While the person to whom an approval is granted has no direct control over the users of the product, it is an offence for the user not to comply with the requirements on the product's label — Control of Pesticide Regulations 1986 (S.I. 1986 No. 1510). This enables dosage rates and other important parameters of usage to be controlled.

Even though conditions of use of pesticides can be controlled by the imposition of restrictions on all users, the concentration a pesticide will reach in water supplies will depend on factors beyond human control, such as soil type and weather, as described above in the case of nitrates. Partly because of this inherent variability of natural processes and partly because of the very strict level of the E.C. standard, water companies need to maintain a facility to remove or dilute pesticides in water.

It has been suggested that pesticides in water could be controlled by means of protection zones analagous to nitrate vulnerable zones. However, whilst this idea has been circulating for a number of years, it has not been taken up by the regulatory authorities either in the United Kingdom or in Europe. It appears unlikely that such measures will be adopted in the foreseeable future.

Table 1 **Pesticides in surface water samples: 1992–1994**

England and Wales

Pesticides	Total number of samples			Number of samples over 100 ng/l			Number of samples over 500 ng/l			*Percentage of samples over 100 ng/l*			*Percentage of samples over 500/ng/l*		
	1992	1993	1994	1992	1993	1994	1992	1993	1994	*1992*	*1993*	*1994*	*1992*	*1993*	*1994*
Most commonly found pesticides[1]															
Isoproturon	2.041	2,977	3,374	194	179	625	46	35	289	*9.5*	*6.0*	*18.5*	*2.3*	*1.2*	*0.0*
Mecoprop	1,358	2,082	2,121	229	376	347	41	118	117	*16.9*	*18.1*	*16.4*	*3.0*	*5.7*	*0.0*
Bentazone	0	196	64	0	17	9	0	1	4	–	*8.7*	*14.1*	–	*0.5*	*0.0*
Diuron	693	1,598	2,426	100	287	323	37	112	113	*14.4*	*18.0*	*13.3*	*5.3*	*7.0*	*0.0*
2,4-D	363	1,615	603	53	104	51	47	36	28	*14.6*	*6.4*	*8.5*	*12.9*	*2.2*	*0.0*
Chlorotoluron	2,130	2,389	2,378	94	124	131	24	29	37	*4.4*	*5.2*	*5.5*	*1.1*	*1.2*	*0.0*
Simazine	4,065	4,094	4,324	516	375	220	59	32	12	*12.7*	*9.2*	*5.1*	*1.5*	*0.8*	*0.0*
Dicamba	369	315	281	20	8	12	5	2	0	*5.4*	*2.5*	*4.3*	*1.4*	*0.6*	*0.0*
Atrazine	3,965	4,100	4,387	672	574	176	77	42	10	*16.9*	*14.0*	*4.0*	*1.9*	*1.0*	*0.0*
Pentachlorophenol(PCP)	6,299	5,478	6,553	401	340	239	134	173	59	*6.4*	*6.2*	*3.6*	*2.1*	*0.1*	*0.0*
Lindane (Gamma HCH)	8,141	7,793	8,280	58	56	85	13	10	13	*0.7*	*0.7*	*1.0*	*0.2*	*0.1*	*0.0*
Other selected pesticides															
Permethrin	816	958	1,608	53	38	11	3	3	2	*6.5*	*4.0*	*0.7*	*0.4*	*0.3*	*0.0*
Dieldrin	7,865	7,371	6,828	28	21	34	7	4	6	*0.4*	*0.3*	*0.5*	*0.1*	*0.1*	*0.0*
Sulcofuron	363	767	420	18	2	1	6	1	1	*5.0*	*0.3*	*0.2*	*1.7*	*0.1*	*0.0*
pp DDT	6,870	6,347	7,055	3	0	0	0	0	0	*0.0*	*0.0*	*0.0*	*0.0*	*0.0*	*0.0*
op DDT	6,715	6,727	7,004	1	0	0	0	0	0	*0.0*	*0.0*	*0.0*	*0.0*	*0.0*	*0.0*
Endrin	7,357	6,813	7,082	1	0	0	0	0	0	*0.0*	*0.0*	*0.0*	*0.0*	*0.0*	*0.0*
Aldrin	7,547	7,025	5,921	00	0	0	0	0	0.0	*0.0*	*0.0*	*0.0*	*0.0*	*0.0*	

[1] All other pesticides exceeded 100 ng/l in fewer than one per cent of samples in 1994.

Source: Department of Environment: Digest of Environmental Statistics, HMSO, 1996.

Table 2 **Pesticides in groundwater samples: 1992–1994**

England and Wales[1]

Pesticides	Total number of samples			Number of samples over 100 ng/l			Number of samples over 500 ng/l			*Percentage of samples over 100 ng/l*			*Percentage of samples over 500/ng/l*		
	1992	1993	1994	1992	1993	1994	1992	1993	1994	*1992*	*1993*	*1994*	*1992*	*1993*	*1994*
Most commonly found pesticides[2]															
Isoproturon	178	186	348	3	5	47	1	0	15	*1.7*	*2.7*	*13.5*	*0.6*	*0.0*	*4.3*
Atrazine	531	612	221	48	66	27	4	7	1	*9.0*	*10.8*	*12.2*	*0.8*	*1.1*	*0.5*
Mecoprop	147	138	110	2	1	6	0	0	2	*1.4*	*0.7*	*5.5*	*0.0*	*0.0*	*1.8*
Diuron	104	129	145	0	6	5	0	3	2	*0.0*	*4.7*	*3.4*	*0.0*	*2.3*	*1.4*
2,4-D	118	114	108	0	0	3	0	0	2	*0.0*	*0.0*	*2.8*	*0.0*	*0.0*	*1.9*
Chlorotoluron	177	178	348	1	4	6	0	1	0	*0.6*	*2.2*	*1.7*	*0.0*	*0.6*	*00*
ppDDT	15	292	235	0	1	3	0	0	0	*0.0*	*0.3*	*1.3*	*0.0*	*0.0*	*0.0*
Linuron	137	172	332	1	6	3	0	0	1	*0.7*	*3.5*	*0.9*	*0.0*	*0.0*	*0.3*
Dieldrin	48	391	293	0	0	2	0	0	2	*0.0*	*0.0*	*0.7*	*0.0*	*0.0*	*0.7*
Simazine	523	603	228	4	12	1	0	1	0	*0.8*	*2.0*	*0.4*	*0.0*	*0.2*	*0.0*
Lindane (Gamma HCH)	48	422	395	0	1	1	0	1	0	*0.0*	*0.2*	*0.3*	*0.0*	*0.2*	*0.0*
Other selected pesticides[3]															
Trietazine	106	42	6	3	2	0	3	1	0	*2.8*	*4.8*	*0.0*	*2.8*	*2.4*	*0.0*
Terbutryn	106	134	128	4	3	0	4	3	0	*3.8*	*2,2*	*0.0*	*3.8*	*2.2*	*0.0*
opDDT	12	291	239	0	1	0	0	0	0	*0.0*	*0.3*	*0.0*	*0.0*	*0.0*	*0.0*
Bromoxynil	102	31	21	1	0	0	1	0	0	*1.0*	*0.0*	*0.0*	*1.0*	*0.0*	*0.0*
Dicamba	112	74	14	1	0	0	0	0	0	*0.9*	*0.0*	*0.0*	*0.0*	*0.0*	*0.0*
2,3,6 TBA	112	0	0	1	0	0	1	0	0	*0.9*	–	–	*0.9*	–	–
Aldrin	4.8	387	283	0	0	0	0	0	0	*0.0*	*0.0*	*0.0*	*0.0*	*0.0*	*0.0*
Endrin	29	292	237	0	0	0	0	0	0	*0.0*	*0.0*	*0.0*	*0.0*	*0.0*	*0.0*
Permethrin	16	0	11	0	0	0	0	0	0	*0.0*	–	*0.0*	*0.0*	–	*0.0*

[1] Data only available from five of the eight NRA regions in 1992, six in 1993 and seven in 1994.
[2] No other pesticide exceeded 100 ng/l in 1994.
[3] Some of those detected in 1992 and 1993 or featuring in Table 00.

Source: Department of Environment: Digest of Environmental Statistics, HMSO, 1996.

Chapter 6

Water Pollution—Point Sources

Introduction

Pollution of water may be described, for the sake of expediency, in two forms. Diffuse pollution from diffuse sources is covered in Chapter 5. In this Chapter, however, we look at point sources of pollution. This may be defined as pollution caused by an incident, or series of incidents, which have immediate impact on the quality of controlled waters (that is to say surface waters or underground aquifers). Controlled waters m Part III of the Water Resources Act 1991 (WRA l991) are defined in section 104. The term covers territorial and coastal waters, inland waters and lakes and ponds. Artificially created lakes, ponds and reservoirs which are without inlet or overflow, that is to say they are landlocked, are excluded from the definition although it remains an offence under section 85(4)(b) to discharge sewage or trade effluent, including slurries, into them. Importantly, the definition also covers any waters lying below the surface of the land, thus including underground streams, springs, aquifers and percolating water. An example may be where silage liquor escapes from an underground tank (perhaps because it is not emptied quickly enough) and the overflow is washed into a watercourse by a flash flood. The result may be a substantial fish kill. So the point pollution leads to a tangible and visible effect upon the quality of the watercourse. Silage effluent is extremely high in chemical oxygen demand (COD) resulting in the available oxygen in the water being used up. Fish quickly are unable to breath and therefore die. There may be other effects which are less easy to spot. Plant life may also be affected as may the many micro-organisms and invertebrates which often form part of the diet for the larger fish. Damage may not stop there. Should the watercourse lead to a river with an abstraction point for drinking water purposes, emergency action will be necessary by the water company. There is usually an early warning system provided by remote telemetry so that the water treatment plant may close off its water intake at the valves to prevent the contamination entering the plant. If the contamination were to enter an underground aquifer, perhaps through an underground river system, the effects could be much more damaging and long lasting.[1] 6–01

Acute or chronic

The example above of a silage liquor escape, causing immediate damage, provides an acute problem which requires immediate reaction and remedy. It is easy to identify many situations whereby a release or discharge of a 6–02

[1] *Cambridge Water Company v. Easterm Counties Leather plc* [1994] 1 All E.R. 53.

polluting substance found readily on a farm, may have immediate impact. On the other hand, there may be steady flows of small quantities of polluting matter which may escape undetected into watercourses over very many months and years. It is often only when another incident occurs that the necessary testing and monitoring of a watercourse brings such a problem to light. This may therefore be termed "chronic". An instance may be where a slurry pit or lagoon is situated above or close to a land drain. Small quantities of effluent have been seeping into the drain and being carried direct to the watercourse. There is an immediate problem in the possibility of a trickle becoming a torrent, should some major part of the structure give way. Then a full scale pollution incident might ensue.

Some pollutants

6–03 Farms are trade premises where a very wide range of substances may be kept and used. It is impossible to identify all potential pollutants but, as an indication of different classes of polluting matter, some of these are identified as follows:

1. Livestock effluent: the excreta, faeces and urine from all classes of livestock, whether mixed as a slurry or separated into solids or semi-solids and liquids. The problems created are caused by large quantities, potency (particularly poultry and pig effluents), storage and handling facilities, the exclusion of rainwater and land-spreading.
2. Dairy and parlour effluents: these include cleaning chemicals, milk spillages (highly potent), chemical spillages, drainage systems. It is important that drainage from livestock buildings, "dirty" yard areas such as feed and collecting areas, together with parlour and dairy buildings, should all be connected to collection tanks or lagoons for later land distribution.
3. Silage liquor: this has a very corrosive effect on standard concrete and, in poorly made clamps, may escape to cause pollution. A small amount of effluent may have devastating effects on water-eco systems. Liquor should be diluted and spread on to appropriate land.
4. Agro-chemicals: a wide range of chemicals are used on farms such as pesticides, fungicides and other crop sprays, weed killers, sheep dips and veterinary medicines. Synthetic fertilisers, particularly with concentrated ammonia, also require careful handling. Spray operators are now licensed and the use of sprays governed by Statutory approved codes of practice, the "Green Code". Chemical containers such as spray cans require careful washing out and disposal, again in accordance with codes of practice.
5. "Red" diesel (*i.e.* which is coloured to indicate a reduced tax component), is subject to the Control of Pollution (Silage, Slurry and Agricultural Fuel Oil) Regulations 1991 (S.I. 1991 No. 324).
6. Dangerous substances: the use of certain poisons on farm for pest and vermin control, such as strychnine and cyanide are subject to very strict control.

Operators require different protection, methods of handling, storage and use, dependent upon the toxicity of the substance. The first three substances outlined in the preceding paragraph, *i.e.* livestock effluents, dairy and parlour effluents and silage liquor, all cause damage by removing the soluble oxygen from water, causing fish to asphyxiate. The normal measure of this process is bio-chemical oxygen demand (BOD). It measures the amount of effluent which is oxidised, thus using up natural oxygen in water. Examples of BOD loading are given in the Table below measured in milligrams per litre. **6–04**

TABLE 3

	BOD
Treated domestic sewage	20–60
Raw domestic sewage	300–400
Vegetable washings	500–3,000
Dilute diary parlour and yard washings (dirty water)	1,000–2,000
Liquid waste draining from slurry stores	1,000–12,000
Liquid sewage sludge	10,000–20,000
Cattle slurry	10,000–20,000
Pig slurry	20,000–30,000
Silage effluent	30,000–80,000
Brewer's grain effluent	30,000–50,000
Milk	140,000
Whisky	20,000

The remainder cause damage directly by poisoning the water eco-system, through chemical or toxic contamination. In either case, the result tends to be similar with a resulting fish kill and damage to micro-flora and fauna living in water. Synthetic fertilisers, particularly with concentrated ammonia, also require careful handling. The danger of a release into the environment, and particularly into a watercourse, requires all precautions to be properly taken.

Should a release occur, then an immediate response is required. Good practice means a telephone list including the water company, the Environment Agency, the emergency services will be available. Also, should an operator succumb to one of the highly dangerous and poisonous substances, an immediate antidote should be available and should also be kept on the premises.

Legislation—water pollution

Part 3 of the Water Resources Act (WRA) 1991 deals with the control of pollution of water resources. Additionally Part 2A of the Environmental Protection Act (EPA) 1990, brought into effect by the Environment Act **6–05**

1995, also deals with contaminated land sources of water pollution. There is also the Salmon and Freshwater Fisheries Act 1975 with an offence of causing waters to be poisonous or injurious to fish or to their spawning grounds or food.

The basis of assessment of potential pollution or contamination of water is to have a system of classification of waters against which to measure pollution. Such classification systems are the precursors of statutory water quality objectives under sections 82 to 84 of the WRA 1991, and five areas of classification have so far been made under regulations.

These are:

1. Surface Waters (Classification) Regulations 1989 (S.I. 1989 No. 1148). It allows assessment of appropriateness for abstraction for use as drinking water.
2. Surface Waters (Dangerous Substances) (Classification) Regulations 1989 (S.I. 1989 No. 2286) classify waters in accordance with a concentration of certain dangerous substances which are listed.
3. Surface Waters (Dangerous Substances) (Classification) Regulations 1992 (S.I. 1992 No. 337) add to the list contained within the 1989 Regulations.
4. Bathing Waters (Classification) Regulations 1991 (S.I. 1991 No. 1597) classify certain sea and estuarine waters as well as inland waters which are used for bathing. These are important in relation particularly to certain micro-biological parameters contained in Schedule 3, relating particularly to faecal coliforms, salmonella, enteroviruses, all of which may be produced from animal wastes.
5. Surface Waters (River Ecosystem) (Classification) Regulation 1994 (S.I. 1994 No. 1057). Again a most important classification for certain rivers or watercourses, which takes critical values of various criteria including bio-chemical oxygen demand (BOD).

In broad terms the classification under the various regulations can be adjusted by alterations to the regulations themselves. They do, however, provide a framework against which, at any point in time, regulatory action can be taken and measured. The further intention of water quality objectives is to improve the quality of water over time.

The criteria for the classification of waters will grow in importance with the determination by the EA to improve the overall standard and quality of rivers and lakes. However, when action is taken under statute or common law, evidence of a discharge to controlled waters is normally sufficient to secure a prosecution. Should the discharge cause a fish kill or other damage, then it is possible for a civil claim for damages and an injunction to follow.

Offences

6–06 The main offences of polluting "controlled waters" are set out in section 85 of the Act. This states:

> (1) A person contravenes this section if he causes or knowingly permits any poisonous, noxious or polluting matter or any solid waste matter to enter any controlled waters.

(2) A person contravenes this section if he causes or knowingly permits any matter, other than trade effluent or sewage effluent, to enter controlled waters by being discharged from a drain or sewer in contravention of a prohibition imposed under section 86 below.

(3) A person contravenes this section if he causes or knowingly permits any trade effluent or sewage effluent to be discharged—
(a) into any controlled waters; or
(b) from land in England and Wales, through a pipe, into the sea outside the seaward limits of controlled waters.

(4) A person contravenes this section if he causes or knowingly permits any trade effluent or sewage effluent to be discharged, in contravention of any prohibition imposed under section 86 below, from a building or from any fixed plant—
(a) on to or into any land; or
(b) into any waters of a lake or pond which are not inland fresh waters.

(5) A person contravenes this section if he causes or knowingly permits any matter whatever to enter any inland fresh waters so as to tend (either directly or in combination with other matter which he or another person causes or permits to enter those waters) to impede the proper flow of the waters in a manner leading, or likely to lead, to a substantial aggravation of—
(a) pollution due to other causes; or
(b) the consequences of such pollution.

(6) Subject to the following provisions of this Chapter, a person who contravenes this Section or the conditions of any consent given under this Chapter for the purposes of this Section shall be guilty of an offence and liable—
(a) on summary conviction, to imprisonment for a term not exceeding 3 months or to a fine not exceeding £20,000, or to both;
(b) on conviction on indictment, to imprisonment for a term not exceeding 2 years or to a fine or to both.

It will be seen that the above offences are extremely wide ranging and it is necessary to look at these in some detail and to determine the implications relating to agricultural land. **6–07**

First, the question of "causing or knowingly permitting" has been examined in many court cases. Perhaps the most important is that of *Alphacell Ltd v. Woodward* ([1972] 2 All E.R. 475, HL). In that case it was shown to be unnecessary for the defendant to be proved either guilty of negligence or that he knew that pollution would take place and allowed it to occur in any event. This case was important in emphasising that there is strict liability in such cases. In the case of *Southern Water Authority v. Pegrum and Pegrum* ((1989) C.L.R. 44) a slurry lagoon became full of stormwater and there was an escape into the local river. The fact that it was rainfall which essentially caused the escape was not felt to be defensible as an Act of God.

The charge of "knowingly permit" can deal with those areas where there is no "active" cause. It has, however, to be shown that there was, or there should have been, some reasonable foreknowledge. In *Price v. Cromack* ([1975] 2 All E.R. 113), the defendant permitted certain things to happen which would have resulted in pollution. With an ever increasing coverage of environmental matters in the media, with better education and dissemination of knowledge, the question is not merely whether the polluter was in possession of that foreknowledge but whether in fact it was reasonable for him to have had it. So, if under any set of circumstances, a reasonable man should have foreseen that the result of certain actions would have lead to pollution or contamination of controlled waters, his lack of foreknowledge is no longer a sustainable defence. But, knowledge is relevant to the circumstances at the relevant time. If new and unexpected information comes to hand later, and that is quite outside the reasonable knowledge at the time then there may still be a defence.

There have been wide ranging attempts to overcome the question of "cause or knowingly permit". A further case was the *N.R.A. v. Welsh Development Agency* (WDA). The WDA were landlords of an industrial estate and had received consent for discharge of surface water run off into a stream. The unit on the estate was let to tenants with a clause containing a covenant against pollution. It was decided that the word to "cause" required an active role, not merely a passive one. In line with this there was also reliance on the case of *Impress v. Rees* ([1971] 2 All E.R. 357), where an intruder had opened a valve on an oil storage tank. The spillage and pollution which followed resulted in a conviction which the company was successful in appealing. The valve was not locked and there was no night time security but neither was there any active "cause" of pollution.

6–08 There are statutory defences to prosecutions under section 85, which would otherwise be offences of strict liability, and these are found in sections 88 and 89 of the WRA 1991. There are some which are relevant to agriculture and they include a discharge consent given under the Water Resources Act, a licence under Part 2 of the Food and Environment Protection Act 1985 (which concern certain deposits into the sea) and discharges in accordance with local byelaws or other statutory procedure. Further statutory defences are found under section 89 where the substance is allowed into water in the case of an emergency to avoid danger to life and limb, and where all practicable steps are taken to minimise the damage and the EA is informed as soon as possible. There is also a defence of permitting waste water from an abandoned mine to cause pollution which will only be available until the end of this century, *i.e.* December 31, 1999. This is a particular point to be borne in mind by the owners and occupiers of land. Where a land owner is also the owner of an abandoned mine, he becomes responsible for any pollution caused by any escape from it, at the start of the new millennium. It is likely that there would be substantial costs involved in taking remedial action.

In all other cases there is no statutory defence against the commission of an offence in strict liability, thus leaving the only means of reducing the impact of the court's decision as mitigation. (Under COPA 1974 and earlier legislation there was a defence of using "best practicable means". This defence is now found only against certain types of statutory nuisance—see Chapter 9).

A further aspect of section 85 concerns the relevant persons who have "caused or knowingly permitted" contamination to take place. A wide range of people including employees are potentially liable. It is not just individuals who are liable for offences. Directors of companies and others are also made liable under section 217. Sub-section (1) states "where a body corporate is guilty of an offence under this Act and that offence is proved to have been committed with the consent or connivance of, or to be attributable to any neglect on the part of, any director, manager, secretary or other similar officer of the body corporate or any person who was purporting to act in such capacity, then he, as well as the body corporate, shall be guilty of that offence and shall be liable to be proceeded against and punished accordingly". We have already seen company directors imprisoned for environmental offences and fines levied against them in addition to sanctions and fines taken against the company itself. This is important bearing in mind the number of farming companies in existence. **6–09**

Section 88 provides defences where discharges to water are authorised under Chapter 2 of Part 3 to the WRA 1991. (Such consents may be made conditional where the discharge may impact on a "European Site" under regulations 48 and 49 of the Conservation (Natural Habitats, etc) Regulations 1994 (S.I. 1994 No. 2716). So, provided that the consent has been authorised and a discharge was strictly in accordance with the conditions of the relevant consent or licence, then the defence is available. An important defence relates to a waste management or disposal licence, since there is a good deal of leachate which comes from waste disposal sites. This could be a licence under the Control of Pollution Act 1974 or Part 2 of the EPA 1990 (see Section on contaminated land). There is a separate regime under the EPA to deal with statutory nuisance caused from contaminated land sites. Protection does not appear to be afforded for a waste management licence under the EPA 1990.

Defences

Section 97 of the WRA 1991 states that the Minister may approve any code of practice "for the purpose of— **6–10**

(a) giving practical guidance to persons engaged in agricultural with respect to activities that may affect controlled waters; and
(b) promoting what appear to them to be desirable practices by such persons for avoiding or minimising the pollution of any such waters."

Contravention of codes of practice do not *per se* give rise to liability either criminal or civil. Their importance lies in following good agricultural techniques in order to avoid pollution and secondly, having followed such codes, to provide for mitigation in the event that pollution does occur. The Codes of Good Agricultural Practice relating to air, soil, water and the use of pesticides, are examined in more detail at Appendices 1–3.

Silt and vegetation in rivers

6–11 Section 90 of the WRA 1991 states:

(1) A person shall be guilty of an offence under this Section if, without the consent of the Environment Agency, he—
  (a) removes from any channel or bed of any inland fresh waters a deposit accumulated by reason of any dam, weir or sluice holding back the waters; and
  (b) does so by causing the deposit to be carried away in suspension in the waters.

(2) A person shall be guilty of an offence under this Section if, without the consent of the Environment Agency, he—
  (a) causes or permits a substantial amount of vegetation to be cut or uprooted in any inland freshwaters or to be cut or uprooted so near to any such waters that it falls into them; and
  (b) fails to take all reasonable steps to remove the vegetation from those waters.

(3) A person guilty of an offence under this Section shall be liable on summary conviction, to a fine not exceeding Level 4 on the Standard Scale.

(4) Nothing in sub-section (1) above applies to anything done in the exercise of any power conferred by or under any enactment relating to land drainage, flood prevention or navigation.

(5) In giving a consent for the purposes of this Section the (EA) may make the consent subject to such conditions as it considers appropriate.

(6) The Secretary of State may by regulations provide that any reference to inland freshwaters in sub-section (1) or (2) above shall be construed as including a reference to such coastal waters as may be prescribed.

It should also by noted that there are two further applications under section 90. Section 90A sets out requirements for obtaining consent, in writing from the EA. Section 90B covers the issue of enforcement notices where the EA considers that a consent licence holder is or is likely to contravene any condition of that consent. At the time of writing, neither section 90A nor 90B have been brought into effect.

Breach of section 90 initially leads only to a relatively small fine (section 90(3)). However, where a consent is obtained and conditions of a consent are contravened, then the full environmental procedures, sentencing and fines, come into operation (section 90B(3)).

Salmon and Freshwater Fisheries Act 1975

6–12 Section 4 of the Act states

"(1) Subject to sub-section (2) below any person who causes or knowingly permits to flow, or puts or knowingly permits to be put, into any waters containing fish or into any tributaries of waters containing fish, any liquid or solid matter to such an extent as to cause the waters to be poisonous or injurious to fish or the spawning grounds, spawn or food of fish, shall be guilty of any offence.

(2) A person shall not be guilty of an offence under sub-section (1) for any act done in the exercise of any right to which he is by law entitled or in continuance of a method in use in connection with the same premises before July 18th 1923, if he proves to the satisfaction of the court that he has used the best practicable means, within a reasonable cost, to prevent such matter from doing injury to fish or to the spawning grounds, spawn or food of fish.

(3) Proceedings under this Section shall not be instituted except by the Water Authority [now EA] or by a person who has first obtained a certificate from the Minister that he has a material interest in the waters alleged to be affected."

Contaminated land

Part 2A of the EPA 1990 provides for wholly separate controls where waters are affected by land which is contaminated. This is a complex regime which is examined in more detail in Chapter 9. **6–13**

Preventative Measures

Part 3 of the WRA 1991 details requirements for owners and occupiers of land to take steps to prevent pollution from occurring. Section 92 allows regulations to be made which provide for the prohibition of potentially contaminative substances from being kept by any person, unless certain prescribed precautions are first put in place. The major regulation, currently under review, is the Control of Pollution (Silage, Slurry and Agricultural Fuel Oil) Regulations 1991 (S.I. 1991 No. 324)—A precis is found below which gives the salient points but reference should always be made to the full text. Guidance notes for farmers were produced in 1991 by the Department of Environment. There are detailed rules for silos including methods of construction, capacity, silage resistant materials, wall loadings, depths of silage and use. The latter is important in regard to the notices to be displayed, the silo and its tank must not be nearer than 10 metres of a controlled water, it must be properly maintained and be effective for at least 20 years. In the case of a below ground effluent tank, the tank must be able to have a life of at least 20 years without *the need for maintenance*. **6–14**

The construction of slurry storage systems must also be sited no nearer than 10 metres of controlled waters and should last at least 20 years with "proper maintenance". Design loadings are required and storage capacities must be adequate. Proper calculations must have been made to provide adequate storage capacity with head space. The head space or free board is most important and must be 750mm in the case of an earth wall store and 300mm in other cases. This is to allow for excess rainfall and surplus storage when the container is unable to be emptied.

Fuel oil stores, which exclude domestic heating oil, receive detailed instructions for the construction of appropriate sized bunds. These must at all times be greater than the volume contained in the tank, by specified amounts. Again a 20-year life for the bund and base of the storage area is required. Lockable valves and taps should be used and again the 10 metre distance from controlled waters is mandatory.

There are certain exemptions based on initial dates of March 1 or September 1, 1991. Such exemptions may be lost subsequently by the service of a notice requiring works (under section 9) or by substantial enlargement or reconstruction. There may be appeals against a works notice. Failure to comply with certain parts of the regulations, *i.e.* the making of silage and storage of slurry and fuel oils, are criminal offences.

6–15 There is a substantial onus on the person who is responsible for maintenance to ensure that there are proper inspections made at regular intervals. Such inspections should be exact, and include an examination of all the relevant constituent parts of the structure. A report should be written, signed and dated and any remedial action which is necessary should be undertaken as a result. This process serves two purposes. It enables the structure to be put into a state of good repair at a stage before there is a pollution incident. But if such an incident were to occur, and there was a properly documented history of inspections and reports, these would be most useful by way of mitigation in the event of a prosecution.

Section 161 of the Act gives to the EA the power to carry out certain works and operations where there appear to it the probability that pollutants will enter any controlled waters. Furthermore they are able to remove matter which has entered such waters with a view to mitigating or remedying the pollution caused. Such action is normally to be exercised only when there is an emergency or when no one can be found to whom a works notice should be served. Expenses may be recovered. The EA is likely to use this power very sparingly but it is unlikely to hesitate where it is clearly necessary.

Section 161 allows the EA to serve a works notice on a person who has:

(a) caused or knowingly permitted the matter in question to be present at the place from which it is likely, in the opinion of the Agency, to enter any controlled waters; or
(b) caused or knowingly permitted the matter in question to be present in any controlled waters.

This is the direct approach which is more likely to be used and, provided the works which are necessary are relatively simple, the responsible person will no doubt act on behalf of the Agency, but under its supervision, in putting the matter to rights. Nevertheless in complex areas, it is likely that the Agency will act as its own agent and will then seek to re-charge the costs. Where a third party's land has to be crossed or used in the execution of the works or operations, proper compensation is payable to that third party under section 161(b). There is provision for an appeal against the works notice under section 161(c) but, where a works notice is not complied with, an offence is committed under section 161(d).

The Control of Pesticides Regulations 1986 (S.I. 1986 No. 1510) indicates that all reasonable preventative measures should be taken to avoid polluting waters. There is an important recommendation concerning the construction of bunds around storage areas for chemical in the "Storage of Approved Pesticides: Guidance for Farmers and other Professional Users" (Guidance Note CS19, HSE 1998). There is also a short Code of Practice produced by the British Agro Chemicals Association, set out in the Table 4 below:

TABLE 4

The best approach is to avoid producing any waste at all **6–16**

DISPOSAL OF SURPLUS SPRAY AND WASHINGS

* Mix just enough to complete a task; no more;
* Avoid being caught out by changes in the weather;
* Never pour pesticide in any form into public sewers or drains;
* Wash the sprayer out in the field of use and spray out on a headland or on a relatively weed or pest free part of the field left unsprayed for the purpose. Make sure you do not exceed the maximum dose approved for the crop;
* Alternatively, choose areas of uncropped land (not fallow or stubble) of minimal wildlife value, which are well away from waterways, ditches and ponds, drains and environmentally sensitive areas and which are not liable to surface run-off. Make sure you have approval of the area from the National Rivers Authority or River Purification Board (and in England and Wales Her Majesty's Inspectorate of Pollution for Red List substances);
* Where land is limited, approach your local Waste Disposal Authority, National Rivers Authority or River Purification Board, to discuss alternative methods of disposal.

DISPOSAL OF EMPTY CONTAINERS

* Triple-rinse all containers, with the washing going into the spray tank. Pressure rinsing is the quickest, most efficient and consistent method. The exceptions are cyanide gassing powders or aluminium, magnesium or zinc phosphides; fill these containers with dry earth instead of rinsing;
* Puncture or crush them so that they cannot be re-used;
* Store cleaned waste containers safely where they are not accessible to animals or children;
* **BURN** containers and other packaging on a very hot fire, a few at a time, at least 15 metres from a public highway and where smoke will not drift across people, animals or garden crops;

  DO NOT BURN containers from products classed as "highly flammable", pyrotechnic devices such as smokes, atomisable fluids or ones which held:

benazolin	MCPB	2,4,5–T
clopyralid	mecoprop	oxadiazon
2,4–D	fenoprop	2,3,6–TBA
dicamba	sodium chlorate	triclopyr
dichlorprop		

* **BURY** cleaned and crushed containers where they cannot pollute surface or ground water, at least 0.8 metres deep and below any land drains;

  DO NOT BURY containers which held "Red List" substances without approval from Her Majesty's Inspectorate of Pollution (HMIP). The List includes:

atrazine	malathion
azinphos-methyl	mercury and its compounds
dichlorvos	pentachlorophenol
endosulfan	simazine
fenitrothion	trifluralin
gamma-HCH	

* Licensed disposal sites will generally accept cleaned, punctured or crushed containers, subject to conditions allowing acceptance of such waste.

DISPOSAL OF UNWANTED PRODUCTS

* Order only enough product to do the job in hand;
* Keep careful records of the movement of stock in and out of the agrochemical store; rotate stock on the "first-in, first-out" principle;
* Check agrochemical stores annually, if not more frequently. Look for containers which are losing their labels, products which are no longer needed because of cropping changes, part-filled or deteriorating containers;
* Your local distributor may consider taking back sound unopened containers with complete and up-to-date label instructions. Alternatively a neighbouring farm may be willing to take such products if it is still growing crops for which the products are approved.
* In all other cases, contact a reputable waste disposal contractor. These can be found in Yellow Pages or through the National Association of Waste Disposal Contractors (tel 0171 824 8882). The following took part in the 1991 National Pesticides Retrieval Scheme:

  Chemclear Ltd, Station Hill, Bury St Edmunds, Suffolk IP32 6AE tel 01284 761291

  Chemlock Environmental Services, 2 Trinder Road, Easton-in-Gordano, Bristol BS20 OLX tel 01275 372763

  Cleanaway Ltd, Technical Services, Airborne Close, Arteval Road, Leigh-on-Sea, Essex SS9 4EL tel 0151 357 3377

  Leigh Enviromnental Services, Lindon Road, Brownhills, Walsall, West Midlands WS8 7BB tel 01902 455666

Envirogreen Ltd, 612 Reading Road, Winnersh, Wokingham Berkshire RG11 5HF tel 01734 785655

The building of bunds around any area where potentially contaminative liquids are to be kept will always ensure that the capacity of such outer storage area is at least 125 per cent of the holding tank size. In our view there should wherever possible be a secondary back-up system, although not mandatory or even recommended elsewhere, as a fall-back position. This may be the use of a blind ditch, having sandbags close to hand so that entry to watercourses can be prevented quickly, or other means of secondary defence. The use of buffer strips is also recommended by the EA. **6–17**

Water protection zones may be put in place by orders which may either restrict or ban completely certain activities within the designated area. Such orders could be made, but have not yet been, in relation to areas which provide for water sheds to reservoirs and other catchments for drinking water purposes, to areas around bore holes used for drinking water abstraction and even above Grade 1 aquifers, again used for the provisions of potable water supplies. In many areas there are already restrictions on farming activities in such areas and these have often been in place for many years.

A more specific provision relates to nitrate sensitive areas and sections 94 and 95 deal with the arrangements. Section 95 provides for voluntary agreement whereby compensation can be paid. However under section 94, mandatory areas can be either with or without compensation.

Discharge consents

Schedule 10 of the WRA 1991 provides for the submission of an application for consent to make such a discharge. The consent and adherence to it will provide a statutory defence under section 88 to any offence under section 85. Applications must be on a prescribed form and advertised, giving third parties six weeks for making representations. There is a deemed refusal unless the consent is granted within four months of the application's receipt and the Secretary of State may issue a direction against determination, should he think fit. Consents normally contain detailed conditions and absolute limits of constituent quantities, together with BOD and suspended solids. The EA may also grant a consent without any application being made, where there has been a previous discharge and it seeks to lay down strict parameters. Such consent is not retroactive. Consents may be revoked or modified at intervals. Additionally farmers with older consents under section 40 of the Control of Pollution Act 1974 may continue without condition until they are replaced by formal consents. **6–18**

Trade effluent consents

Under section 118 of the WRA 1991 there may be consent to discharge trade effluent, which includes all types of farm effluent, into a public sewer. There will be a few farms, mainly situated in or on the edge of settlements, **6–19** or close by a watercourse, where normal means of disposal are inappropriate. Section 119 covers applications for consent for which there is no prescribed form of notice and no publicity procedure. (Special category effluents require consents under section 120 but this process is unlikely to apply in regard to agricultural units). Under section 121 the EA may grant consent which is conditional on quantity and quality combined with a whole range of other conditions. All conditions are appealable. If it is essential for connections to be made direct to the sewer, then any pre-treatment which can take place will reduce either quantity or strength and is likely to reduce the annual costs of such consent. Again consent variations may be made and appeals lodged against these.

Powers of entry under WRA 1991

6–20 Sections 169 to 174 deal with powers of entry. Section 169 concerns powers of entry in regard to enforcement, by permitting persons who are authorised by the EA, or the Secretary of State, or the Minister of Agriculture, Fisheries and Food, to enter premises. They may also inspect, take necessary measurements, and take samples of water, effluent, land or articles. Where the EA takes its powers under section 108 of the Environment Act 1995 concerning its "pollution control functions", section 169, which relates to enforcement, is not applicable. It should be noted that Schedule 20 to the Act sets out in detail how the powers should be applied, through sections 169 to 172 of the Act, including obtaining a warrant and the power to make compensation to anyone who has been caused loss or damage as a result of the entry.

Section 170 permits outside agents of the EA, which would cover the use of outside consultants, contractors and others to obtain entry for purposes of survey, tests, experimental borings and sampling and analysis. Section 171 provides power to carry out surveys and to search for water where the EA consider it may be appropriate to use compulsory purchase powers under section 154 or to use a Compulsory Works Order under section 168. Section 172 provides powers of entry for any purpose of the EA or the Ministry of Agriculture. Finally, section 174 concerns impersonation of those who may lawfully exercise powers of entry. It is an offence which is triable either way. However, the fine on summary conviction must not exceed the statutory maximum and there is a maximum 2-year term of imprisonment, on conviction on indictment.

Environmental information

6–21 The Agency must keep a Pollution Control Register under section 190 of the WRA 1991, which contains a large amount of information on discharge consents, offences, enforcement notices, works notices and convictions. Only information which is contrary to the interests of national security or liable to breach commercial confidentiality are to be excluded under section 191A. The Register must be kept up to date and is available for inspection by the public free of charge at all reasonable times. Copies of relevant entries should be obtainable at reasonable cost. Publicly available information of this type is extremely valuable both to individuals and to pressure groups who may bring private prosecutions themselves for environmental offences.

Civil Liabilities

Actions by fishing clubs are becoming increasingly common, following a pollution incident and a fish kill. Not only is there an immediate loss of fish stocks, which need to be replaced, but the lesser members of the aquatic food chain may also have suffered from the pollution incident. It takes time for an area to be re-stocked, the fish to grow to a worthwhile size, and the food sources to replenish themselves. In the meantime the club will have lost its fishing, possibly some of its membership and income, and has suffered environmental damage with longer term consequences. Such civil actions normally follow a successful prosecution, but are certainly not dependent upon it (see Chapter 2 for further details). **6–22**

Summary

It can be seen from this Chapter that there is a strict regulatory regime in place which covers the maintenance, the use and the construction of certain areas of containment such as silos, slurry stores and fuel oil tanks. There are also codes of good practice relating both to these and to the spreading of a wide range of effluents, both liquid and solid on to land. Codes are non-mandatory and will not be a defence against a prosecution, except that by following such codes, the offence may be mitigated. The results of successful prosecutions are increasingly large fines (to be paid for out of earned income) occasionally coupled with a spell of imprisonment or a community service order, extreme bad publicity and inclusion within a register of offences which is open to public scrutiny. Accidents and incidents will occur, but it is vital to prevent them from happening by following the steps laid out in the relevant regulations and GAP codes, for the person in charge together with all the staff to be aware of proper procedures and "best practice", to have that information in writing together with emergency contacts with telephone numbers. Best practice is becoming a common epithet but it encapsulates the use of systems, not merely to protect the environment, but to protect the farmer and the farm business. **6–23**

The EA has produced a number of pollution prevention guidelines which are confusingly known as PPG's. (These are not to be confused with planning policy guidance notes relating to town and country planning). Those of most interest on farms are:

PPG 1— General guide to the prevention of pollution of controlled waters.
PPG 2— Above ground oil storage tanks.
PPG 5— Works in, near or liable to affect watercourses.
PPG 6— Working at demolition and construction sites.
PPG 8— Safe storage and disposal of used oils.
PPG 9— Nature Conservation.
PPG 12— Sheep dip.
PPG 13— Guidance note on the use of high pressure water and steam cleaners.
PPG 17— Dairies and other milk handling operations.

Chapter 7
Soil pollution and wastes

Introduction

Land has long been used for disposal of unwanted materials. Farmers in particular have disposed of many of their own wastes in this way, either through burial or by depositing them on the land surface. Examples include casualty animals, building rubble, machinery parts and even whole machines left to rot in a bramble patch! Agriculture has also been the traditional outlet for other wastes which have a beneficial use on the land. "Night soil" from villages and towns is an early example, which now takes the form of sewage sludge. **7–01**

Because farmers depend on their land they could generally be relied upon not to dispose of materials onto their land, which could affect their livelihood. But this presumption is no longer always sufficient. The toxicity of many substances is not always apparent, some substances, for example, becoming toxic after building up in soils over a long period of time to levels which have become regarded as unacceptable only more recently.

Its very nature means that most pollution damage to soils tends to be insidious and piecemeal and contamination is perhaps a rather more appropriate description in most circumstances. As a result it has tended not to attract much attention, with more emphasis being placed on protecting air and water than soil. But the changing nature of the materials and contaminants involved, together with a greater appreciation of the attendant risks and a growing aversion to such risks, has led governments and other institutions to recognise the need for policies to protect soils in order to safeguard human and animal health and the environment. There has been a growing recognition that what may be no more than contamination today may be pollution in the future, if levels and accumulations are not controlled. The approach to policy has largely been precautionary with control regimes generally aimed at preventing pollution from occurring.

The Council of Europe has adopted both the European Soil Charter (in 1972) and "Recommendations on Soil Protection" in 1992. These emphasise the need for soils to be protected from damaging farming practices, erosion, pollution and degradation caused by human activity. The United Kingdom has begun to address the issues in both the 1990 White Paper on the Environment "This Common Inheritance" and also in the 1994 Sustainable Development Strategy. In 1996 the government published a series of 120 proposed "Indicators of Sustainable Development in the United Kingdom". Amongst these are two relating to soil, one to soil quality and the other to heavy metals in topsoils. Quality is assessed on organic matter content, acidity and plant nutrient content (phosphorus and potassium only, nitrogen being too difficult to interpret), whilst heavy metals assessed are copper, cadmium, zinc and lead. Organic matter, acidity in grassland soils and phosphorus levels suggest deterioration over **7–02** the past 15 to 25 years, while there is as yet no time series data for heavy metals to assess whether there is an appreciable deterioration in the position.

The first comprehensive action taken by the government to promote the protection of agricultural soils was the publication in 1993 of the Code of Good Agricultural Practice for the Protection of Soil (the Soil Code). This has been published by MAFF as a guide to help farmers and growers avoid causing long-term damage to the soils which they farm, and provides practical information on a range of topics dealt with in this chapter.

Soil

7–03 Soil is a limited natural resource. It comprises topsoil and subsoil and is a complex material which is still relatively poorly understood. It is made up of minute weathered fragments of rock and a variable proportion of organic matter derived from dead plant and animal matter, together with many living microscopic plants and animals. It is a living system with a combination of biological, physical and chemical properties which allow it to be used for growing food and raw materials, including those for energy production. Maintenance of a healthy soil life is essential for life on earth, at least as we currently know it.

Soil develops very slowly over hundreds or thousands of years, but it can easily be damaged or destroyed. This is not only by the more obvious forces of erosion which remove soil, but also by degradation in which pollution can play a part. Although soil can be cleaned up following pollution, the cost of remediation is high and generally outweighs its agricultural value. For all practical purposes, pollution damage is usually irreversible in terms of its agricultural use and it is therefore particularly important to avoid pollution occurring. This was recognised by the Royal Commission on Environmental Pollution (RCEP) in its 1996 Report on the sustainable use of soils, in which the RCEP considered that temperate countries such as the United Kingdom will have an increasing role to play in meeting world demand for food in future years, as pressures from other uses and poor land management in other parts of the world are reducing its availability for agricultural use. Fortunately, agricultural soil in the United Kingdom is relatively undamaged and, as such, is a valuable resource not only to farmers but to the nation as a whole.

The purpose of this chapter is to take stock of the threats to soil from wastes, the regimes which exist for their control, and the implications of these for agriculture. It outlines possible pollutants, their sources and associated problems; the control regimes affecting these pollutants and how they may affect farmers, together with any responsibilities farmers may have. We deal with the spreading of non-agricultural wastes and sewage sludge onto land, the potential for agriculture itself to contaminate the soil, together with problems which can arise from activities outside agriculture but which may impact upon it. We do not enter into detail with the complexities of regulations relating to the large number of potential pollutants, but rather aim to identify the legislation and its broad scope. Both the interpretation of the legislation and the management of pollution risks may require professional skills. The Soil Code and the Environment Agency may provide some guidance, but in some cases the need for expert advice may remain.

The nature of soil pollution

The precise nature of pollution threats to agricultural soils are varied. Soil can be contaminated directly by wastes being deposited on it, or indirectly via the atmosphere. Direct deposition can arise from a number of sources, some of which may be incidental to other operations, for example, dredging and mine wastes, or accidental, for example flooding or spillages. Purely accidental incidents do happen and can be serious, but in terms of the total amounts of contaminants going onto land, they are probably relatively minor. Potentially far more significant sources of contaminants are those applied directly to soil from the disposal of industrial and household wastes onto land. Sewage sludge is well known to contain pathogens, metals and organic chemicals, all of which may be harmful in excessive concentrations. There are also concerns about possible pollutants contained in materials such as paper wastes which have recently begun to be spread on land in much larger quantities. And from agriculture, there are potential risks from fertilisers, manures and crop protection chemicals used in agricultural production itself. Airborne pollutants, which may arise from industrial emissions and transport, have also recently been identified as a major source of soil contaminants by the RCEP. **7–04**

Contaminants may be inorganic materials, such as simple zinc, copper and lead, or man-made organic materials such as industrial chemicals and pesticides. Certain elements, mostly heavy metals, are toxic in varying degrees should they exceed certain threshold concentrations. Some can kill plants, or at least retard growth, for example zinc, copper, nickel, and arsenic. Others are more harmful to man or animals, such as lead, mercury, fluorine, selenium and molybdenum. Some, like arsenic, cadmium and copper, are harmful to both. Some of these are essential nutrients in trace amounts, for example zinc and copper, yet can be highly toxic at higher but still relatively low concentrations. Whilst some of these substances are present in wastes which may be applied to land, particularly sewage sludge, they can also occur naturally in certain soils at concentrations which exceed the threshold for toxic effects. They may also be present in products applied to land for beneficial use, as is the case with cadmium in phosphate fertilisers and copper in some manures. Cadmium is highly toxic and is present in the parent phosphate rock from which the fertilisers are made. Similarly, some manures may contain quite large amounts of copper as a result of it being included in feeds as a growth promoter, particularly in the case of pig feed. Yet sheep are particularly sensitive to copper and may be poisoned if grazed on land where slurry containing high levels of copper has been spread.

The intake of these substances by animals is often mainly from ingestion **7–05**
of soil with forage rather than from the forage itself. The extent to which

herbage is contaminated with soil will depend on the thickness and type of sward, weather conditions and time of year, grassland management and stocking density. Contamination can range from 3 per cent in thick sward to 20 per cent in newly seeded pastures where grass cover is incomplete. Appendix 1 of the Soil Code provides a useful summary of the risks from metal contaminants in soil.

Organic contaminants can occur in a wide range of chemical compounds in common use, and include those contained in household disinfectants and detergents derived from benzene. These will occur in sewage sludge. Some extremely toxic compounds, like dioxins and furans, and to a lesser extent polychlorinated biphenyls (PCBs), may be present in sludge, although usually at very low levels. Pesticides are a potential source of organic contamination and capable of damaging soil fauna and flora, although the RCEP found no evidence of any lasting problems from these products.

In general, it is industrial pollution rather than that from agriculture, which are seen as the greater threat to soil. This is particularly the case when land is used intentionally as a matter of policy to dispose of industrial wastes and sewage. These are dealt with in the two following sections.

Control mechanisms

7–06 To cause pollution of soil is not in itself a specific offence, in the way that it is for water and air. Nor is it an offence to use polluted soils for agriculture. Rather the legal framework is preventative, aimed at preventing pollution occurring or contaminated produce entering food supplies. There are a number of legal mechanisms relating to specific wastes or categories of wastes. These govern their treatment, handling and disposal, such targeting allowing the individual characteristics of the wastes and their sources to be accommodated in the control mechanism. There are also a number of codes of practice and guidance notes, again relating to different materials. Most are not statutory and will not give protection against legal action, but following them should help to prevent pollution occurring. Use of contaminated soils for growing crops is indirectly controlled through legal controls on the level of contaminants in food and in livestock feedstuffs under the Food and Environment Protection Act 1985 (FEPA).

The different types of contaminants and their control mechanisms are dealt with in this section under the following headings:

— Controlled waste.
— Sewage sludge.
— Other non-agricultural sources.
— Agricultural contaminants.

Controlled wastes

7–07 Requirements for control measures relating to handling and disposal of waste must comply with the relevant E.C. legislation. In the case of waste, this is the Framework Directive on Waste (75/442, as amended by 91/156).

The United Kingdom government had already introduced new measures for regulating wastes in its "Waste Management Licensing" (WML) under the provisions of the Environmental Protection Act 1990 (EPA). But in order to comply with the Directive, the United Kingdom government had to add to its existing legislative provisions and subsequently introduced the Waste Management Licensing Regulations 1994 (S.I. 1994 No. 1056). The regime covers "controlled waste" which, under section 75(7)(c) of the EPA 1990, is currently defined as domestic, industrial and commercial wastes. It is the principal mechanism for regulating many of the wastes which are or could be disposed of to land.

At present, wastes from premises used for agriculture, along with those from any mine or quarry are not included in the EPA definition of "controlled waste" (section 75(7)), and sewage is also excluded (section 75(8)). Article 2(1)(b) of the Framework Directive allows the exclusion of natural, non-dangerous substances used in farming provided they are covered by other legislation. The United Kingdom government takes the view that this includes national legislation, but since there is none governing some non-natural agricultural wastes, these will need to be regulated. The government's proposals for meeting this obligation have yet to be published, but given that some agricultural wastes will be drawn within a control regime, the main features of the waste management licensing regime are worth noting in this text.

Notwithstanding the position that agricultural wastes are not controlled at present, some uncertainties remain. These may arise where farms are not used entirely for agriculture. Farm shops, vegetable processing, packhouses, controlled environment stores and haulage operations are examples of businesses which increasingly tend to operate on farms, and, depending on their scale and nature, may or may not be regarded as agriculture. It is ". . . waste arising from premises used for agriculture within the meaning of the Agriculture Act 1947" which is excluded from the definition of controlled wastes (section 75(7)(c)), and in order to decide if the exclusion applies in such cases it will be necessary to determine whether the premises are used for agriculture.

One of the principal features of the 1994 WML Regulations is that the **7–08**
government has significantly altered the definition of waste to align it with the Directive's definition. Whereas for many years the United Kingdom operated on the broad definition contained in section 75(1) of the EPA 1990, which included materials having usefulness or value and likely to be re-used, recovered or recycled, Government policy now is explicitly to reduce the amount of waste going to final disposal, and to apply regulation only where necessary (see paragraphs 9–10, Department of Environment Circular 11/94 "Environmental Protection Act 1990: Part II Waste Management Licensing"). Accordingly, the definition of waste now excludes some classes of materials previously defined as waste. These are materials which remain within the "commercial cycle" or "chain of utility", although materials which require a "specialised recovery operation" before they can be used (Annex 2 of Circular 11/94) may remain "waste" until they are recovered.

Some materials which are still waste in the circumstances in which they are used have been given exemptions from full licensing under Schedule 3 of the Waste Management Licensing Regulations. The intention is to encourage recycling of materials, but it has also meant that increasing quantities of non-agricultural wastes which can be used as soil conditioners or fertilisers are being disposed of on to agricultural land. The introduction of the landfill tax in October 1996 is likely to provide further impetus to this trend since the current rate of £2/tonne for inert materials and £7/tonne for other wastes, in combination with stricter requirements for landfill sites, means that the cost of landfill disposal is rising sharply.

The application of the altered definition of waste does require careful interpretation and the relevant questions to be addressed are set out in a detailed 15-page Annex to the Circular (Annex 2). Responsibility for interpretation falls to the Environment Agency (EA), although ultimately the position can be tested in the court.

The Regulations governing those handling and disposing of controlled wastes are described in the Circular and accompanying Annexes. They are complex and detailed treatment is outside the scope of this book. Rather, we aim to place in context those materials which find their way to agricultural land, and to outline the position as it may apply to those agricultural wastes which the government decides to include within the definition of "controlled waste" in its forthcoming proposals.

Implications for agriculture

7–09 A farmer will need to be aware of the provisions of the waste legislation:

(i) if he receives, or considers receiving non-agricultural wastes which are defined as "controlled waste" under the Regulations; ((a) below)
(ii) if he transports controlled waste to a farm for re-use (he will need to register with the Environment Agency as a carrier of controlled waste); ((b) below)
(iii) if some agricultural wastes are controlled in the future. ((c) below)

(a) Using and storing controlled waste on the farm

7–10 If the material in question is regarded as a controlled waste by the EA, then in principle anyone handling, storing or disposing of it will require a waste management licence from the EA. It is possible that its storage and/or use may fall within one of the exemptions contained in Schedule 3 of the 1994 WML Regulations (see para. 7–07, above). However, in the context of the exemption for spreading wastes on land, it is important to realise that the inclusion of a material in Table 2 of Schedule 3 does not necessarily mean that it is controlled waste in every situation. Paragraph 5.71 of the Circular specifically states: "The inclusion or exclusion of something in or from Table 2 does not imply anything about the circumstances in which such a thing is or is not a waste. The Department's advice in Annex 2: The Definition of Waste should be considered in deciding in particular circumstances whether a material spread on land for beneficial purposes is waste at all." In other words, the question of whether a material is controlled waste in any set of circumstances needs to be considered in the light of the new definition of waste (see para. 7–07, above).

The exemptions from licensing which may be relevant to farmers include, sometimes with qualifications in addition to the need to pre-notify the EA: **7–11**

— materials spread on land, at rates of up to 250 tonnes/hectare, or 5,000 tonnes/hectare for dredgings from inland waters, where benefit to agriculture or ecological improvement results (paragraph 7 of the Schedule). The categories of materials qualifying for this exemption are shown in Table 2 of the Schedule, and are as follows:

Waste soil or compost.
Waste wood, bark or other plant matter.
Waste food, drink or materials used in or resulting from the preparation of food or drink.
Blood and gut contents from abbatoirs.
Waste lime.
Lime sludge from cement manufacture or gas processing.
Waste gypsum.
Paper waste sludge, waste paper and de-inked paper pulp.
Dredgings from any inland water.
Textile waste.
Septic tank sludge.
Sludge from biological treatment plants.
Waste hair and effluent treatment sludge from a tannery.

— storage of sewage sludge which is to be used on agricultural land in a secure lagoon, container or place on agricultural land (paragraph 8 of the Schedule);

— the reclamation or improvement of agricultural land by spreading of waste soil, rock, ash or sludge, or waste arising from dredging an inland water, construction or demolition. This is subject to the following provisions: (a) the site is otherwise incapable of beneficial use because of industrial or other development; (b) that there is benefit to agriculture or ecological improvement; (c) that no more than 20,000 tonnes/hectare is spread; and (d) that the spreading is in accordance with planning permission. Storage associated with these activities is also covered. Sites designed or adapted for disposal of waste by landfill are not included in this exemption (paragraph 9 of the Schedule);

— making of compost from biodegradable waste, or storing the waste prior to use, by the person producing the waste or using the compost, provided that the annual quantity does not exceed 10,000 cubic metres for mushroom compost, or 1,000 cubic metres for other purposes (paragraph 12 of the Schedule);

— the beneficial use of waste if it can be put to use without further treatment, and the use does not involve disposal. Storage of waste to be used under this exemption is also covered, again provided that the storage does not amount to disposal. There is a specific exclusion from this exemption of waste covered by paragraphs 7, 8, 9, 19 or 25, or which would be covered by those paragraphs except for some condition or limitation in them (paragraph 15 of the Schedule);

— swill boiling and related activities governed by the Diseases of Animals (Waste Food) Order 1973 (S.I. 1973 No. 1936). (paragraph 16 of the Schedule);

— the storage of construction and demolition wastes, or road planings, which are to be used in the construction, maintenance or improvement of a transport facility or building. Storage is limited to three months, except on the site where the waste is produced (paragraph 19 of the Schedule);

— the deposit of dredgings or plant matter from inland waterways on a towpath or bank of the water from which the waste is removed, or in the case of moving the waste to other towpaths or banks where there is benefit to agriculture or ecological improvement, subject to a limit of 50 tonnes per metre of bank per day (paragraph 25 of the Schedule).

Registration of exemptions

7–12 Where an exemption from waste management licensing applies, the person carrying on the exempt activity must register with the appropriate registration authority, which will place the relevant information on a register (Regulation 18). The Regulation excludes the spreading of waste on agricultural land, which is subject to notification requirements described below, the details of which will be included in the register, and no separate registration is required for making mushroom compost where the process has an authorisation under Part 1 of the EPA. The fee for registration is £300. Failure to register when carrying on an exempt activity involving the recovery or disposal of waste is an offence, the penalty for which is a fine not exceeding £500 on summary conviction for most categories of exempt activities (Regulation 18(6)).

Spreading waste on agricultural land under the exemption

7–13 If a material is deemed to be controlled waste and it is intended to spread this on agricultural land under the exemption in paragraph 7(3)(c) of Schedule 3 as described above, the Environment Agency must be notified in advance (or at least every six months where regular applications are involved). There is no fee for notification. Responsibility for notification rests with the "body" intending to spread the waste. It appears that no registration is necessary when the activity is carried out by an individual (para. 6.19 of Circular 11/94). The information required is set out at paragraph 7(4) of Schedule. It includes;

(a) a description of the waste and its origin;
(b) pre-spreading storage location;

(c) estimated quantity of waste;
(d) location and proposed date of spreading.

Waste spreading operations must be carried out in a way that does not ". . . cause pollution of the environment or harm to human health" (section 33(1)(c) of the Act), and the person applying waste under the exemption in paragraph 7 should be able to demonstrate, on the basis of qualified advice, that benefit to agriculture or ecology will result from its use in the particular circumstances in question. The exemption will not apply if there is no benefit. For example, gypsum can be beneficial for some soils, but not for others. Where it is not beneficial, its application would not fall within the exemption. The Department of Environment considers that expert advice will be needed to identify the appropriate application rate for each site and each soil type. (See Circular 11/94, para 5.66 *et seq.*).

Amplified advice to farmers is contained in the Soil Code (paragraphs 104 to 107) which recommends that applications should not contain more than the nutrient requirements for the crop or the rotation, and that where the presence of contaminants is suspected, expert advice should be obtained on the desirability and rate of application.

Dredgings from inland waters

The amount which can be dredged from inland waters and spread onto farmland under the exemption is limited to 5000t/ha by paragraph 7(3)(c). **7–14**
There is also an exemption under paragraph 25 for dredgings deposited on a bank or towpath, up to a limit of 50 tonnes per metre of the bank or towpath. (See Circular 11/94, paras. 5.171 *et seq*). Sediments dredged from some inland waters (settlement ponds, lakes, rivers) can contain contaminants which have built up there, having entered the water environment from various sources. The Soil Code advises that analysis for suspected contaminants should be carried out where there is reason to suspect the existence of a problem. It also points out that where problems do exist, the dredgings may be subject to the hazardous waste legislation.

Sewage sludge

The supply and use of sewage sludge on agricultural land is taken entirely **7–15**
out of the controlled waste regime by regulation 7 of the Controlled Waste Regulations 1992, being regulated by the Sludge (Use in Agriculture) Regulations 1989 (S.I. 1989 No. 1263). The storage of sewage sludge is exempted from licensing under the conditions set out in paragraph 8 of Schedule 3 to the 1994 Regulations, but the use of the exemption must be registered. (See Circular 11/94, paras. 5.87 *et seq*).

Septic tank sludge

The spreading of septic tank sludge on agricultural land, together with its **7–16**
storage prior to such use, falls within the scope of the exemption in paragraph 7 of Schedule 3.

Compost

7–17 It is only the ingredients and process of compost-making which might be considered to involve waste. Once the process has been completed the compost is a product with an established use and market. The exemption does not apply to operations taking in waste from outside sources and sending the compost on to other users. (See Circular 11/94, paras. 106 *et seq*).

The beneficial use of waste put to use without treatment

7–18 It seems that this category might include materials such as old telegraph poles used in pole barns or railway sleepers forming slurry lagoon walls. Other examples might be reject materials from food or drink manufacture fed to livestock without further treatment. Where the materials can be used directly, there would seem to be a particularly strong case for arguing that such materials are not waste within the meaning of the new definition. (See Circular 11/94, paras. 5.121 *et seq*).

Swill boiling

7–19 This and any other activities already regulated by licences issued under the Diseases of Animal (Waste Food) Order 1973 (S.I. 1973 No. 1936) are exempted to avoid dual regulation. (See Circular 11/94, paras. 5.130 *et seq*).

Wastes from construction and demolition, and road planings

7–20 One disadvantage of this exemption is the limitation of storage to three months, whereas farm construction or track maintenance may take place only at less busy times when labour is available. However, since these materials can often be used without further treatment, for example, those to be used as hard core, the exemption for storage without a time limit under Paragraph 15 (beneficial use of waste without further treatment) would appear to be available. In many situations such materials may not be "waste" at all. (See Circular 11/94, paras. 5.152 *et seq*).

(b) Transport of controlled waste

7–21 While the storage, treatment, handling and disposal of "controlled waste" is regulated by the Waste Management Licensing Regulations 1994 (S.I. 1994 No. 1056), those who transport controlled waste are required to be registered with the Environment Agency under a different set of regulations, namely the Controlled Waste (Registration of Carriers and Seizure of Vehicles) Regulations 1991 (S.I. 1991 No. 1624), made under the Control of Pollution (Amendment) Act 1989.

Under these Regulations, any person who transports controlled waste in the course of his business, or otherwise with a view to profit, is guilty of an offence unless he is registered with the appropriate authority, now the Environment Agency. A farmer may be affected by this where he imports controlled waste onto his farm with his own transport. Examples might be old telegraph poles, railway sleepers, road planings or wastes from food factories used for livestock rations, although often these will not be waste. There is no standard guidance available from the Agency as to what it regards as controlled waste for the purpose of the Regulations, and it is therefore necessary to consult it on each material and set of circumstances as to whether it is deemed to be controlled waste.

Registration costs £95 for three years initially, and £65 on renewal. Should certain wastes from premises used for agriculture be included in the definition of controlled waste in the future, as is expected, farmers may need to register with the EA if transporting these materials off the farm. The implications of this will need to be assessed once the Government's proposals have been published.

The Duty of Care

Section 34 of the EPA 1990 introduced an explicit "Duty of Care" for all those involved in handling controlled wastes. This places a duty on those involved to take all reasonable measures to: **7–22**

(a) prevent others contravening WML requirements
(b) prevent the escape of waste under their control or that of any other person, and
(c) ensure that waste is only transferred to an authorised person, and that when waste is transferred, it is accompanied by an adequate written description to enable the person receiving it to comply with duty of care requirements.

The general effect of the Duty of Care is set out in DoE Circular 19/91. In plain English, it requires all those who deal with controlled waste to take all reasonable steps to ensure that waste is handled in accordance with the law, and that the waste does not escape. This means that the necessary steps to ensure the waste is safely contained should be taken. The duty is set out in a Code of Practice published by the Department of Environment in 1991 and entitled "Waste Management. The Duty of Care. A Code of Practice." The Environmental Protection (Duty of Care) Regulations 1991 (S.I. 1991 No. 2839), made under the 1990 Act, impose requirements to complete transfer notes recording details of waste transfers, to keep both descriptions and transfer notes (or copies) and to make copies available (on request) to the EA. Farmers should be aware that in practice, their responsibilities will include checking that those from whom controlled waste is received, and those to whom it is consigned, are properly authorised (or exempted). Once again, farmers will become affected by these requirements for any agricultural materials defined as controlled wastes in the future.

(c) Agricultural wastes which may be controlled in future

7–23 Since the content of the Regulations which are to be introduced to regulate non-natural agricultural wastes are not yet known, there is little that can be usefully said at the time of writing. It would appear that materials such as waste oil and plastics need to be addressed, although some exemptions may be introduced.

Enforcement and penalties

7–24 The authority for all aspects of implementing the controlled waste legislation, including the registration of carriers and the seizure of vehicles, is the Environment Agency, which took over the functions of the former waste regulation authorities in April 1996. It is an offence to keep, treat or dispose of controlled waste without a licence, or in breach of a licence, except under an exemption. The maximum penalty on conviction in the magistrates' court is a fine of £20,000, and/or six months imprisonment. In the crown court fines are unlimited, and imprisonment can be for up to two years.

Flytipping

7–25 This is a problem which already afflicts farmers in many areas, particularly close to centres of population. There is concern that the unauthorised dumping of waste on any land without the consent of the owner or occupier may increase following the introduction of the landfill tax. Where controlled waste is deposited on land unlawfully, the EA has powers under section 59 of the Act to require the occupier of the land to remove the waste or take other steps specified in a notice. However, if the occupier can show that he neither deposited nor knowingly caused nor knowingly permitted the waste to be deposited, he may be able to appeal successfully to a magistrates' court against the requirement.

Sewage sludge

7–26 Sewage sludge is the concentrated solids from sewage which has undergone treatment to a greater or lesser degree. Application to farmland completes the natural cycle of nutrients and this recycling is regarded as an environmental benefit. It does, however, carry risks which necessitate its control. Sewage sludge, particularly from areas where industry discharges to sewers, can contain significant amounts of heavy metals. These can be poisonous to humans and animals and to soil flora and fauna in which case it can also damage soil fertility. Metals can remain in the soil for very long periods and their potential to damage fertility and retard crop growth may increase as the organic compounds in which some of the contaminants are contained are broken down by soil processes, and the contaminants released in more active form.

Sludge also contains significant amounts of nitrogen which, depending on the type of sludge, can convert swiftly into nitrate. If the sludge is applied in excessive quantities or at inappropriate times, it can cause significant amounts of nitrate to leach into water supplies. Nitrate pollution is dealt with in Chapter 5.

The risks presented by sewage sludge have long been recognised. It is excluded from the waste management licensing regime by virtue of regulation 7 of the 1992 Regulations, and has its own system of control. Prior to 1989 the government issued guidance on an advisory basis to sewage undertakers and farmers. The report of the Department of the Environment's Sub-Committee on the Disposal of Sewage Sludge to Land (STC Report No. 20, 1981) provided the definitive guidance, but this was superseded by the Sludge (Use in Agriculture) Regulations 1989 (S.I. 1989 No. 1263), (as amended), which implemented the 1986 European Directive on the Use of Sewage Sludge on Agricultural Land (86/278).

The Directive's purposes are to protect man, wildlife and the environment from harmful effects of spreading sewage sludge on land, and to protect the long-term viability and quality of agricultural soils. The potential for harmful effects on soil arises principally from the metal content of some sludges, particularly those from industrial sources. The Directive requires sludges and soils to be analysed for their metal contents. The quantities permitted to be added in sludge are limited by either;

(a) setting a maximum quantity of sludge which may be applied per hectare per year (provided the maximum permitted concentrations of metals in the sludge are not exceeded), or
(b) setting a maximum annual addition of metals to soil per hectare per year.

Sludge application is only permitted where soil concentrations remain below the maximum levels set by the Member State, except that they may be exceeded at "dedicated sites". Dedicated sites are those which on June 17, 1986 were dedicated to the disposal of sewage sludge and on which any commercial food crops were being grown exclusively for animal consumption. Regulation 8(2) requires sludge producers to notify the Secretary of State for the Environment as soon as possible after Septenber 1, 1989 of the address and area of every dedicated site to which sludge was applied. Regulation 8(3) prohibits the occupier of such sites from growing commercial food crops on that land other than those intended for animal consumption. Regulation 8(4) provides that where the level of a specified metal in the soil exceeds the prescribed value on a dedicated site, no further sludge may be applied or crops sold other than in accordance with written advice from the appropriate Minister (in England, the Minister of Agriculture). Such farms are often owned by water companies and may be farmed by tenants under special controls imposed by the landlord. Tenants and prospective tenants may need to obtain independent advice on the management of the inherent risks. **7–27**

Old sewage farms were at one time raised as candidates for inclusion in the government's Contaminated Land Register put forward in Section 143 of the EPA (see paragraph 13 of Code). In the event, the government has not enacted section 143 and the issue of contaminated land has been dealt with in the Environment Act 1995 (See para. 4–29). Those involved in property transactions should bear this in mind.

Comprehensive records must be kept of the quantities of sludge produced and used in agriculture, its composition, treatment and where it was used. The responsibility for keeping these records normally rests with the sludge producer. While records are kept of nutrient and metal levels, the Regulations do not however address any organic chemicals, such as dioxins, which may be contained in sludges.

The maximum levels of metals permitted in land to which sewage sludge is applied is less rigorous in the United Kingdom than in other European countries (see Table below). Indeed, some countries, such as Sweden, prohibit the use of sludge from virtually all land-growing crops for human consumption.

7–28 A comparison of present E.C. and U.K. and E.C. Member States maximum permissible total metal concentrations (mg/kg) in sludge amended soil (pH 6–7)

	E.C.[1]	U.K.[2]	Denmark	Germany	France	Italy	Spain
Zinc	150–300	300	100	200	300	300	150
Copper	50–140	135	40	60	100	100	50
Nickel	30–75	75	15	50	50	50	30
Cadmium	1–3	3	0.5	1.5	2	3	1
Lead	50–300	300	40	100	100	100	50
Chromium	—	400[3]	30	100	150	150	100

Notes:
[1] *Limits from CEC (1986).*
[2] *Limits from U.K. (1989).*
[3] *Provisional limit from DoE Code of Practice (DoE, 1989).*

The Regulations set minimum harvesting/grazing intervals following the application of sewage sludge. No livestock may be grazed, or forage harvested, for three weeks following the application of sludge. In addition, sludge may not be applied within 10 months before harvesting fruit trees, or before the planting of fruit or vegetables which are normally in contact with the soil and may be consumed raw. There are also restrictions on the lifting of turf, and prohibitions on sewage sludge use on land where basic seed potatoes or basic nursery stock is to be grown, or where seed potatoes or nursery stock for export will be produced. Untreated sludge must not be applied to orchards or to land used for growing nursery stock, including bulbs. The use of septic tank sludge is also controlled under the 1989 Regulations by the same restrictions on grazing and cropping.

Producers of sludge will be guilty of an offence if they cause or knowingly allow sludge to be used on agricultural land when it exceeds the legal concentrations of metal contaminants set down in the Regulations. The general position when the sludge is applied, other than by or on behalf of its producer, is that the occupier of land is responsible for complying with the Regulations. For example, if sludge is handed on to a farmer to apply, or if he was in a position to cause or knowingly permit the Regulations to be broken, he could be guilty of an offence. Farmers accepting sewage sludge on their land will be responsible for ensuring that the "no grazing" and "no harvesting" periods are observed. The EA is responsible for enforcing the Regulations.

The practical application of the Regulations is set out in a Department of Environment Code of Practice for Agricultural Use of Sewage Sludge (Second Edition, Department of the Environment, 1996). The government has used the second edition of the Code to tighten limits for zinc and cadmium, as recommended by an independent report (MAFF, 1993). The Code also gives recommended limits for molybdenum, selenium, arsenic and fluoride, which are not included in the Regulations. For grassland, the Code includes more stringent requirements for sampling depths, and for concentrations of certain elements to take account of the potential for materials to accumulate in the surface layers. Whilst the water companies have accepted the recommendations of the Code, the RCEP in its 1996 Report found that little more than half of sludge applied to farmland had been treated by methods recommended in it.

Currently, about 50 per cent of sewage sludge is applied to agricultural land. This amounts to 0.5 million tonnes/annum dry weight (c. 10 million tonnes/annum wet weight), and quantities are expected to at least double as a result of a ban on the dumping of sewage sludge at sea, due to come into effect in 1998, and the increased treatment of sewage required by the Urban Wastewater Treatment Directive. In recent years metal contents of sludges have tended to decline as traditional metalworking industries have closed and as a result of tighter controls on trade effluent discharged to sewers. The capacity of farm crops to utilise the nutrients in sludge (nitrogen and phosphorus) tends to be the limiting factor on application rather than metals determining the amounts which can be applied without causing pollution. However, metals do retain the potential to cause harm and should not be overlooked. As indicated above, the standards for zinc and cadmium in the DoE Code of Practice have been tightened in 1996 as a precaution, following research results pointing to impaired soil fertility. **7–29**

The RCEP found grounds for concern in the arrangements for the application of sewage sludge to land, and devoted four of its 18 key recommendations for action to this subject. It recommended that all sludge should be treated by one of the methods in the Code of Practice, rather than about 60 per cent as at present. It also called for steps to be taken to further reduce the zinc content of sludges, to keep a watching brief on new contaminants such as platinum group metals from catalytic converters on cars and for a group to be set up to examine the options for reducing loads of heavy metals and persistent organic compounds. It also recommended that the uncontrolled use of sewage sludge on "dedicated sites" should be phased out as soon as possible to avoid permanently damaging the soils, and that materials from smaller treatment works, septic tanks and cesspits, which may be spread on land without treatment, should be subject to stronger regulation.

The message from the Commission's consideration of the position appears to be that present controls and standards offer insufficient protection against potential risks to the soil. Farmers taking, or considering taking sewage sludge, from water companies—who often supply it free would be well advised to obtain copies of the DoE Code of Practice and the MAFF leaflet, and to ensure that the Regulations and application rates are strictly adhered to. Farmers should be supplied with analyses of their soils before application takes place, and also with the analysis of the material to be applied. However, the safeguards from these procedures will only be effective if the quantities and analysis of the sludge actually applied match those specified.

Some water companies may seek the agreement of farmers to site sludge storage lagoons on their land. These allow sludge to be stored close to where it is to be applied to arable land in the frequently short period after harvest and before the next crop is sown, and are predominantly in arable areas. While the water company will normally bear the cost of construction, it is also important to consider who will be responsible for meeting planning requirements, solving odour problems, and restoring the site. Such storage is exempt from the requirements of waste management licensing under paragraph 8(1) of Schedule 3 to the 1994 Regulations, although the need to register for the use of the exemption will apply (see para. 7–12 above).

Management of risks arising from wastes applied to land

7–30 Questions have been raised about the adequacy of controls over the application of exempted materials to land by the Royal Commission on Environmental Pollution in its 1996 Report on soil. The Commission established that quantities of wastes being disposed of by this route were increasing rapidly, and that while there was no co-ordinated information on the total quantities involved, these were already about 2.8 million tonnes/annum. Within this, waste from the paper industry was predicted to rise from 0.4 million tonnes/annum to 1 million tonnes/annum between 1996 and 1998. While there were statutory controls in place over the disposal of sewage sludge to land to provide protection from some potentially polluting contaminants, the Commission felt it was inconsistent that there should be no equivalent controls over these exempted wastes, which may contain heavy metals, organic chemicals and pathogens and carry a consequent risk of causing harm to the soil or to agriculture. The introduction of the landfill tax subsequent to these exemptions could divert more wastes to land, particularly if there is any increase in the rates of tax levied.

The Commission recommended that the government should conduct an immediate review of these exemptions for materials applied to land, and should develop guidance for owners and occupiers of land. Pending the availability of this guidance, the advice is that owners and occupiers obtain expert assessments from independent consultants before accepting such materials. The Commission also identified a need to ensure that adequate standards of treatment for sewage sludge applied to farmland are respected, that efforts are made to further reduce levels of contaminants in sludge and that acceptable levels of specific contaminants are reviewed. Work is in hand at the time of writing jointly by the EA, the Water

Research Centre and ADAS which may result in the production of guidance for owners and occupiers of land.

Although relatively few farms are affected by soil pollution problems, farmers would be well advised to exercise caution in agreeing to accept non-agricultural wastes onto their land. They should consider seeking full analyses for potential pollutants, and ensure that the waste provider accepts liability for unforeseen pollution problems as well as having the means to meet such liabilities if they should arise. Farmers should also take care in the disposal of any agricultural wastes which have the potential to harm soils. There are some concerns that present no grazing/no harvesting periods might need to be increased, at least in some circumstances. Farmers should also consider the likely requirements of purchasers of their commodities, particularly fruit and vegetables.

Other non-agricultural sources of soil pollution

Pollution can also arise as a result of other activities where wastes are deposited, accidentally or otherwise, on land which is used for agricultural production. Application to land of materials dredged from inland waters falls within this category, and while such materials are controlled waste, the deposit on land of uncontaminated dredgings is usually exempt from waste management licensing, as described at paragraph 7–13, above. **7–31**

Pollution with oil is a special case, and can arise from agriculture, although this risk is reduced by the requirement for bunding around new oil stores introduced in 1991 in the Control of Pollution (Silage, Slurry and Agricultural Fuel Oil) Regulations (S.I. 1991, No. 324) (see Chapter 6). External sources, such as road accidents, may also cause problems. The Soil Code sets out much useful advice, although for serious incidents expert advice is likely to be needed.

Flooding of agricultural land by seawater can also damage its agricultural quality, although its effects can be effectively eliminated within a few years once the sea is excluded. One of the means of achieving this is by application of gypsum (calcium sulphate) to soils of certain types. The main sources of gypsum are waste from industrial processes, and the waste legislation must be considered. The use of gypsum is specifically mentioned as an exemption from the requirements of waste management licensing in Schedule 3 of the 1994 Regulations, although there would be a requirement to pre-notify the Environment Agency (see para. 7–13, above). Remedial measures are described in the Soil Code.

Reclamation of land is also an area of potential concern. Land previously used for a non-agricultural activity may in certain situations be reclaimed for agricultural use, for example old mineral workings, or closed landfill sites, both of which may pose some threat of contamination. In certain areas, old mine workings may contain lead, which is particularly toxic to animals. The Interdepartmental Committee on the Redevelopment of Contaminated Land (ICRCL) has prepared a Guidance Note 70/90 for grazing such areas, whilst for crops the ICRCL thresholds for gardens and allotments should apply. Leachate from abandoned mines can also be a problem, and has been exempt from pollution control legislation until the introduction of the Environment Act 1995. In the case of the former British Coal mines, responsibility rests with the residuary body.

Some farmers have taken advantage of the need for landfill sites and have made sites available with a view to restoration to agriculture at a future date. These sites may have been used for a variety of domestic and/or industrial wastes and farmers need to be aware that gases such as methane may be generated from the waste which can migrate through the soil to the surface. These gases may be harmful to crops being grown on the site. Leachate from landfill sites can also be a problem, finding its way to watercourses, both surface and underground, and onto adjacent land which in some instances may be that of a neighbour. Although Part 2 of the EPA introduced much stricter regulations governing the operation of landfill sites, control has been less stringent in the past and a number of pollution incidents have occurred. Landfill is a very specialised area with very significant potential liabilities and it is therefore essential for owners and occupiers of land, or prospective purchasers, to obtain expert advice from several quarters including legal and environmental appraisals. Completed landfill sites were also included in the initial list for the proposed Contaminated Land Register, but like sewage farms, were not included in the revised list. Again, it should not be assumed they won't be in the future.

A new contaminated land regime has been set out in the Environment Act 1995 requiring the identification of contaminated sites, and providing powers for the EA or the local authority to clear up the contamination (see Chapter 4). No regulations have yet been made to bring the regime into effect.

7–32 Apart from the physical risks in holding contaminated land, there are legal risks and farmers are advised to seek specialist advice, particularly in the area of landfill. It is established in English law under the *Rylands v. Fletcher* principle that a person is liable for damage caused by the escape of substances brought onto their land, but increasingly power has also been given to the Environment Agency aimed at preventing pollution occurring at all. It has statutory powers to reclaim moneys they expend on any clean up deemed necessary. Such provisions are in section 161 of the Water Resources Act 1991 relating to water pollution, and in sections 59 and 61 of the EPA relating to land. Section 59 deals with waste unlawfully deposited, and section 61 relates to risks from closed landfills. The necessary costs are recoverable from anyone who caused or knowingly permitted the problem (section 61), the occupier (section 59) or the owner of the land (section 61). It appears that section 61 applies to the owner of any land affected by pollution of the type in question, so that where the pollution migrates the owners of adjoining land could be charged for clean up on their land.

Turning to atmospheric pollutants, the RCEP identified atmospheric deposition as an important source of soil pollution. These may arise from sources such as power stations, smelters, brickworks, incinerators and chemical plants. Examples of serious harm to agricultural land from such sources are relatively few, but in one recent case at Bolsover, Derbyshire, milk and meat were excluded from the human food chain due to contamination with dioxins, which it was claimed had been released into the air from a chemical process. (The ENDS Report, July 1995.) Farmers in some areas are concerned about the impact of emissions from toxic waste incinerators, although the evidence of damage remains controversial. Transport also releases a number of pollutants into the air such as lead from petrol, platinum and palladium from catalytic converters, and zinc from tyres.

Indirect airborne pollution is controlled by air pollution legislation and monitored and enforced by the Environment Agency, and local authorities. Part 1 of the EPA covers both large industrial plants subject to integrated pollution control (IPC) under the auspices of the EA, and smaller processes where air pollution alone is regulated separately by local authorities. Under both systems, operators are required to hold an "authorisation" and to comply with the limits it imposes on discharges to air. There are also a number of provisions in the Clean Air Act relating to matters such as smoke control zones in cities. Legislation on the control of emissions from road transport mainly relates to specifications for engine emissions from new vehicles or at regular tests, together with fuel standards, or tax incentives (as for unleaded petrol or ultra-low sulphur diesel).

A further form of pollution arising from atmospheric deposition is acidification. This is particularly significant for uplands where deposition levels of compounds of sulphur and nitrogen may be high, or where the ability of the soil to offset the acidifying effects is low. Acidification of soils may in turn lead to acidification of water draining from them, and cause serious harm to the ecology of streams, rivers and lakes. Some lowland areas are also affected. Whereas sulphur compounds from industry and electricity generation were predominant in the past, these have now been reduced dramatically, and nitrogen compounds, largely in the form of nitrogen oxides from electricity generation and transport, and ammonia from agriculture, have increased sharply. Lowland agricultural land is normally limed where necessary to maintain pH at suitable levels, and acidification is not therefore an issue for lowland agriculture. Indeed, farmers now increasingly have to apply sulphur to meet crop requirements, whereas previously these had been supplied through atmospheric deposition.

Contamination arising from agriculture

Finally, we address agriculture's ability to contaminate land. Earlier in the chapter we touched on the inorganic and organic substances in products which agriculture applies in the course of animal and crop production, namely fertilisers, manures and pesticides. Controls on these largely centre on preventing inappropriate use and consequent risks to safety or harm to the environment. **7–33**

In the case of fertilisers, the Soil Code refers farmers to the MAFF/ADAS "Fertiliser Recommendations for Agricultural and Horticultural Crops"

(MAFF Reference Book 209). The main concerns regarding soil pollution are cadmium and to a lesser extent fluoride and uranium, contained in phosphate rock. The Soil Code states that fertiliser manufacturers should monitor the concentrations to ensure that soil is not polluted.

The main contaminants of soil contained in manures are copper and zinc, although once again inappropriate applications can cause increased levels in soil. E.U. feedingstuffs legislation has reduced the concentrations allowed to be added to animal feeds as growth promoters. However, the Soil Code advises farmers to check the concentration in slurries and in their land, especially where there have been repeated applications. Soils should be analysed to 15 or 25 cm in arable soils and 7.5 cm in grassland, and expert advice obtained if the levels exceed the ceiling for sewage sludge application (see Appendix 3).

Although there is concern over the long-term build up of pesticides in soils, the RCEP found no evidence of this in its 1996 Report. There are rigorous legal controls affecting pesticide use in the United Kingdom, with extensive testing of the environmental effects and pollution potential of pesticides required before they are approved for use. The Food and Environment Protection Act 1985 (FEPA) and the Control of Pesticides Regulations 1986 (S.I. 1986 No. 1510) (COPR) govern a range of activities from the selling and advertising to the storage and use of pesticides, and this was added to in 1990 by the MAFF/HSE Code of Practice for the Safe Use of Pesticides on Farms and Holdings. This Code is statutory and provides guidance on the use of pesticides, including the disposal of washings and containers. Guidance in the Soil Code also refers farmers to the MAFF Water Code.

Liability for damage caused by waste

7–34 It is apparent from the matters dealt with in this chapter that soil pollution is inextricably linked with the whole issue of waste. We have seen how legislation has been largely focused on preventative measures, but there is also a recognition that this may not always be sufficient and that the legislation also needs to address damage caused. Section 73 of the EPA does include provisions concerning liability for damage caused by the illegal deposit of waste. These place liability for damage caused by the waste on the person depositing it, or on a person who knowingly caused or knowingly permitted it to be deposited. Exceptions to this are made where damage was wholly the fault of the person who suffered it, or where a person voluntarily accepts the risk of damage.

The principle that a person is liable for damage caused by the escape of substances brought onto land, more or less regardless of precautionary measures taken, has long been established in United Kingdom civil law by *Rylands v. Fletcher*. This has tended to have most impact where damage is to property rather than to the environment, in contrast to other E.U. Member States where the principle of strict or "no fault" civil liability is much more widely instituted for environmental damage. The European

Commission is also moving towards establishing civil liability on a community-wide basis, seeing it as an extension of the "polluter pays" principle, and in 1989 it published a proposal for a Directive to introduce such liability for producers of waste in relation to damage to the person, property and to the environment. Essentially, strict liability means that the plaintiff would no longer have to prove fault before being able to sustain a claim for damages.

This proposed Directive on Civil Liability for Damage caused by Waste (COM (89) 282) covers all waste defined in the current Framework Directive on Waste and the Commission apparently intends that the same exclusions would apply. It would not, therefore, include those agricultural wastes excluded from the Directive, namely animal carcasses and faecal wastes, but would include any agricultural wastes currently subject to review, which may be classified as controlled waste in due course.

Chapter 8
Air pollution

Introduction

8–01 In considering air pollution, we first need to be clear what we mean by this term. For the purposes of this chapter, it will cover pollution of the air by agricultural activity. Those air pollutants which arise from other sources and which contribute towards pollution of agriculture are not addressed in this chapter, but in those dealing with the media through which they exert their effect. These are principally water and soil (Chapters 5, 6 and 7 respectively).

Air pollution from agriculture gives rise to broadly two types of pollution. The first tends to give rise to purely local problems and is not what would normally be thought of as harmful or noxious but rather as having nuisance value. Odours and noise fall into this category. The second type stems from emissions which contribute, along with those of other industries and activities, to problems in the wider atmosphere such as global warming and ozone depletion. Remedying these problems requires different approaches. Nuisances tend to be addressed by regulations which tackle problems as and when they occur, whereas the wider issues are more likely to be the subject of general controls or regulations aimed at pre-empting emissions at unacceptable levels. This chapter deals with the latter, whilst nuisances are addressed in the next chapter.

Over the course of many years governments have introduced various measures to improve the quality of air. The problems addressed have not involved agriculture to any significant extent and it has remained relatively free of controls. However, this situation is unlikely to continue since agriculture has been found to contribute to a number of issues recognised more recently as of concern.

This chapter sets out the current legislation on air pollution control where it applies to agriculture. It then proceeds to give an outline of the range of wider-scale air pollution problems in which agriculture plays a part and where control measures are either already under consideration, or where they are a possibility in the future.

Legislation

8–02 Early United Kingdom legislation focused on local pollution issues, and it is not until the last 20 years that wider concerns have been generally accepted. These have been addressed by European legislation, through the 1984 Air Framework Directive and a number of daughter Directives which have tackled emissions of sulphur dioxide, nitrogen dioxide/oxides, black smoke, suspended particulates, lead and ozone. Since the industry is not thought to make a significant contribution to these problems, this group of

Directives have not impacted on agriculture. In 1995, the second Air Framework Directive extended the list of substances "for consideration" to benzene, poly-aromatic hydrocarbons, carbon monoxide, cadmium, arsenic, nickel and mercury, but again there does not appear to be direct implications for agriculture from this Directive. It is only with the 1996 Directive on Integrated Pollution Prevention and Control that agriculture is specifically identified, and this has yet to be implemented.

At present, air pollution legislation impacting on agriculture is almost exclusively of United Kingdom origin. It is supplemented by the MAFF Code of Good Agricultural Practice for the Protection of Air (the Air Code), which offers guidance and encouragement to farmers in addressing air pollution issues.

Clean Air Act 1993

Measures to reduce atmospheric pollution were introduced in the 1950s to cope with the smogs during certain weather conditions in urban areas. The Clean Air Act 1956 introduced various controls in urban areas, and also prohibited the emission of dark smoke from chimneys on industrial or trade premises. Section 1 of the 1968 Act extended this prohibition to industrial or trade premises generally. The provisions contained in these Acts have now been consolidated into the Clean Air Act 1993, and the original Acts repealed. **8–03**

Dark smoke arises when combustion of organic compounds in the burning process is not complete. For the purposes of the legislation, smoke is defined as dark when it is as dark or darker than Grade 2 on the "Ringelmann Chart". This has a scale of 0–5, and is described in British Standard 2742—"Use of Ringelman and Miniature Smoke Charts". Grade 2 represents 40 per cent obscuration. It is not necessary for the emission to be witnessed. Unless the defendant proves to the contrary, dark smoke will be considered to have been emitted if material has been burnt on the premises in circumstances likely to have given rise to dark smoke.

Agriculture was generally believed to fall outside the definition of trade premises. But in March 1990 a DoE Minister expressed the view that agriculture was included, and the Air Code, published in 1992, specifically states in paragraph 14 that land on which an agricultural or horticultural business is carried on is considered to be trade premises. There has been at least one successful prosecution of a farmer by a local authority.

Certain exceptions to the scope of the offence are set out in the Clean Air (Emission of Dark Smoke) (Exemption) Regulations 1969 (S.I. 1969 No. 1263). Of interest to farmers are those for containers contaminated with pesticide, and animal carcasses in certain situations. Essentially, these are where there is no other reasonably safe and practicable method of disposal, where the burning is carried out under the direct and continuous supervision of the occupier or a person authorised to act on his behalf, and where the emission of dark smoke is minimised. In the case of carcasses, the exemption covers animals which have died of or been slaughtered because of disease. Further detail is provided in the Air Code. **8–04**

There is a statutory defence under section 2(4) that the offence was inadvertent and all practical steps had been taken to minimise the emission of dark smoke. It is also a defence, under section 51(1) of the Act, that the local authority did not give notice to the occupier within four days of having become aware of the offence (unless the officer had reason to believe that notice had already been given).

Tyres are notorious for producing "dark smoke", and burning plastics and oils is also likely to do so. Other materials can also cause a problem, depending on the conditions under which the burning takes place. Guidance on methods of burning to minimise the risk of creating dark smoke is also contained in the Air Code.

Environmental Protection Act 1990 (EPA), Part 1—Integrated Pollution Control (IPC) and Local Authority Air Pollution Control (LAAPC)

8–05 Apart from the Clean Air Act, the United Kingdom's main air pollution legislation is contained in Part 1 of the EPA. This falls into two sections, "Integrated Pollution Control" (IPC) for larger processes or those with more potential to cause pollution, and "Local Authority Air Pollution Control" (LAAPC) for medium-sized processes and those with more modest potential to pollute.

IPC, as its name implies, is an integrated system of control. It concentrates on a small number of large operations and regulates emissions to water and land as well as air. It enables the regulatory authority, the Environment Agency (EA), to take a holistic view of the process and its impact on the environment. This is an important development in view of the interchangeability of some polluting substances between different emission routes, depending on the detail of the design or management of the process. The IPC system operates by requiring operators of "prescribed processes" listed in Part A of Schedule 1 of the Environmental Protection (Prescribed Processes and Substances) Regulations 1991 (S.I. 1991 No. 472) to obtain a prior authorisation for the carrying on of the process from the EA, through which it is then able to limit the emissions.

LAAPC applies to a larger number of less polluting processes. The regulatory authority is the local authority environmental health department. It operates on similar lines to IPC, with prior authorisations required for prescribed processes, but in this instance for those listed in Part B of Schedule 1 to the Regulations. There is, however, an important difference in that local authority environmental health departments deal only with air pollution, and do not take an integrated approach. Discharges to water or to land are therefore controlled separately, and without formal integration, by the EA, to whom potential dischargers should apply for consent.

8–06 No agricultural operation falls within IPC, and only a small number of activities carried out on farms are covered by LAAPC. These are listed in the Air Code. In brief, they are as follows:

(a) general incinerators under 1 tonne/hour capacity;

(b) animal incinerators under 1 tonne/hour capacity, although incinerators of less than 50 kg/hour capacity are exempt;
(c) waste oil burners;
(d) wood, straw or poultry litter combustion processes of between 0.4 and 3 MW net rated thermal input (exempt below 0.4 MW);
(e) treatment or processing of animal or vegetable matter including:
  (i) fur breeding;
  (ii) animal feed compounding;
  (iii) production of compost for mushrooms.

For all of the processes under category (e), there is an exemption if the processing of animal or vegetable matter is carried out on a farm and does not involve the manufacture of goods for sale. The transfer of the product of the process to another site under the same management is not a sale and so remains within the scope of the exemption. There is also a general exemption for the manufacture or preparation of food and drink, although this does not extend to certain processes relating to animal or vegetable fat or oil, to some processes involving the use of stomachs and intestines or blood boiling, or to the cooking of tripe for human consumption on other premises.

Even where a farmer finds that his operations fall within an exemption, he should be aware that the Air Code advises that he should comply wherever practicable with the Process Guidance Note (see below) to minimise the risk of a nuisance arising. He will be subject to the statutory nuisance provisions contained in Part 3 of the EPA. Processes which are subject to authorisations under Part 1 are not generally subject to controls under Part 3 (section 79(10) of the EPA).

Official guidance on the approach to, and standards to be adopted by, **8–07**
the regulatory authority in setting authorisations is contained in published Guidance Notes issued by the EA's Chief Inspector in the case of IPC, and by the Secretary of State for the Environment in the case of LAAPC. Guidance Notes have been prepared for each process and are drawn up in consultation with the industry concerned and are reviewed from time to time in the light of developing technology and economic circumstances.

The guiding principle in authorisations under the EPA is BATNEEC (Best Available Techniques Not Entailing Excessive Cost). The interpretation of this may pose some challenges, but the Department of the Environment has provided some guidance:

> "Best" should be taken to mean the most effective in preventing, minimising or rendering harmless polluting emissions. There may be more than one technique which achieves the best standard, but the technique's effectiveness should have been demonstrated to qualify as best. "Available" means procurable by any operator, even if the supplier is outside the United Kingdom and/or has a monopoly.
>
> "Techniques" includes both the process and its operation, and includes matters such as staff numbers, training supervision and manner of operating the process.
>
> "Not entailing excessive cost" allows the degree of environmental benefit obtained to be balanced against the cost. For example, a

technique which gave only a marginal improvement for a heavy additional expenditure could be held to entail excessive cost.

8–08 The approach to processes which already existed prior to the need for authorisations may differ relative to more recent processes which required authorisations from the outset. Older plants will be allowed a period in which to upgrade which will reflect the cost of such upgrading in relation to the plant's characteristics and life expectancy. For new plants, the cost of installing new techniques will normally be lower than for existing plants, and such techniques will normally be required from the outset.

BATNEEC therefore envisages that the business will use the best technology currently available for preventing, minimising or rendering emissions harmless, subject to reasonable economic criteria. These economic criteria are determined for the industry as a whole, and not on the basis of the financial circumstances of the individual business. If an individual business is unable to afford a technique which is generally viable for the industry, it may have to close. BATNEEC would normally be applied at the point at which a plant is constructed or refurbished. Operators are not expected to purchase new equipment every time there is a development in pollution abatement technology, although, as mentioned above, there may be a timescale for older processes to upgrade. The Guidance Note may indicate the timescale for the regulator to review authorisations and to require improvement to meet modern standards.

Not all conditions attached to an authorisation are necessarily subject to the BATNEEC test. The enforcing authority may impose other conditions, which may relate to the process, the way it is carried out, staff levels and training, emission levels, monitoring, insurance against clean-up costs, etc. As with other conditions, these can be appealed if they are felt to be unreasonable.

Applications

8–09 Applications for both types are made on forms available from the appropriate enforcing authority. Details of applications, authorisations and other relevant information are advertised, and representations can be made to the enforcing authority, which takes any representations made by third parties into account when determining the application. The authorities have wide powers to secure information. Under paragraph 5 of Schedule 1 to the Act, if the application is not decided within four months it is deemed to be a refusal, and the applicant can appeal to the Secretary of State. The Secretary of State also has the power to call in applications to be determined by him rather than by the enforcing authority (paragraph 3 of Schedule 1). There are substantial application fees for authorisations, and annual subsistence fees to maintain the validity of the licence.

Authorisations

8–10 Authorisations contain conditions which may include specific limits for relevant pollutants, and may be reviewed from time to time, and indeed must be at least every four years. There is an appeal system by which applicants can appeal to the Secretary of State for the Environment if they are dissatisfied with the Agency's or local authority's refusal to grant or vary an authorisation, a decision to revoke one, or if the conditions attached to an authorisation are unacceptable. Appeals can also be made against various notices served by the enforcement agency (section 15 of the EPA). The appeal systems is covered by the Environmental Protection (Applications, Appeals and Registers) Regulations 1991 (S.I. 1991 No. 507) (as amended).

Public registers

Details of applications, authorisations, notices served and information obtained in pursuance of authorisations are amongst the information kept on public registers maintained by the enforcing authorities. There is provision for information not to be included in the register on grounds of commercial confidentiality. **8–11**

Transfers

An authorisation for a prescribed process may be transferred from the holder to a person intending to carry on the process in the holder's place, although the enforcement authority must be notified within 21 days (section 9 of the EPA). The authority may decide to review the authorisation in the light of the new holder's circumstances. **8–12**

Enforcement

The enforcing authorities have powers to withdraw authorisations, provided at least 28 days notice is given, and can serve enforcement notices to secure the remedying of specified contraventions, or likely contraventions. In the event of an imminent risk of serious pollution a prohibition notice can be served, the effect of which is to suspend the authorisation, wholly or partially, until the relevant steps are taken. A prohibition notice can be served regardless of whether a breach of the authorisation has occurred. **8–13**

Offences and penalties

A number of offences are laid down in section 23 of the EPA, the principal ones being to carry on a prescribed process without an authorisation or in breach of the conditions contained in an authorisation. The burden of proof is on the operator to show that, on the balance of probability, he complied with the implied conditions of BATNEEC, although there are some conditions to which this does not apply. On summary conviction, a fine of up to £20,000 may be imposed, while on indictment the penalties are an unlimited fine and/or up to two years imprisonment. **8–14**

Integrated Pollution Prevention and Control Directive (96/61)

This Directive is modelled on the United Kingdom system of IPC and effectively extends IPC to Europe for a wide range of industrial processes. It was adopted in September 1996. Some agricultural processes will be affected, namely intensive livestock units which exceed the following sizes: **8–15**

Poultry	—	40,000 places
Production pigs over 30kg	—	2,000 places
Sows	—	750 places

The Directive must be brought into force within three years and will then apply to all new units. Units already in operation at the date of coming into force must be brought under control within a further eight years. The main objective includes the use of the "best available techniques" to prevent pollution, the avoidance, minimisation and recovery of waste production, and the effective use of energy (Article 3). The interpretation of best available techniques will clearly be important, but one obvious difference from the United Kingdom BATNEEC approach, described above, is the absence of "NEEC". However, the Directive's definition of "available" includes taking into consideration economic viability, and the costs and benefits. There may, therefore, turn out to be less difference between E.U. "BAT" and United Kingdom "BATNEEC" than first appearances suggest.

The Directive includes at Annex III a list of the main polluting substances to be taken into account. Those relevant to agriculture include the following:

— oxides of nitrogen and other nitrogen compounds	(*e.g.* ammonia)
— volatile organic compounds	(*e.g.* methane)
— metals and their compounds	(*e.g.* zinc and copper)
— dust	
— biocides	(*e.g.* disinfectants, antibiotics)
— materials in suspension	(*e.g.* suspended solids in water)
— substances which contribute to eutrophication	(*e.g.* nitrates and phosphates)
— substances which remove oxygen from water	(*e.g.* manure)

It remains to be seen what approach the government will adopt for those businesses not already subject to IPC or LAAPC.

8–16 The intensive livestock thresholds (see paragraph 8–15, above) would appear to include much smaller businesses than other categories within the Directive's scope. Businesses with one or two employees, or in some cases possibly only family labour, are covered and these clearly will not have the resources to administer a complex system of control. The Directive accords special recognition to this category in Article 9(4), where it requires the limits on emissions to take into account "practical considerations appropriate to these categories of installations".

While the United Kingdom regulation bringing the Directive into effect is not required to be introduced before September 1999, farmers constructing or extending intensive livestock units in the meantime may wish to be mindful of the sizes triggering control listed above. It is not yet clear how "intensive livestock" or a "unit" will be defined. It seems likely that adjoining units on separate farms will be regarded as separate, but what distance must there be between separate units on the same farm for them to be considered as separate? These and other important issues regarding the scope, nature and content of the regulations will need to be addressed. Since approximately 1,000 units are thought to fall within the Directive's scope in this category alone (almost as many as are currently regulated under the entire United Kingdom IPC system), it therefore seems likely that an administratively simple approach will be adopted compared to IPC as it is currently operated.

Atmospheric pollution problems

Introduction

We now turn to the air pollution problems stemming from emissions from agriculture which affect the wider atmosphere. Little action has as yet been taken on these. This is partly because the identification and acceptance of the problems themselves is relatively recent, and partly because tackling emissions from most forms of agriculture is more difficult than for the majority of non-agricultural sources. Some agricultural emissions can be traced to fairly precise locations or activities, but others are simply part of the general nature of agriculture, and modern intensive agriculture in particular. The latter will be especially difficult to address. The following section describes the problems, identifies the sources of the various pollutant gases, and where relevant, also describes the measures in hand. They are dealt with in the following order: **8–17**

Ammonia;
Greenhouse gases;
 (i) Carbon dioxide;
 (ii) Methane;
 (iii) Nitrous oxide;
 (iv) CFCs;
Ozone depletion;
Ground-level ozone.

Ammonia (NH_3)

Ammonia is one of the major contributors to nitrogen deposition, together with nitrogen oxide emissions from electricity generation and transport. Emissions of ammonia into the atmosphere have two major impacts, both of which arise from their subsequent deposition onto land or vegetation. They contribute to acidification of soils and water bodies, and they enhance the levels of nitrogen available to plants. These levels of nitrogen may then exceed the critical level for particular natural or semi-natural plant communities and lead to changes in the species balance, favouring those which are able to make best use of the extra nitrogen. Since ammonia tends to be deposited more rapidly than nitrogen oxides, it travels less far and so may contribute proportionately more close to its major sources, and rather less in other locations. **8–18**

Agriculture has been identified as the major source of ammonia emissions in the United Kingdom, contributing about 80 per cent of the total. Livestock husbandry is responsible for the bulk of emissions. It is thought that these arise from buildings in which livestock are housed, manure stores and the spreading of manures on land, in roughly equal proportions. The application of fertilisers and the breakdown of crop residues also make smaller contributions, as do human beings themselves through sweat and breath, sewage treatment and miscellaneous sources.

Techniques for measuring and controlling ammonia emissions are not yet well advanced, although injection of slurry or rapid incorporation of manures into the soil (within a few hours of application) has a considerable effect. Such advice as is available is included in the Air Code for both housing and spreading.

Control of ammonia has been on the agenda for some little time, having been identified by the European Parliament's Environment Committee as suitable for inclusion under the 1995 Air Framework Directive. In the event, neither ammonia nor acid deposition, which might have provided a means of addressing ammonia emissions, were included. It is, however, expected that the reduction of ammonia levels from larger housed livestock units will be one of the aims of the recently adopted E.U. Directive on Integrated Pollution Prevention and Control, described above, although the extent and timescale of any measures remains to be decided by individual governments. In practice, these rely on progress with research and development of techniques to both measure and control emissions.

Greenhouse gases

8–19 Certain gases in the atmosphere, together with water vapour, trap the sun's heat by reducing the amount re-radiated to space, similar to the effect of glass in a greenhouse. This keeps the earth's temperature about 30 °C higher than would otherwise be the case. However, gases released by man's activities are causing the effect to increase, giving rise to the phenomenon known as global warming, the existence of which, after some years of uncertainty, is now internationally accepted. The Air Code describes this as one of the biggest environmental problems facing the world.

The main gases involved, and their approximate contributions to increased heat retention, are carbon dioxide (70 per cent), methane (25 per cent), nitrous oxide (4 per cent) and to a lesser extent chlorofluorocarbons (CFCs). The concentration of these gases has increased since the industrial revolution as a result of human activities, and particularly so in this century. Most of the gases persist for long periods in the atmosphere, and it is therefore important to make reductions sooner rather than later because of the time lag before the total amount of such gases in the atmosphere starts to reduce. There is also concern that the further the process of warming is allowed to proceed, the greater is the likelihood of passing a point beyond which it develops its own momentum and the situation can no longer be retrieved by human action.

The impact and extent of climate change is the subject of much uncertainty, and will vary from place to place. In general, it is expected that many areas will become warmer. While this may be beneficial for temperate and cool regions in terms of their ability to grow crops, it could have serious impacts in arid and semi-arid parts of the world. Rainfall patterns are also expected to alter, and the frequency of climatic events such as floods and droughts is expected to increase, with consequences for agriculture. The general trend towards higher temperatures will lead to the reduction of icecaps and a consequent rise in sea level which could ultimately be as much as 30m according to some predictions. Since the circulation of ocean currents is likely to be affected, current climatic patterns could also shift. This may lead to some areas becoming colder, in spite of the general warming trend.

In terms of action to control emissions from agriculture, this is one of **8–20** the harder sectors to address. As the Air Code recognises, it is impossible to prevent all emissions, some simply being part of the natural cycle and some part of the intensification of agriculture. The growth in world population necessitates greater production from agriculture generally, and the United Kingdom now provides more of its own food than it has for a very long time.

Whilst the Air Code was published in 1992 and may not be up to date on certain points, it does nevertheless set out certain action that farmers can take to reduce emissions of these pollutants. But no one country or region of the world can solve the problem on its own. Emissions need to be controlled on a global scale, and efforts are being made to develop agreements. The E.U., as one of the most developed areas, is attempting to give a lead by setting its own targets, and the United Kingdom has agreed to reduce its emissions of carbon dioxide to 1990 levels by the year 2000 if other countries do the same. However, this is only a first step and much more will need to be done.

Carbon dioxide (CO_2)

The main source of increasing CO_2 levels in the atmosphere is the burning **8–21** of fossil fuels (coal, oil and gas), which contain large quantities of carbon obtained from the atmosphere by prehistoric forests and other plant growth and locked up in these fossil reserves for many millions of years. The use of agricultural products as fuel is a positive environmental advantage compared to burning fossil fuels since the CO_2 released has been directly obtained from the atmosphere in recent times and is simply recycled.

Agriculture in the United Kingdom contributes about 1 per cent of CO_2 emissions, excluding fertiliser and machinery manufacture. Including these activities approximately doubles the figure. There is some scope to reduce emissions by ensuring that energy is used efficiently, both in vehicles and in heated structures such as glasshouses and mushroom houses, and by replacing fossil fuels with renewable energy sources. A number of recommendations for efficient use of energy on the farm is included in the Air Code.

Official figures show that between 1970 and 1993 the United Kingdom's CO_2 emissions declined by 17 per cent (Department of Environment,

1996). The government has sought to encourage the use of renewable sources of energy by the Non-Fossil Fuel Orders (NFFOs), which offer enhanced prices for electricity generated by novel technologies utilising such sources. As technologies develop, the degree of subsidy has tended to reduce, and under any individual contract there is a time limit for which the subsidy is provided. The scheme is operated by the Department of Trade and Industry, which appears to view it partly as a means of developing new technology to generate business opportunities overseas. Of relevance to farmers are contracts let for plants burning poultry litter, straw, forestry wastes and coppice grown on farms.

Methane (CH_4)

8–22 Whilst methane contributes less to global warming than CO_2 on account of its much lower concentration, it is almost 25 times more powerful than CO_2 as a global warming agent. This means that any savings in emissions are particularly worthwhile. Agriculture is responsible for about 32 per cent of methane emissions (the ENDS report January 1996), other sources being landfill sites, coal mining, leakage from gas distribution systems and other miscellaneous sources (see Table 5). Within agriculture, the main sources of methane are ruminant animals (mainly cattle and sheep in the United Kingdom) and stored slurry.

It is not considered likely that methane from the animals themselves can be greatly reduced, nor that research on ruminant diets will bring major reductions in methane emissions in the foreseeable future. But measures to address methane escaping from slurry stores were included in the European Commission's draft strategy for reducing methane emissions published in late 1996. It is likely that this would be achieved by some kind of roofing, with the methane either flared off, or utilised for on-farm energy generation. In either case it would be converted to the much less powerful global warming gas, CO_2 (Air Code).

It is officially estimated that methane emissions have declined by 19 per cent in the United Kingdom between 1970 and 1993 (Department of Environment, 1996) although the figures are rather uncertain. Globally, rice paddies are a major source of methane, although this is of little importance in Europe.

Nitrous oxide (N_2O)

8–23 While nitrous oxide is a lesser contributor to global warming than CO_2 or methane, it is an extremely powerful agent, being 10 times more powerful than methane and 320 times more powerful than CO_2. The contribution of different sources is shown in Table 6, but the most recent information suggests that agriculture contributes up to 17 per cent of United Kingdom emissions (the ENDS report January 1996). Of the greenhouse gases produced by agriculture, it is nitrous oxide which makes the largest contribution to global warming. There is, however, relatively little which can be done to reduce emissions, at least in the present state of knowledge.

Table 5 Estimated emissions[1] of methane (CH^4) by UNECE source category: 1970–1994

United Kingdom Thousand tonnes

	Note	1970	1980	1985	1986	1987	1988	1989	1990	1991	1992	1993	1994	*% of total in 1994*
(a) By UNECE source category														
Power stations	2	2r	2r	2r	2r	2r	5r	6r	6r	7r	8r	10r	11	–
Domestic	3	197r	93r	87r	86r	76r	65r	58r	52r	56r	50r	53r	46	*1*
Industrial combustion		17	9r	9	9	9	9	9	9	9r	8	8	8	–
Deep-mined coal		1,419	1,166	779	936	887	864	820	750	754	675	516	316	*8*
Open-cast coal		3	5	5	5	5	6	6	6	6	6	6	6	–
Gas leakage	4	42	343	382	386	405	383	378	386	381	375	370	365	*9*
Offshore oil and gas	5	11	54	77	82	88	90	92	96	100	102	116r	122	*3*
Road Transport	6	16r	23r	24r	25r	27r	29r	31r	30r	30r	28r	26r	24	*1*
Landfill	7	1,580r	1,870r	1,910r	1,910r	1,900r	1,900r	1,890r	1,890r	1,860r	1,840r	1,820r	1,790	*46*
Other waste treatment & disposal		69	70	70	70	71	71	71	71	71	72	72	72	*2*
Cattle	8	866	918	887	865r	839	815	816	817r	803	797	792r	803	*21*
Sheep	8	159	190	215	223	232	246	258	263	262	264	264	261	*7*
Other animals	8,9	50	49	49	49	50	51	48	48	49	49r	51	51	*1*
Other agriculture		1	1	1	1	1	1	1	1	1	1	1	1	–
Total		**4,433r**	**4,793r**	**4,497r**	**4,649r**	**4,592r**	**4,535r**	**4,484r**	**4,426r**	**4,388r**	**4,276r**	**4,104r**	**3,876r**	***100***
(e) Emissions (tonnes)/ GDP (£million)	10	12.7r	11.3r	9.6r	9.5r	9.0r	8.4r	8.2r	8.0r	8.1r	8.0r	7.5r	6.8r	

Source: *NETCEN; CSO*

[1] Most of the figures in this table are based on a single methane emission factor for each fuel which is held constant over time. It should be noted that these figures are approximate and represent best current estimates; they will be revised as more accurate information becomes available. The number of significant figures quoted in this table should not be taken as an indication of the accuracy of the estimates.

[2] New series includes methane emissions from biogas combustion and emission factors have been revised.

[3] New series includes methane emissions from wood combustion and emission factors have been revised.

[4] Gas leakage is an estimate of losses during transmission through the distribution system and does not include beyond-the-meter non-combustion losses. The 1990 to 1994 estimates are derived from leakage measurements performed by British Gas. Pre-1990 estimates are based on a fixed proportion of throughput and are more uncertain.

[5] The 1991 figure for methane emissions from offshore oil and gas is taken from the Watt Committee report. Data for previous years are based on the number of installations and may underestimate emissions from flaring in the late 1970s.

[6] Revised time series reflects improved emission factors.

[7] Estimates of landfill emissions are very uncertain. See paragraphs 1.19 and 1.20 of text for further explanation.

[8] These figures include emissions from animal respiration and manure and have an uncertainy of +/− 20–30 per cent.

[9] Pigs, poultry and horses.

[10] GDP measured at 1990 prices.

Table 6 Estimated emissions[1] of nitrous oxide (N_2O) by emission source: 1990–1994

United Kingdom — Thousand tonnes

	1990	1991	1992	1993	1994	*% of total in 1994*
(a) By UNECE source category						
Power stations	2.9	2.9	2.7	2.4	2.3	2
Domestic	0.3	0.3	0.3	0.3	0.3	—
Commercial/public service	0.2	0.2	0.1	0.1	0.1	–
Industrial combustion [1]	0.6	0.6	0.6	0.6	0.6	*1*
Non-combustion process [2]	95.2	89.7	73.1	63.1	73.6	79
Road transport	3.1	3.3	3.9	5.2	6.8	7
Waste treatment and disposal [3]	0.2	0.2	0.1	–	–	–
Animal wastes	3.5	3.5	3.5	3.5	3.5	4
Soils	6.6	6.7	6.4	6.2	6.3	7
Total	**112.6**	**107.4**	**90.9**	**81.4**	**93.6**	***100***
(b) Emissions (tonnes)/GDP (£million) [4]	0.32	0.25	0.19	0.17	0.18	

Source Netcen; CS0

[1] Excludes emissions from solid fuel transformation.
[2] Emissions arise from adipic and nitric acid production.
[3] Comprises emissions from field burning which was discontinued in 1993.
[4] GDP measured at 1990 prices.

It is released by the reaction of nitrogen compounds in manures and soils, and the best advice to farmers on minimising losses is to avoid excessive use of manures and fertilisers, and to ensure they are not applied to waterlogged soils. (Air Code)

Chlorofluorocarbons (CFCS)

Although better known for their effects in depleting ozone levels in the upper atmosphere, CFCs are also powerful greenhouse gases, and it is therefore doubly important to ensure their release into the atmosphere is avoided. They are not widely used in agriculture, other than in older refrigeration equipment which may be used for cooling milk tanks or for temperature-controlled crop stores. The best advice is to maintain and dispose of the refrigerant and equipment carefully to ensure that CFCs are recovered. (Air Code) **8–24**

Ozone depletion (O_3)

Ozone in the upper atmosphere forms a screen against potentially harmful levels of ultraviolet radiation from the sun penetrating to ground level. Major reductions in ozone levels have been identified in recent years over both the Arctic and the Antarctic, and they appear to be increasing in intensity and extent. These ozone "holes" appear in the spring when the sun returns to these regions and causes chemical reactions which lead to the loss of ozone. While CFCs have been found to be among the most damaging gases, they are by no means the only problem. Methyl bromide used for fumigating stored crops and for sterilising horticultural soils also plays a part in reducing ozone levels. A 1996 review of the use of methyl bromide in horticulture by ADAS found that the major sectors contributing to the 481 tonnes used were crops grown under cover, such as lettuce, celery and mushrooms (276 tonnes) and soft fruit, principally strawberries (160 tonnes). Use on tomatoes grown under cover has declined due to the increasing adoption of artificial growing media instead of soil. The study found that the scope for replacement with alternative techniques was limited in the short to medium term, and that several of the principal uses were likely to be designated "Critical Agricultural Uses" and so exempted from the aim of the Montreal Protocol of 1987 to phase out methyl bromide use by the year 2010. **8–25**

International agreements such as the Montreal Protocol have resulted in major reductions in emissions of CFC and other ozone depleting gases, particularly in developed countries. However, global emissions still exceed the rate at which the problem gases are being destroyed. If all countries comply with the Montreal Protocol, the level of damaging gases are expected to peak in the late 1990s, and decline slowly thereafter. Slight reductions in the concentrations of damaging gases in the atmosphere above two United Kingdom sites have been recorded (Department of Environment, 1996).

The major effects of the increased levels of UV radiation experienced at the earth's surface as a result of depletion of the ozone layer would be on human and animal health, and also on crop yields. The contribution which farmers and growers can make to resolving this problem lies in ensuring that any CFCs contained in refrigeration systems on farms are not released to the atmosphere, and that the use of methyl bromide is minimised.

Ground-level ozone

8–26 Although not strictly conforming to our definition of air pollution, it is nevertheless thought appropriate to deal with ground-level ozone caused by non-agricultural air pollutants in this chapter, since it affects agriculture directly through the air rather than through other media. Unlike ozone in the upper atmosphere, ozone at ground level is harmful. It is an aggressive gas, which may have damaging effects on both plants and animals, including humans. It arises largely from the action of sunlight on combinations of pollutants, particularly nitrogen oxides and volatile organic compounds (VOCs) such as solvents from paint. The process is heavily temperature-dependent, and so is more of a problem in a hot summer. However, it is not rapid, and by the time peak levels of ozone have been generated, the polluted air masses have usually drifted from their predominantly urban sources to rural areas. The highest ozone levels do in fact tend to be recorded in the countryside, and health related guideline figures are also exceeded in urban areas.

Measures are in hand to reduce levels of VOCs emitted from many industries, using the authorisation mechanism provided by Part 1 of the EPA. Nitrogen oxide emissions are being addressed through changes in fuels and technology in electricity generation, and by the phasing in of catalytic converters for petrol-engined cars, although the forecast growth in traffic is expected to offset reductions from the latter in the next century. There is no clear trend in levels of ground level ozone, due in part to the variability of levels according to summer weather. However, there is agreement that levels should be reduced. Agriculture has not been identified as a significant contributor to ground-level ozone pollution.

Conclusion

8–27 While agriculture has been little affected by air pollution legislation in the past, it is clear from this chapter that it makes significant contributions to a number of problems of current concern. We have seen that action has already been taken at European level to introduce controls for larger intensive livestock units, with only the precise nature of implementation at national level remaining to be decided. But so far as most of the wider air pollution problems arising from agriculture are concerned, there is as yet little indication of how these will be tackled. While it may be possible to address agricultural activities carried on within buildings, such as the keeping of intensive livestock, by established methods of pollution control, agricultural activities in the open air are very much more difficult to tackle. It is possible that for some problems at least, the very large number of farms involved would make individually determined and monitored permits or authorisations impractical and a "Code of Practice" approach is likely to be a more realistic option. A permit system could be more feasible where it is possible to identify a smaller number of units, such as those involved in large scale poultry rearing operations, should it be considered that this was justified by the pollution potential involved.

The pressure for agriculture to reduce its contribution to air pollution results in part from the growing awareness of the need to adopt good practice to minimise pollution. This is the main approach of the Nitrates Directive, but in future we can also expect to see direct controls extended to larger numbers of smaller sources, such as individual farms. The need for the United Kingdom to fulfil its commitments to international agreements, such as the Montreal Protocol, will also be part of this trend and it is perhaps not impossible ultimately that practices which cause the release of unacceptable quantities of pollutants may be prohibited entirely where control is not a realistic option.

Increasingly most nations do not consider the current levels of emissions to the air and their effects on global climate and the ozone layer to be acceptable. There is a growing recognition that these problems are one aspect of the sustainability of a whole range of activities and of whether these can be sustained in the long-term without unacceptable damage to the environment. How to pursue the concept of sustainability has therefore become one of the major thrusts of environmental policy in the 1990s. Unfortunately, the willingness of countries to take the necessary steps to achieve this is less apparent and the question of which countries will shoulder the burden of reductions in emissions, and whether less developed countries should be able to continue increasing theirs, presents a major challenge to world politicians in the coming years.

Chapter 9
Nuisances

Introduction

9–01 The word "nuisance" in common usage is a very general term. What is annoying or a "nuisance" to one person, may not be so to another—or at least not to the same degree. The word is applied to a wide variety of situations, ranging from anything disagreeable or mildly annoying, to something which is obnoxious and even injurious to health, not only to an individual but also to the community at large. Distinguishing between these extremes is not always easy. This is a problem which assumes particular significance when it comes to ascertaining whether the nuisance in question is severe enough for a remedy to be available through the courts.

This chapter is essentially about the more extreme forms of nuisance where the possibility of legal action arises. But there may be valuable lessons for a wider variety of situations, if only to preserve good neighbour relations, which itself may prevent disputes or legal actions arising at a later date. Farmers need to recognise that their activities may be constrained by the need not to cause a legal nuisance to neighbours. Similarly, members of local communities may need to be tolerant and show a greater understanding of the needs of agriculture, which does still constitute the primary economic activity in the countryside where they have chosen to live. This chapter also addresses the legislation which has been put in place to regulate specific nuisances, such as dark smoke.

From a legal point of view, nuisances can be divided into three categories. That which arises most frequently is "statutory nuisance" and is the aspect we deal with in most depth. As its name implies, it is founded in statute law. We also describe the law relating to public nuisance, and to private nuisance, which is used less frequently and which derives from the development of the general law, common law.

Public or common nuisance

9–02 Public nuisance is some unlawful act or omission which endangers or interferes with the lives of the public generally or some section of the public within the neighbourhood of the nuisance's operation. Public nuisance is a civil wrong (a tort) for which the remedy is compensation or damages and is also a crime punishable by law. Criminal prosecutions can be taken by the Attorney-General, either alone or on behalf of an individual or a local authority. A local authority may also institute civil proceedings in its own name under section 222 of the Local Government Act 1972, and may seek an injunction against a public nuisance.

Private nuisance

9–03 Private nuisance is an interference with another person's use or enjoyment of his property. It constitutes a tort for which the remedy is compensation or damages. Nuisance itself is not actionable and damage must have occurred before a person is able to sue. Examples are damage arising from noise, fumes, smell, smoke, dust, etc. Actions may be taken only by those who have a legal interest in the land, although this does include tenants. Actions are brought by the aggrieved party in the civil court, either the county court or the High Court.

The distinction between public and private nuisance was provided by Lord Denning (in *Attorney-General v. PYA Quarries Ltd* ([1957] 1 All ER 894; [1957] 2 QB 169), who said:

> ". . . a public nuisance is a nuisance which is so widespread in its range or so indiscriminate in its effect that it would not be reasonable to expect one person to take proceedings on his own responsibility to put a stop to it, but that it should be taken on the responsibility of the community at large."

It is, however, possible for nuisance to be both public and private (*Halsey v. Esso Petroleum Co. Ltd*), as well as being subject to further statutory provisions.

In both public and private nuisance, actions are taken against the person causing the nuisance. The remedies are injunctions and damages. Where the nuisance has been abated between the time of issuing the writ and the trial, the court may withhold action and allow the plaintiff leave to apply for an injunction if the nuisance recurs.

Where the matter is one of private nuisance, a number of points will need to be considered, including the following: **9–04**

1. It is not an absolute defence for the defendant to show that he has taken all reasonable steps. The court may place considerable weight, however, on whether the defendant has sought to be reasonable. For example, it is accepted by the courts that a certain amount of noise is inevitable in building works, albeit for a limited period, whereas a nuisance which is permanent will be looked at closely.
2. It is no defence that the nuisance existed before the plaintiff arrived, and that the plantiff thereby came to the nuisance. An exception to this appears to be where there has been a nuisance for 20 years about which neither the plantiff, nor his predecessors, have complained. In such a case, the nuisance has been uninterrupted and it has been held that a prescriptive right to continue to cause the nuisance has been acquired as an easement attaching to the property (*Sturges v. Bridgeman* (1879)). Right by prescription is not a defence available in public nuisance.
3. Neither is it a defence that the activity concerned is for the public benefit, although it may be a defence in certain situations that the activity was carried out with statutory authority. While farming meets one of the most basic of human needs—food production—this is not carried out with statutory authority and this defence is therefore not likely to be applicable.
4. In deciding what is a nuisance, the courts will have regard to the character of an area. For example, in a country district, farmyard

odours are to be expected from time to time and will not be regarded as a nuisance, while the same odours in an urban area could be a nuisance.

5. The damage which the plaintiff must show is that he has been prevented from enjoying the normal comforts of life in the context of his property rights. There need not be direct injury to health.
6. On occasions, private nuisance actions may involve a degree of ill-will between neighbours. The court will take this into account in deciding whether action taken by the plaintiff was reasonable in the circumstances and whether the nuisance is in fact genuine.

Statutory nuisance

9–05 Most cases of nuisance fall within the range defined by statute. Currently this is Part 3 of the Environmental Protection Act 1990, which allows action to be taken in respect of nuisances which are occurring, may occur (although they have not yet) or may recur. Action may be taken either by a local authority or an aggrieved person (although in the latter case action cannot be taken in respect of a nuisance which has not yet occurred).

Other statutory provisions also apply to certain specific nuisances and may be used from time to time. In the case of "dark" smoke, for example, actions are likely to be taken under the Clean Air Act 1993.

Nuisance-type causes of air pollution are generally prejudicial to enjoyment, comfort or health. They are all essentially very localised in their effects, and include the following:

— noise, for example from cockerels crowing, cows lowing, milking machines, crop-drying fans, mobile machinery and auditory bird scarers, particularly when the noise arises at unsocial hours;
— dust, for example from crop handling;
— smoke, for example from bonfires of farmyard wastes, including plastics and rubber, especially tyres;
— flies and other insects which may breed in farm manures and livestock buildings;
— odours, for example from livestsock, livestock housing, manure stores, manure composting and manure spreading.

Why do these conflicts occur?

9–06 Agriculture and society have both changed greatly since the Second World War and it is these changes which explain much of the conflict arising in recent years. Very often it is not appreciated that these changes have resulted from the long-standing government commitment to encourage greater production and economic efficiency in the agricultural industry, aimed at delivering food at declining real prices. This policy has been successful, particularly in the intensive pig and poultry sectors, which is where for these very reasons that many of the conflicts occur.

A particular feature of the changes which have occurred is the progressive concentration of the industry into a diminishing number of units of increasing size. Quite apart from the concentrations of animal numbers, and the amounts of waste produced in modern units, systems for the storage and handling of manures have often involved the introduction of liquid slurries. These can produce stronger odours than traditional straw-based solid manure and have been the cause of many problems. Another important feature has been the substitution of machinery for labour as the drive for greater efficiency in agriculture has continued. At the same time, machines have become larger and noisier as farm size has increased.

As machines have replaced manpower, the number of people engaged in agriculture has fallen markedly. In the United Kingdom it is now less than 2 per cent of the population and one of the lowest figures in Europe. This has meant that fewer and fewer country dwellers retain links with agriculture or have an understanding of it and many villages are now principally occupied by those who earn their livings elsewhere. Very often these residents are well-educated professionals, with a greater awareness of their rights and who are willing to assert themselves if their expectations of rural peace and tranquillity and quality of life do not materialise. Often the problems are due to very fundamental conflicts arising from differences in working hours, but they also arise from a failure to appreciate that the countryside is not necessarily a quiet place. It is a living and working environment which by the very nature of agricultural crop and animal production and the vagaries of the weather means that agricultural working hours do not conform with the five-day week of the newer country dwellers.

The type of conflict which can occur can be illustrated by the following example. 9–07

On a fine evening in late summer a family hold a barbecue for friends. But the party is spoiled by a strong smell of manure which drives everyone indoors with the windows tightly shut. The embarassed host and hostess, proud of their expensive dwelling in a rural village to which they moved for an improved quality of life, resolve to take the matter up with the offending farmer.

The farmer is running a long-established business which was set up by his father more than 60 years earlier and is now one of the last surviving mixed farms in the area. It has been a difficult and late harvest, and it is only now that the land is clear of crops and able to receive the year's manure for ploughing in before the next seasons winter cereals are sown in a few weeks' time. He and his staff are working long hours seven days a week to catch up, while the recent incomers to the village, almost all commuters and office-workers, apparently with "9 to 5" jobs, are able to relax in their gardens.

The farmer receives a phone call complaining about the nuisance he has caused. He regards this as an impertinence from a village newcomer who is obviously entirely unfamiliar with farming and the pressures of an agricultural business. There is an angry exchange. Later, the farmer regrets his unsympathetic approach, but hopes nothing more will be said. But the complainant's anger has been made worse by the farmer's reaction and he registers a complaint with the local authority. Two days later an Environmental Health Officer from the local district council pays a visit to the farmer.

This example includes features of actual cases and illustrates how quickly an unfortunate incident can lead to the local authority becoming involved, action perhaps being taken under the Environmental Protection Act 1990, as well as damage—perhaps permanently—to relations between neighbours. Considerable expense in fees for solicitors and specialists in odours and farm-waste management may be incurred, although the diversion of time and energy from the farm business may be of even greater significance. Whilst confrontation and recourse to the law may be unavoidable in some situations, the chances of avoiding this can be increased if both parties have a clear understanding of their mutual obligations under the law, and how these manifest themselves in practice. This is set out in the next section of this chapter which deals with the essential elements of the statutory nuisance legislation.

The law

9–08 The changing character of rural businesses and communities demands an approach which reflects the new circumstances in the countryside by meeting the reasonable expectations of both parties involved. This has been encompassed in Part 3 of the Environmental Protection Act 1990, which sets out the framework on which much of this approach is based. Essentially it provides a vehicle for defining the limits of acceptability and allows action to be taken in respect of nuisances which are occurring, may occur (although they have not yet) or may recur.

The essentials of the position are that the public can expect protection from nuisances which are sufficiently intrusive or offensive, long-lasting and frequent to be regarded as a statutory nuisance, and that the person responsible can be expected to take all reasonably practicable steps to abate or minimise it. However, if the problem still persists, even to a level which constitutes a statutory nuisance, the person responsible may be able to rely on the statutory defence of "best practicable means". This is available if the nuisance arises in the course of a trade or business, subject to certain limitations described below. This concept is of particular importance in defining the parameters for settling disputes because it establishes the principle of what action the originator of the nuisance may or may not be required to take.

Most legal actions for nuisance are taken by local authorities on behalf of local residents under the provisions of this Act. We feel they represent an improvement on the previous legislation under the Public Health Act 1936 and the Public Health (Recurring Nuisances) Act 1969, where any challenge to an abatement notice issued by the local authority had in effect to be made by non-compliance which would mean an offence would have been committed if the challenge was unsuccessful. Under the new legislation, the provision for appeal provides a more transparent process by which an abatement notice can in most situations be appealed before it becomes effective. This enables most contested Abatement Notices to be tested before the courts *before* either expensive compliance measures have to be put in hand or a possible offence of non-compliance with the notice is committed.

Generally speaking, the subject of the notice must be either prejudicial to health or a nuisance, in which case it is likely to involve some interference with personal comfort. The question then arises of how much interference constitutes a statutory nuisance. At the end of the day, this is decided by a court, usually a magistrates' court, and may involve the hearing of evidence and opinion from experts, both professional environmental health officers (EHOs) employed by local authorities, and independent consultants. Clearly, the environmental health department of the local authority will only issue an abatement notice where it takes the view that a statutory nuisance exists, but the courts do not always not adopt the same view as the local authority. It is not infrequently the case that the local authority has been subjected to political pressure by the complainants, through the elected members of the authority, with the risk that the decision to proceed with the abatement notice may not be as objective as it ought to be. **9–09**

Matters which may constitute statutory nuisances are detailed in section 79(1) of the Act. These are:

(a) any premises in such a state as to be prejudicial to health or a nuisance;
(b) smoke emitted from premises so as to be prejudicial to health or a nuisance;
(c) fumes or gases emitted from premises so as to be prejudicial to health or a nuisance;
(d) any dust, steam, smell or other effluvia arising on industrial, trade or business premises and being prejudicial to health or a nuisance;
(e) any accumulation or deposit which is prejudicial to health or a nuisance;
(f) any animal kept in such a place or manner as to be prejudicial to health or a nuisance;
(g) noise emitted from premises so as to be prejudicial to health or a nuisance;
(h) any other matter declared by any enactment to be a statutory nuisance.

The various terms used in section 79(1) are defined in section 79(7). **9–10**
Important definitions are as follows:

"dust" does not include dust emitted from a chimney as an ingredient of smoke;

"fumes" means any airborne solid matter smaller than dust;

"gas" includes vapour and moisture precipitated from vapour;

"industrial, trade or business premises" means premsises used for any industrial, trade or business purposes or premises not so used on which matter is burnt in connection with any industrial, trade or business purposes, and premises are used for industrial purposes where they are used for the purposes of any treatment or process as well as where they are used for the purpose of manufacturing;

"noise" includes vibration, but does not include noise from aircraft other than model aircraft;

"person responsible", in relation to statutory nuisance, means the person to whose act, default or sufferance the nuisance is attributable;

"prejudicial to health" means injurious, or likely to cause injury, to health;

"premises" includes land and, subject to subsection 79(12), any vessel;

"smoke" includes soot, ash, grit and gritty particles emitted in smoke, but dark smoke emitted from industrial or trade premises, with certain limited exceptions, is excluded by section 79(3). Dark smoke is dealt with under the Clean Air Act 1993.

Although not defined in the Act, "accumulation or deposit" has been held in previous legislation to involve "an accumulation of something which produces a threat of disease, vermin or the like" rather than inert deposits, such as broken glass, which could only threaten health by physical injury.

The main provisions of Part 3 of the Environmental Protection Act 1990 in relation to statutory nuisances are as follows.

Local authority action

9–11 Section 79(1) states that local authorities have a duty to inspect their areas from time to time to detect any statutory nuisances which ought to be dealt with. They are also required to take all reasonably practicable steps to investigate complaints by persons living in their areas. In practice, local authority investigations tend to arise from complaints made to them rather than as a result of their own inspections of their areas.

Abatement notices

9–12 Where a local authority is satisfied that a statutory nuisance exists, or is likely to occur or recur, it is obliged under section 80 to serve an abatement notice. The notice may require the abatement of the nuisance, or prohibit or restrict its occurrence or recurrence, or require works or other steps which may be necessary for these purposes. These must be carried out within a specified time. One implication of this provision is that the local authority does not have to wait for a nuisance to occur but may anticipate it doing so, although this power is little used in our experience.

Service of notices

9–13 Notices are normally served on the person responsible for the nuisance. There are two main exceptions, namely when the nuisance arises from a structural defect, in which case the notice is served on the owner; and when the person responsible cannot be found (or the nuisance has not yet occurred), then the notice should be served on the owner or the occupier of the premises. Farmers should be aware that an occupier of land may be held responsible for what happens on it and they should therefore ensure that activities which they permit, including contractors operations, do not cause nuisance.

One anomaly in the present position relates to the duty imposed on local authorities to serve an abatement notice where a statutory nuisance exists, regardless of the fact that it is satisfied that the best practicable means have been used and that a successful appeal is probably inevitable. Nor is there provision for a notice to be withdrawn by the local authority once it has been served. It seems that only a court can do this by quashing a notice on the application of the parties.

Appeals

Anyone on whom on abatement notice is served has 21 days in which to lodge an appeal to a magistrates' court if they wish to do so. Magistrates have the power to quash a notice, to vary it or to let it stand. The list of grounds for appeal is set out in "The Statutory Nuisance (Appeals) Regulation 1995 (S.I. 1995 No. 2644) and include the following: **9–14**

- that the notice is not justified by section 80 (*i.e.* that there has not been or will not be a statutory nuisance);
- that there is a material informality, defect or error in or in connection with the notice;
- that the local authority has refused unreasonably to accept compliance with alternative requirements to those contained in the notice, or that the terms of the notice are otherwise unreasonable or un-necessary;
- that the time specified for compliance in the notice is not reasonably sufficient;
- that the best practicable means have been used to prevent or counteract the effect of the nuisance (applies only to certain situations where the nuisance arises on industrial, businesss or trade premises);
- that the notice should or might lawfully have been served on some other person instead of, or as well as, the appellant, and it would be equitable for this to happen;
- that, in the case of noise, the requirements of the abatement notice are more onerous than the requirememts in force under sections 60, 61, 65, 66 or section 67 of the Control of Pollution Act 1974.

Suspension of the notice pending determination of an appeal

Paragraph 3 of the Appeal Regulations provides for an abatement notice to be suspended pending the outcome of an appeal if it involves expenditure, but the local authority may include a statement on the notice that it shall not be suspended, specifying which of the following applies: **9–15**

- that the nuisance is injurious to health;
- that the nuisance is likely to be of such limited duration that suspension of the notice would render it of no practical effect;
- that the expenditure which would be incurred in compliance with the notice would not be disproportionate to the public benefit in the period before the appeal is determined.

Failure to comply with an abatement notice

9–16 Failure to comply with an abatement notice is a criminal offence and atracts a maximum penalty of a level 5 fine (currently £5,000) together with a maximum further penalty of one-tenth of that amount for each day that the offence continues after conviction. In addition, the local authority can do whatever is necessary to abate the nuisance and secure compliance with the notice and recover any reasonable expenses incurred from the person responsible, and if that person is not the owner, from whoever is currently the owner. The current owner may not be the person who caused the nuisance, and so could find himself taking on the liabilities of the previous owner.

Deciding whether to appeal

9–17 When deciding whether to lodge an appeal, it should be remembered that there is no provision for an abatement notice to be withdrawn. Its requirements will therefore be permanent if it is not quashed or varied on appeal. The decision to appeal is therefore an important one and professional help in the form of a solicitor is essential at this stage. The effects on the enterprise or business will have to be assesssed. In cases where it is the sole enterprise the whole business can be threatened. The value of the property may also be affected, particularly if the use of specialist buildings is constrained. These costs will need to be set against the costs of appealing and the prospects of success. For this it is necessary to consider the strength of the case against the grounds of appeal available having regard also to the reasonableness of the notice given the state of the farm operations. An independent assessment may be required, preferably by a specialist consultant. The 21 days allowed for an appeal to be lodged is not in fact very long in which to make such an important decision and if in doubt it may be best to lodge an appeal and be prepared to withdraw it subsequently. This allows more time for a considered decision. Even if an appeal is successful, not all costs are recovered. In our experience of these cases, a successful appellant is usually awarded about 75 per cent of his costs by the court, but even the remaining 25 per cent can amount to a large sum.

The appeal provisions were introduced for the first time by the Environmental Protection Act 1990. In practice, they are quite widely used and a substantial proportion are successful. A common problem has been the confusion of professional judgments made by environmental health officers with decisions made by the elected members of local authorities. The imposition of costs in cases where notices have been served due to political pressure on elected councillors rather than on the merits of the case are proving a valuable check on local authorities resorting to the hasty or inappropriate use of abatement notices. The number of notices used in inappriopriate situations now seems to be declining.

Defences

9–18 When proceedings for an offence are taken either by a local authority or by an aggrieved person, it is often a statutory defence to show that the best practicable means have been used to prevent, or counteract the effect of, the nuisance. The fact that a defence is statutory means that the court cannot convict the defendant if the defence is proved to the court's satisfaction. The defence of best practicable means is available where the nuisance has arisen on industrial, trade or business premises, although there are the following exceptions:

(a) smoke, except where it is discharged from a chimney;
(b) fumes or gases;
(c) matters which are declared to be nuisances by other enactments;
(d) a nuisance which renders premises unfit for human habitation, where the proceedings are brought by an aggrieved person.

The defence of best practicable means is only available in the magistrates' court. Section 79(9) of the Act provides for "Best Practicable Means" (BPM) to be interpreted by reference to the following:

> "'practicable' means reasonably practicable having regard among other things to local conditions and circumstances, to the current state of technical knowledge and to the financial implications.
>
> The means to be employed include the design, installation, maintenance and manner and periods of operation of plant and machinery, and the design, construction and maintenance of buildings and structures.
>
> The test is to apply only so far as compatible with any duty imposed by law.
>
> The test is to apply only so far as compatible with safety and safe working conditions, and with the exigencies of any emergency or unforeseeable circumstances."

Where a code of practice under section 71 of the Control of Pollution Act 1974 (noise minimisation) is applicable, regard shall also be had to guidance given in it. This is not a reference to the MAFF Codes of Good Agricultural Practice, but to DoE codes for specific noise nuisances, of which a number have been adopted covering matters such as construction noise and model aircraft. **9–19**

It is important to note that financial considerations are specifically included within the scope of BPM, a point which was frequently argued under the previous legislation and which has now been clarified. Measures which are not financially viable cannot be considered to be required as part of BPM. However, in our view the interpretation of what is viable does not turn on the finances of the individual business. This could mean that a poorly-run business might never be required to remedy inadequate facilities, for example, whereas a well-run one would have to take much more expensive measures. We believe that the financial test applies to what would normally be viable in typical circumstances of the business in question.

A further statutory defence exists in the case of noise nuisances, namely that the noise complies with levels set under sections 60, 61, 65 or 66 of the Control of Pollution Act 1974. This is unlikely to be relevant to agriculture, except in rare situations.

Action by an aggrieved person

9–20 Section 82 of the Act also provides for action to be taken by an aggrieved person. The procedure differs from action by a local authority in certain respects, with the principles of the previous system under the Public Health Act 1936 having been retained. This does not provide an opportunity to establish before a court what action ought to be taken in advance of proceedings under which penalties may be imposed. In view of the disputes which often arise as to the methods to be adopted and indeed whether a statutory nuisance exists, this can be a very real problem. However, these provisions are rarely used in practice, the bulk of cases being taken by local authorities under the reformed procedure under which appeals against the terms of an abatement notice are usually possible before substantial expenditure has to be incurred.

The procedure involves an aggrieved person applying directly to the magistrates' court, without having to go through the local authority. No abatement notice is served, but the aggrieved person must give 21 days notice in writing (three days in the case of noise) to the person about whom he is complaining before taking proceedings. If the existence of a statutory nuisance is established to the court's satisfaction, the court may issue a nuisance order requiring the offender to abate the nuisance, prevent a recurrance of it and to execute any necessary works. The defence of "best practicable means" is also available for proceedings under section 82 for nuisances arising on industrial, trade or business premises.

A fine not exceeding level 5 (currently £5,000) may also be imposed. A further fine of the same size may be imposed for subsequent contravention of the order, together with one-tenth of the maximum for each day after conviction that the order is contravened. The court may also award costs.

In the event of non-compliance with a nuisance order, or if neither the person responsible nor the owner can be found, the court may direct the local authority to take any necessary action. No provision is made for complaints about anticipated nuisances to be heard, unlike the position where action is taken by a local authority.

High Court proceedings

9–21 A local authority is empowered by section 81(5) of the 1990 Act to take proceedings in the High Court to secure the abatement, prohibition or restriction of the nuisance when it is of the opinion that proceedings in the magistrates' court afford ". . . an inadequate remedy". What is meant by "an inadequate remedy" raises an interesting question. The statutory defence of "best practicable means" which is available in the magistrates' court does not apply in the High Court and some local authorities have appeared to regard High Court actions as a means of circumventing the best practicable means defence, although the question of reasonableness is still likely to be relevant. There is an alternative view that recourse to the High Court is provided to deal with cases where the penalties available in the magistrates' court are insufficient to secure compliance.

As mentioned in the section dealing with public nuisance, it is also possible for a local authority to take action in the High Court under section 222 of the Local Government Act 1972 on the grounds of public nuisance. The local authority may apply for an injunction to prevent a nuisance under this provision. The penalty for breaching an injunction is an unlimited fine or imprisonment.

There are no statutory provisions enabling an aggrieved person to take action in the High Court, but such an action is possible as a private action under common law. High Court proceedings by local authorities or individuals are infrequent, no doubt partly on account of the costs involved. Where private actions do occur it is usually where a local authority has not become involved, and a neighbour with sufficient resources seeks a final resolution to a dispute.

Sources of nuisance and their control

The main nuisances of agricultural origin are odour and noise, with complaints about odours being the most numerous and also the most difficult to resolve. Many nuisances can in fact be minimised by adopting various measures which involve little or no cost to the business and are really a matter of good agricultural practice. However, being able to minimise a nuisance does demand some understanding of the factors which influence the degree of nuisance arising. This section describes the main sources of agricultural nuisances, their measurement, the factors influencing them and suitable control mechanisms. **9–22**

Odours

The main sources of farm odours are livestock farming, and animal manures in particular. Others include feed preparation (especially boiling of human food residues for swill feeding of pigs), and silage, which is grass fermented under airtight conditions to preserve it for winter use. **9–23**

While many farms no longer keep livestock and so cause few odour problems, specialist livestock farms, which may have many more animals than hitherto, have the potential to cause much greater problems as a result of both their size and also as a result of modern management systems. Combining this with the rural population's reduced involvement with and tolerance of agriculture, it can be understood why farm odours have become a matter of increasing concern.

Livestock odours may arise from farm buildings where the animals are kept, from contaminated yards or other areas of concrete fouled with excreta, from stored manures or from manures spread on land. Figures for public complaints received by local authorities show that spreading on land generates most complaints, followed by livestock buildings and manure stores. Recent figures of complaints based on returns from local authorities in England and Wales, taken from the Chartered Institute for Environmental Health Annual Reports for 1994–1995 and 1995–1996, are as follows:

ENVIRONMENTAL MONITORING — COMPLAINTS OF ODOURS

	1994/95	*1995/96*
Number of complaints received regarding odours nuisance from agricultural practices	8,408	9,005
Complaints per million population	235	280
Premises subject to complaint	3,481	3,646
Notices served	67	63
Prosecutions	0	2
Convictions	0	2

The most important factors determining the existence of odour nuisance is the distance from the source. Odours are not a problem provided one is sufficiently far away! The inappropriate location of farm buildings or other facilities in relation to housing is an important issue. This may arise either from the traditional location of farms within or adjacent to villages, or from the siting of new farm or housing development through the development control system operated by local planning authorities. This raises issues of planning policy, some of which have been addressed by government in planning policy guidance notes issued to the planning authorities. These are dealt with in Chapters 3 and 4.

9–24 Methods of husbandry also have a considerable influence on the odour characteristics of manure. Two of the most significant factors are the type of manure—solid farmyard manure or liquid slurry—and the feed. Some species create odours which humans find more unpleasant than others. Pigs generate most complaints, while poultry and cattle make smaller contributions to the total. Even horses kept for riding, which are rarely in large concentrations, generate a small but significant number of complaints which are considered to be justified by the local authorities.

Why and how are odours created and how do they move? Can they be measured or assessed? Can they be controlled and how? These are important questions which need to be addressed by anyone dealing with odour problems.

Odours are caused by a large number of chemical compounds. Each of these is derived principally from dietary sources, some from carbohydrates but most from proteins. Over 160 chemical compounds have in fact been identified in farm odours, but of these only about 15 are of real significance. These fall into four groups:

— sulphides	*e.g.* hydrogen sulphide, dimethyl sulphide
— volatile fatty acids (VFAs)	*e.g.* acetic acid, butanoic acid
— phenols	*e.g.* phenol, 4-methyl phenol
— indoles	*e.g.* indole, skatole

Although the behaviour of these compounds is easy to predict in theory, it is complicated by the properties of the manure and is not well understood from a scientific viewpoint. Simple observations and experience have however identified a number of key points which influence the formation of odours.

Aerobic versus anaerobic activity

Manures are a hotbed of microbial activity with some microbes thriving in the presence of oxygen (aerobic type), and others taking over when oxygen is absent (anaerobic type). Aerobic activity produces much less unpleasant odours than aneraobic. Air, and with it oxygen, penetrates solid manure relatively easily, and is excluded only when it is densely compressed or waterlogged, or when it contains insufficient straw. Solid manures are therefore predominantly in an aerobic state, and tend not to create offensive odours. On the other hand, slurries will usually become anaerobic after being stored for only a couple of days. This factor has important implications for management with a view to odour control. For example, the onset of anearobic conditions can be deferred indefinitely if the slurry is efficiently aerated. **9–25**

Temperature

At higher temperature, most chemical processes speed up and in consequence greater amounts of odourous compounds can be generated. Odour problems therefore tend to be more severe in summer, at the same time as many people spend more time out of doors. **9–26**

Surface area

The amount of odour actually emitted is related to the surface area of manure that is exposed to the air. This is the underlying explanation of the peak of odour emissions which occurs when manure is spread thinly over the ground, creating a very large surface area. **9–27**

Air movement

Odours are carried from the source to the nose in the air we breathe either as gases, in very small water droplets called aerosols, or attached to dust particles. The strength of an odour is determined by its concentration. Odours are carried by movements of the air mass and these are generally determined by wind direction, although eddies and turbulence can carry part of the air mass for short distances in a different and sometimes unexpected direction, sometimes directly against the wind direction. **9–28**

Under different meteorological conditions there may be very distinct layers of air which hardly mix, or there may be currents of air rising from the ground which cause mixing of air masses on a large scale. These movements affect dilution and therefore the concentration of odour perceived. In the latter situation, where there are usually at least moderate wind speeds, odours are rapidly diluted below the threshold of detection, while in the former, where winds speeds are usually very low, they may persist at detectable levels for considerable distances downwind. As an extreme example, there have been a number of occasions when odours have been detected over wide areas of eastern England and have been attributed to extensive manure spreading activity in the Netherlands. Such incidents tend to occur at times of light easterly winds in the spring, when such winds are particularly frequent and when manure spreading becomes feasible as the soil begins to dry out after the winter.

Measuring odours

9–29 Odour detection in humans is closely allied to taste. It is very variable with individuals varying widely in their sensitivity to and tolerance of the substances which contribute to agricultural odours. While it is technically possible to measure the concentration of various compounds in air by sophisticated scientific techniques, such as gas chromatography, these are expensive and unwieldy and of uncertain relationship to actual nuisance levels.

Olfactometry is one method of measuring odours currently available. Essentially, it relies on the human nose to detect odours in samples of air collected from the site and transported to a laboratory. There, a group of people or "panel" is exposed to an odour under controlled conditions, by decreasing concentrations until it can be detected by only half of the group. The strength of the odour is then expressed as the dilution necessary to make the odour indetectable to half of the panel. This represents the "odour threshold value" and is expressed as an odour concentration in odour units per cubic metre of air. Farm odours, even at source, rarely exceed 5,000 odour units per cubic metre of air, whereas industrial odours may need to be diluted a million times to reach the threshold of detection.

Even this technique is rather expensive and time consuming, and tends to be more suitable for research work than for actual nuisance cases. In practice, the method of odour assessment is usually to rely on the experience of professionals such as environmental health officers and consultants. Through experience of a range of odours and situations these people will be able to give guidance on the general acceptability (or otherwise) of particular odours in individual situations.

9–30 The Ministry of Agriculture (MAFF) has published a Code of Good Agricultural Practice for the Protection of Air. This sets out good agricultural practice for minimising and avoiding nuisance from odour and smoke, but does not address noise. Although compliance with the provisions of the Code is not a statutory defence in court, it is likely to be helpful to the case. The adoption of good agricultural practice is nevertheless normally an essential part of what is held to be "best practical means", which *is* a statutory defence. It is therefore advisable for farmers to give very serious considerations to the provisions of the Code, a copy of which should always be held. Whilst complaints about odour nuisance are the most frequent, there are a range of other occurrences of agricultural origin about which complaints are also made from time to time. These include noise, smoke, dust and insects. Most of these problems can be addressed relatively simply with good will between the parties, although more intractible difficulties tend to arise over noise caused by bird scarers and animals, neither of which can be effectively silenced. The task of finding an acceptable compromise between the interests of the respective parties is most difficult in these cases.

Noise

Noise problems arise from bird scarers, from farm machinery such as milking machines or harvesters, and from animals themselves. Frequently, it is not the noise itself but the time of day (or night) at which it arises that is the real issue. For example, cows are traditionally milked very early in the morning, or there may be round-the-clock working at harvest and at other busy times, especially when unsuitable weather has limited the time available for certain key operations. **9–31**

Bird scarers

In recent decades the automatic gas-fired "banger" has been widely adopted as an effective weapon in the farmer's armoury for protecting vulnerable field-scale crops and orchards against bird pests. It has replaced methods which relied upon visual scaring and shooting. A variety of machines are now on the market. The most basic involve single or multiple discharges similar to a shotgun, but now sirens, bird distress calls and a range of other noises including electronic shrieks may be emitted. All of these rely on the broadcast of noise and so have the potential to create nuisance, particularly when these are used at inappropriate times or in unsuitable locations, and public complaints have ensued. **9–32**

There is no formal MAFF code for noise but the agricultural industry has responded to this concern by producing a Code of Practice under the auspices of the National Farmers Union (NFU). This has been updated on a number of occasions, most recently in 1995. As with other codes, it has no statutory status although it has been drafted in consultation with government departments and other interested organisations.

The Code includes guidance to farmers on both maximising the effectiveness of scarers (which includes not operating them too frequently) and on avoiding or minimising problems for the public. Nearly all rural local authorities are familiar with the Code, and most accept it as authoritative and meeting the "best practicable means" test. It has also been recognised by magistrates' courts as the appropriate standard to which devices should be operated.

The government has considered producing a statutory Code of Practice for possible confirmation under section 71 of the Control of Pollution Act 1974. However, in the face of the existing well-recognised NFU Code, it has not chosen to proceed with this. The effect of making a code statutory is simply to formalise recognition of a code as an appropriate statement of good practice. The status of such a government code would however serve no additional practical purpose when an industry one is already recognised and accepted. The NFU has recently submitted its code for approval by the Government under section 71, and a decision is awaited.

Farm machinery

Other sources of noise problems include crop drying fans, milking machines and animal noise. There have been a number of well-publicised cases relating to cockerels, mostly in non-commercial situations. In many of **9–33** these cases, the noise of cockerels crowing in the early hours of thc morning has been held to be a statutory nuisance.

The Noise and Statutory Nuisance Act 1993 extended Part 3 of the Environmental Protection Act 1990 to include noise arising on the highway. The implications for agriculture are probably small, but there is potential for some difficulty for produce-carrying vehicles fitted with refrigeration units which park in residential areas prior to delivery.

Control of noise

9–34 The need for a farmer to control noise may arise from the comments of neighbours or from the threat or the result of legal proceedings. It may often be less expensive in the long run if action is taken early. Under the statutory nuisance legislation, it will be necessary to control a nuisance to the standard of "best practicable means" and this will very often require a variety of technical measures which are available in the case of noise. The measures adopted are likely to vary depending on whether the noise source is fixed, as with a milking machine, or mobile, such as a bird scaring banger. But, the essential components of the approach are likely to be similar with the difference being one of emphasis. Again, there are a number of critical factors affecting noise emissions and control mechanisms centre around these.

Wind

9–35 Wind has a surprisingly strong effect on the direction and distance over which noises are audible. A noise footprint for a source in the countryside tends to very elongated on the downwind side, and foreshortened upwind.

Topography

9–36 Topographical effects are very site-specific. Noise may be chanelled along a valley, or shielded by solid features such as hills, ridges and even buildings.

Time of day

9–37 The time of day when a noise is emitted also needs to be considered carefully as part of an assessment of the source's capacity to disturb. Milking machines are a good example because they tend to be operated in the early morning, or crop drying and cooling fans which operate at night. One option for addressing problems is therefore to restrict the time when machines are operated, although this may not always be a practical possibility.

Directional sources

9–38 Some sources are directional while others are not. Bird scarers emit most noise in front of the barrel, while crop drying fans tend not to be directional. In the former case, simply rotating the device will achieve an effect which may be beneficial, even where it means bringing it closer but pointing it in the opposite direction. This will be considerably enhanced by adding an effective baffle behind the device.

Clearly the best approach is, wherever possible, to site the source of the noise in such a way that it does not give rise to nuisance in the first place, or so that any unavoidable nuisance is minimised. Once a problem has arisen, re-siting is one of the first considerations for a mobile source such as a bird scarer, but one of the last options for a fixed installation. Correct siting should take into account prevailing winds and topography.

Technical solutions

In some cases, technical modification of the noise source may produce very satisfactory results. The fitting of an approved silencer to the milking machine may well be a simple and effective solution to complaints. In some cases, mounting the noise source—or the part of the machine that is the noise source—on sound or vibration-insulating mountings may bring an improvement. Manufacturers of the original equipment will often be able to offer assistance and guidance, if not replacement parts, which will help to achieve acceptable functioning of their products. **9–39**

The propagation of the energy in sound waves may be altered or reduced by shielding the source with sound-absorbing or reflective baffles. Flimsy materials are of little use. Soft materials such as straw bales or polystyrene absorb the energy, as does as solid structure such as masonry. Straw bales may be very helpful in shielding a bird scarer, whereas masonry, perhaps with an absorbent lining, may serve best for a fixed source. In some cases it may be possible to totally enclose the noise source in baffles. This may be practical with the milking machine, but it would defeat the purpose of a bird scarer. In this case, the object is to limit the noise to the area at risk from birds, and to shield other sensitive areas from the effects of the device. In practice, this can only be done up to a point, but this may be sufficient for the noise to cease to be a problem to the complainant.

Smoke pollution

Smoke is now a less common problem following the prohibition of the burning of most crop residues in the field since the 1992 harvest. However, a small proportion of complaints have always arisen from the burning of various waste materials. Tyres are notorious for producing "dark smoke", emission of which is an offence under the Clean Air Act 1993, although with certain exceptions for trade premises under the Clean Air (Emission of Dark Smoke) (Exemption) Regulations 1969 (S.I. 1969 No. 1263). **9–40**

Straw and stubble burning

During the 1980s, the practice of straw and stubble burning became widespread as autumn-sown crops increasingly supplanted spring-sown ones and the interval between harvest and sowing the subsequent crop was drastically reduced. The advantage of burning was that it removed straw **9–41** rapidly and allowed swift progress with seedbed preparation. The increase in burning, and in particular the fierce fires which sometimes burnt out of control in dry summers, raised public concern about nuisance from smoke and smuts, damage to hedgerows and wildlife and danger to road traffic from smoke.

The industry had first produced its own Code of Practice in the 1960s and this was repeatedly reviewed as public concern developed. Model byelaws were developed by the government to give legal force to the Code, through locally enacted byelaws. Subsequently, national regulations were introduced. However, following a peak in public concern in the dry summers of the late 1980s, the general practice was banned by means of Regulations under section 152 of the Environmental Protection Act 1990, with effect from the end of 1992. These Regulations provide for certain exceptions, such as the burning of broken bales and the straw of certain minor crops such as lavender and linseed.

Miscellaneous nuisances

9–42 Problems with insects usually relate to flies originating in animal housing or manure stores, but there is at least one case of a local authority taking unsuccessful proceedings over a commercial bee operation whose bees were alleged to cause spots on the washing of local residents. Dust from activities such as grain handling also generates occasional complaints, but we are not aware of any case where legal action has been taken.

Practical steps to avoid and resolve problems

9–43 The existence of unresolved problems can be a significant burden on both the person responsible for causing the nuisance and on those experiencing the consequences. In most circumstances it will be advisable for farmers to minimise any unreasonable problem they may cause for their neighbours in the interests of maintaining good relations. Failure to obtain a solution may result in the local authority serving an abatement notice imposing restrictions on the activities which may be carried out, and this may culminate in potentially expensive legal action. This may have serious implications for the farm business.

For its part, the public will need to recognise that it is not feasible to eliminate all nuisance from agriculture. Either techniques do not exist, or where they do exist, they may be too costly to be within the reach of farm businesses and therefore go beyond best practical means, as is recognised in the MAFF Code of Good Agricultural Practice for the Protection of Air. The approach is therefore to ameliorate the problem to the practicable minimum by following a range of good practice measures. The public also need to be aware that the courts have recognised this and have regarded some alleged nuisances, including some farm odours, as being a normal part of the countryside which must be accepted as such.

A mutual understanding reached at an early stage is likely to be to the advantage of both parties. There are occasions, however, when this is not possible and legal action becomes unavoidable. Sometimes this is where a complainant has become very committed to the issue, and is not prepared to accept a compromise, even after there has been a long period of consultation and co-operation with the complainant and/or the local authority's environmental health officer. In these circumstances, the farmer may well feel that the effort involved in seeking a compromise will have been wasted. But in our experience, the fact that the farmer has addressed these issues and been willing to co-operate will often stand him in good stead if the case goes to court.

If a farmer does find that he has a problem, there are a number of practical steps which may help to resolve the situation, or will help to protect his position if the matter should go to court. These are set out below.

Be reasonable

A constructive approach to resolving disputes requires a reasonable approach and a degree of flexibility on both sides. A visible willingness on the part of the farmer to take all reasonable measures to minimise the nuisance should help to avoid confrontation from the outset. This may mean taking positive steps from the time the first complaints are received, which will also demonstrate to the public that their concerns are taken seriously and responsibly. Even in cases where the other party is perceived as unreasonable, it is important to retain a balanced approach and to respond to complaints, as this is likely to be taken into account if the matter ever comes to court. Responding can also prevent positions becoming hardened and polarised. It is also advisable to ask the local authority to inform you of all complaints and to refer complainants directly to you. **9–44**

In many cases, there will be site-specific factors, or "person-specific" factors such as particular sensitivity at certain times of day or to certain aspects of the problem. A trial and error approach to adjusting the management, involving the complainants, often helps to build a joint approach to achieving a solution, or a compromise, and may not be unduly expensive. Even trials of alternative equipment can be organised at little expense, although a purchase may be expected following a successful trial. However, even this may be worthwhile if all parties are agreed that this will solve, or make a large contribution to solving, the problem. Always be seen to co-operate and talk with the environmental health officer, and suggest sensible approaches. Some such officers may have little knowledge of agriculture and constructive suggestions which they can take back to the complainant helps to establish the farmer's credibility.

Follow best practicable means

It is clear that the courts will normally expect compliance with industry codes of practice—such as the MAFF (Ministry of Agriculture, Fisheries and Food) Code of Good Agricultural Practice for the Protection of Air. **9–45**

Whilst compliance with the codes themselves is not a statutory defence, it is evidence of adopting a substantial part of the best practicable means approach. It is therefore important to ensure that all farming operations are in compliance with, or clearly parallel such codes, and it is essential that a farmer, or his adviser, compares his own management practices and operations against these and makes any changes necessary.

A degree of experience is often helpful in interpreting the application of the Code to individual circumstances. For example, BPM may be interpreted to include abatement techniques which are effective and financially viable for that particular business. These may be in addition to the adoption of good agricultural practice. In practice, few abatement techniques available to farmers meet these criteria, but some products may be considered beneficial in certain situations. Again, it may involve a trial and error approach. However, it is not infrequent that complainants consider a "cure" to be worse than the original problem, particularly in the case of masking agents used to disguise farm odours. In the case of bird scarers, the device itself may be more or less indispensible, but there may be variations in siting and direction which should be explored.

Keep records

9–46 A court case will usually centre around consideration of specific occasions when a statutory nuisance is alleged to have occurred. For such allegations to be dealt with effectively, it is extremely desirable, if not essential, to have records covering weather conditions, farm operations, and notes of any nuisances arising from off-farm sources which might be attributed to the farm. In our experience complainants tend to attribute any unpleasant odour to the source they have identified. It is therefore advisable to keep a daily diary of this type of information, at least from the time that complaints are first received. This type of information has been found to be invaluable if the case goes to court. A wind vane is helpful in improving the accuracy of wind direction observations, and as a basis for instructing farm staff, who for example may be required to cease manure spreading operastions if the wind moves to a certain direction. The evidence that such a step has been taken may of itself also be useful.

Conclusion

9–47 The law of nuisance provides both Local Authorities and individuals with opportunities to raise serious difficulties for farm businesses which cause private, public or statutory nuisances. The public is increasingly likely to complain and be more aware of the legal position. Accordingly, it is well worthwhile ensuring that genuine nuisances do not arise, or if they do, that the appropriate action is taken to prevent or counteract their effects. Failure to do so may involve a great deal of time and expense, and may result in the property being subject to a permanent notice which may have implications for its future use and value.

Potential or actual nuisance is also a material consideration in decisions on planning applications. Planning authorities will often be reluctant to grant consent for new agricultural buildings which are close to dwellings, and ought to think twice about permitting dwellings close to potential sources of nuisance. This is dealt with in more detail in Chapter 4, and again has clear implications for the use and value of land.

Chapter 10

Practical steps to avoid and mitigate pollution

Introduction

10–01 As has been seen from the preceding chapters, a wealth of regulations now affect the agricultural industry. These have increased in both number and complexity and have become necessary as pollution threats from modern day agriculture have been identified. Increasingly, there are also concerns about new types of pollution from agricultural activity, such as those contributing to ozone depletion and global warming. A number of E.U. initiatives are being developed and more controls are likely to follow in future.

Given the number of regulatory requirements which have been placed on the statute book, it is perhaps unrealistic to expect individual farmers to be familiar with all those that may affect them. From the farmer's point of view, the aim must rather be to avoid running into conflict with the law by not polluting. To do this, the farmer needs practical guidance on how to go about his activities with a view to minimising the pollution risks inherent in his work. This chapter aims to set out information to help him to do this. It does this under the following headings: Codes of Good Agricultural Practice, Farm Waste Plans, judicious siting of facilities, and professional advice.

Codes of Good Agricultural Practice

10–02 Over the past decade or so, a number of codes setting out practical guidance on minimising pollution and other risks from agriculture have been produced by MAFF. These are known as Codes of Good Agricultural Practice. The first one to be published was in 1985 and, by comparison with the more recent codes, was a very slim document indeed. Its main function was to draw together environmental advice contained in the many advisory leaflets available at the time on various aspects of agricultural development. More recent codes are far more comprehensive and "self-contained", dealing with air, water and soil separately. Nevertheless, the general guidance in these codes can, in the majority of cases, be applied satisfactorily by farmers themselves in their own particular circumstances. The advice has been prepared by the government's extension service, ADAS (which has been succeeded by the Farming and Rural Conservation Agency (FRCA) which will provide advice to government following the privatisation of ADAS).

The first self-contained Code of Good Agricultural Practice was that for the protection of water, the Water Code, produced in 1991. Further codes dealing with the protection of air and soil were produced in 1992 and 1993 respectively. These replace most of the advice contained in the 1985

Code. At the time of writing, the Water Code is under review and will be updated, taking into account developments in legislation such as the requirements of the Nitrates Directive for a mandatory Code of Practice to apply in Nitrate Vulnerable Zones, and is likely to include a section on horticulture. The Air and Soil Codes are also under review.

Although broadly similar in their approach and format, the formal status of the three Codes differs. Only the Water Code is statutory, its status deriving from the requirement in section 116 of the Water Act 1989 (now consolidated as section 97 of the Water Resources Act 1991), that the relevant minister prepares a code. Failure to observe the Code is not in itself an offence, but non-adherence can be taken into account in the event of any prosecution for a water pollution offence. **10–03**

Similarly, it is not compulsory to follow the Air and Soil Codes. But neither will following them give protection from legal action. In practice though, compliance with the relevant Code does tend to be taken into account in court, where arguments in mitigation provide the opportunity to demonstrate that all reasonable steps have been taken to prevent pollution occurring. Conversely, non-compliance can be used by the prosecution in demonstrating that the farmer had not taken all reasonable steps. Compliance with a code can also be used to support a defence, notably that of best practicable means in the case of statutory nuisances, although once again, following a code does not provide a defence in itself. In practice, the fact that the Water Code is statutory and the others are not makes little difference in the authors' opinion.

It is worth remembering that none of the Codes are, or claim to be, exclusive statements of Good Agricultural Practice. There may be alternative practices which are not described in the Codes which are equally good, although these will need to be established as good agricultural practice by showing that a person or organisation of suitable standing recognises them as such in circumstances relevant to the case under consideration. Such situations are most likely to be relevant in specific circumstances not provided for under the Codes. A further point to remember is that the Codes' advice is necessarily general and that in some cases there will be a need for an expert to determine how it should be interpreted and applied on an individual farm.

The principal message of the Codes is that there is a responsibility on farmers to manage their operations in such a way that pollution is not caused, and so that the risk of pollution is minimised. While this is easily grasped in the case of acute pollution, such as silage effluent leaking into and causing serious pollution of a stream, diffuse pollution raises more difficult issues. Often the connection between the agricultural operation and the subsequent problem is not apparent, and the significance of adopting good agricultural practice is not always obvious to a farmer in the same way as visual evidence from an acute incident, such as dead fish. Moreover, in many situations the connection may be generalised, that is to say the particular activity may lead to an undesirable consequence in the majority of cases, but not necessarily in any particular one. **10–04**

In some areas, for example, there is a very high probability that growing a crop such as potatoes will result in water draining from the field in question exceeding the 50 mg/l limit set for the nitrate standard for drinking water. Whether the drainage from the field contributes to a particular drinking water source exceeding the standard or not will depend on other factors not under the control of individual farmers, such as other land use in the catchment and even the weather. In this situation, it is unlikely that a farmer would see himself as polluting. Similar situations arise with pesticides. However, regardless of the level of these contaminants in the water source, it is not currently the position that potatoes should not be grown or that pesticides should not be used. Rather, the principle adopted is that farmers are expected to use best industry practice to minimise the unwelcome effects of their legitimate activities. In the case of Nitrate Vulnerable Zones defined under the Nitrates Directive, this expectation will become more formalised since it is expected to become mandatory for farmers to comply with certain practices laid down as good agricultural practice in the Water Code.

10–05 Unfortunately, despite the Codes of Good Agricultural Practice having been in existence for a number of years, it appears that they are not yet well known or accepted by farmers. A survey carried out on behalf of MAFF in 1995 showed that less than 50 per cent of farmers were aware of the Codes, and that only 20 per cent actually owned one of them (although they are available free of charge—see Appendices 1–3). These facts are not in themselves evidence that farmers do not know what constitutes good practice, or that they do not follow it, since many of the Codes' recommendations are no more than good sense for a professional farmer. What it does indicate is that many farmers are unaware of the value of compliance with the Codes as a means of partial defence or mitigation should problems arise, or indeed of helping to avoid problems arising in the first place.

Any farmer implicated in or suspecting a pollution problem would be well advised to consult the relevant Code, so that he can make any necessary adjustments to the operation in question to bring it into line with good practice. Some farmers will, in addition, prefer to make efforts to avoid pollution problems arising in the first place by comparing their operations with those describe in the Codes and, as a matter of policy, conducting their businesses in accordance with established good practice. In most circumstances this will prevent any offence being committed, and evidence that compliance has been achieved will be very useful in mitigating the seriousness of any offence. One of the most important pre-emptive steps a livestock farmer can take to avoid water pollution is to establish a farm waste plan for his holding.

Farm Waste Plans

10–06 Animal manures are the source of most point source pollution arising from agriculture. They are also thought to be responsible for much of the diffuse pollution which arises as well, contributing to a general reduction in water quality. Avoiding pollution requires waste to be better managed and the government has launched an initiative to encourage farmers to adopt "farm waste plans". The term "farm waste plan" is perhaps an unfortunate one, since manures are a useful source of nutrients and organic matter. The purpose of a plan is to ensure that the benefits to the soil from these "wastes" are realised with the minimum risk of water pollution arising.

Some 80 million tonnes of manures are applied to land by farmers each year, with a further 120 million tonnes deposited on land by livestock as they graze. The value of the main plant nutrients contained in farmer-applied manure alone has been estimated at some £250 million. Yet surveys of fertiliser use have found that few farmers take full account of the nutrients available in manures when calculating the rate of fertiliser to apply. Farm waste plans have been developed as a means of enabling farmers to appreciate the nutrient content of their manures with the aim of encouraging them to adjust their manure and fertiliser application rates accordingly, thereby avoiding excess applications of nutrients and potential pollution. Also, by obeying straightforward rules contained in the plan, they can avoid manure spreading where and when the pollution risk is high.

It is important to recognise, however, that plans do not remove some of **10–07**
the very real difficulties which exist in applying manures safely and rationally. Disposal is not always straightforward, particularly on some farms, such as where the combination of soil and rainfall characteristics are unfavourable. On these farms putting farm waste plans into practice will present extra difficulties and may involve extra costs. Difficulties may include the following:

— the constraints imposed by trafficability of soils due to soil type and rainfall;
— the physical difficulty of spreading manures according to predetermined plans, particularly in the case of poultry manures where low rates are desirable and machinery capable of spreading at such rates is not readily available.

Neither do farm waste plans overcome the following difficulties, although there may be scope to address these further as the results of current research and development become available:

— the variability and difficulty in predicting nutrient levels, especially nitrogen, in manures;
— the difficulty of obtaining reliable and representative samples of manure for analysis;
— the historic absence of simple and accepted methods for testing nutrient levels.

Plans should not therefore yet be regarded as fully evolved or a complete solution to farm pollution problems. They are nevertheless good practice and a major step towards the better management of livestock manures. None of the difficulties outlined above negate the benefits of drawing up a farm waste plan and following its principles as closely as conditions permit. It has to be recognised that there will always be a need for flexibility in the light of changing and sometimes unforeseen circumstances, and that it would be unrealistic to expect a plan for a farm to operate to the same precision as in the controlled environment of a factory floor.

10–08 Plans can be prepared by farmers themselves. In a number of river catchments targeted by the government and the Environment Agency for campaigns to increase the uptake of farm waste plans, pro-forma plans produced by MAFF/WOAD for the farmer to complete have been distributed, and copies are available from FRCA. As part of these campaigns, ADAS check the completed plan. Plans can also be produced professionally, or with professional assistance, and this is particularly advisable in complex situations, for example where there are a number of livestock enterprises on the farm, and especially where extra storage is or may be required.

It is also perfectly possible for a farmer to follow all the principles of a farm waste management plan, as detailed in the Water Code, without producing a formal plan as such. This is likely to be easier where he has ample land available, giving a greater degree of flexibility. A plan will be of the greatest value where opportunities for spreading wastes on the farm are limited or insufficient, or the quantities applied are close to the maximum advised. If a farmer does not have a written plan, he should bear in mind that it may be more difficult to substantiate in court that he has followed good practice.

Within Nitrate Sensitive Areas and Nitrate Vulnerable Zones, the management of manures is of particular importance in view of their potential to cause nitrate to leach into water. It will therefore be particularly advisable for livestock farmers in these areas to develop farm waste plans.

Principles of farm waste plans

10–09 The basic steps in preparing a farm waste plan are set out in the Water Code. They are:

(a) Identifying any land where manures and dirty water (yard washings, etc.) should never be spread, such as close to watercourses or boreholes.

(b) Working out how much land is required to take the nitrogen contained in the material to be spread. The maximum recommended application rate is normally 250 kg N/ha from manures, but lower rates may apply in Nitrate Sensitive Areas and Nitrate Vulnerable Zones. If there is insufficient land available, arrangements will need to be made to spread the excess on other suitable land.

(c) Identifying land where wastes should not be spread at certain times, or reduced rates of application will apply. This may be because of cropping, or because machinery will not be able to access certain soil types when wet without causing unacceptable soil damage.

(d) Working out the greatest quantity of manure to be stored, taking account of the periods when wastes cannot be spread, and ensuring that sufficient storage is available for this.

Further details of the steps involved in preparing a plan are contained in the Water Code, and an example of a pro-forma plan is included at Appendix 6. Professional help can be obtained from members of the National Farm Waste Management Register, who are qualified in the preparation of farm waste plans. An example of such a plan is also included at Appendix 4. Details of members of the Register can be obtained from the British Institute of Agricultural Consultants.

Following a farm waste plan illustrates a responsible approach to the management of livestock manures and dirty water. It demonstrates that efforts have been made to avoid pollution and means that the farmer has done much to minimise the risks of causing pollution from the spreading of wastes on the farm, and wording to this effect is included in the MAFF/WOAD pro-forma plans (1994 edition). Should a pollution incident still occur, it is less likely to be a significant one if a farmer has been following an adequately prepared farm waste plan. However, if it were serious, and a prosecution resulted, any farmer who had a professionally prepared or checked farm waste plan and had complied with it would be well placed to show that he had adopted good practice and taken all reasonable measures to avoid pollution from sources covered by the plan. The farmer would then be able to make a strong plea in mitigation that he had taken all reasonable steps in accordance with current government guidance to avoid pollution occurring. It should be borne in mind that there are also other major pollution risks on livestock farms, notably silage effluent and slurry stores, which are subject to regulations on standards of construction and maintenance (see Chapter 6). **10–10**

Siting of new farm buildings and facilities

Many farm pollution incidents occur or are exacerbated by the inappropriate siting of buildings, tanks, lagoons or stores. For example, a farm complex situated on or near to the bank of a stream is at greater risk of causing a pollution incident from an accident with polluting materials, and will require more expensive measures to give protection. It therefore makes sense, when the opportunity arises, to site farm buildings and other facilities with care, having regard not only to ease and efficiency of operation but also to the most favourable location in respect of potential pollution problems. **10–11**

Paragraph 132 of the Air Code draws particular attention to the siting of new livestock units in relation to housing in view of potential odour problems. Requirements of the planning system, (detailed in Chapter 4) have introduced certain measures for livestock buildings whereby planning permission is required if the proposed site is less than 400m from protected buildings. Even so, the grant of planning permission for such a facility at less than 400m does not mean that pollution problems will not occur. There have been a number of instances where this has indeed happened and abatement notices and court action have ensued, putting farmers to much worry and expense as a result. Of course, it often happens that planning is given for dwellings within 400m of existing livestock buildings or facilities, but the onus remains on the farmer to avoid causing pollution. It is therefore important for farmers to be alert to proposals to build dwellings close to their buildings and to draw any potential problems to the attention of the planning authority before permission is granted. If development does proceed, he should ensure that he adopts best practice to avoid causing pollution problems (see Chapter 4 for further details of planning procedures).

At present, only prior approval rather than planning permission is required for some smaller non-livestock buildings close to dwellings, but it is important to recognise that it is not only livestock units which can cause problems. Noise and dust from crop stores, for example, can cause nuisance, and farmers have found themselves subject to constraints on the use of fans at unsocial hours—an unwelcome development when working under pressure during a wet harvest.

Professional advice

10–12 There is much a farmer can do to ensure that his operation does not cause problems, initially through awareness, common sense and consideration. In many situations this is probably sufficient, but as this book and the Codes, have indicated, this approach will not always be adequate and farmers will need professional assistance. This will obviously be so when threatened with legal action, but it is also advisable in a number of other situations, for example where there is thought to be a greater risk from pollution or where the associated liabilities can be high. Farmers will, of necessity, have to make their own judgments when to call in outside professional help. This will mean recognising their own limits and making realistic estimates of their own ability to carry out the task. If it is decided to call in a professional, it is important to check that the person selected has relevant qualifications and experience, and that he carries adequate professional indemnity insurance to cover a claim in the event of one arising in relation to the work he is asked to perform. Remember that the lowest price may not always be the cheapest in the long run. Names of specialist consultants throughout the country can be obtained from BIAC (see para. 10–09, above).

Measures to reduce risks

10–13 We have looked in earlier chapters at the regimes whereby the regulators give warnings, a range of notices, prosecute and achieve convictions when there is a pollution incident. Allied to increasingly severe fines (or community service orders and imprisonment where offences are wilful) there is unwelcome publicity in the Press and inevitably, inclusion within the Pollution Register. The costs of defence and mitigation, added to the costs of the prosecution, the costs of remediation and prevention of future incidents, possible third-party claims, all contribute to a nightmare scenario. Should such risks really be taken, in the light of the possible consequences?

It should not be a great burden, either in time or expense, to take appropriate measures to reduce risks to a minimum. We therefore list below recommended steps:

1. **Farm Waste Plan:** this is considered absolutely crucial in providing a complete farm strategy for the storage and distribution of farm wastes, chemicals and other contaminants under all circumstances.
2. **Codes of Good Agricultural Practice:** the current Codes are found in this book. They will be updated and copies should be obtained, *and read*, since they are full of good advice and common sense.
3. **Farm Waste Strategy:** the overall strategy is clearly a combination of the relevant elements of the Plan and the Codes.
4. **Use a diary (or a computer) as a reminder of key dates:** these are for example, when certain installations require thorough checking (*e.g.* silage pits). Always make notes of this inspection by way of:
   (i) the date;
   (ii) the condition of the structure;
   (iii) what faults are discovered;
   (iv) action to be taken;
   (v) action that has been taken.

   It is also desirable to take photographs at the time of the inspection, using a camera that records the date (otherwise, who writes dates down on the back of photographs?).
5. **Staff training:** ensure that all members of staff are *thoroughly* conversant with procedures. Anything which may lead to a pollution incident should be immediately reported to the farmer. It might be a crack in a wall or a concrete area, a peculiar smell from an unknown source, a coloured discharge into a ditch. Such are early warning signs and prompt action at that stage may prevent damage occurring.
6. **Notices:** in the staff rest room there should be a notice board displayed with policies and specific instructions. The same board will undoubtedly be used for other matters such as health and safety issues, the farm's certificate of insurance, etc.
7. **Emergency procedure:** it is vital to have a separate emergency procedure in the event of potential or actual pollution. The basis for such a notice is set out below.

EMERGENCY

Procedure for Pollution

1. Report any potentially polluting escape to the person in charge. He, or you must immediately telephone the Environment Agency on their emergency number **0800 807060.**
2. Minimise damage by
   (a) diverting or preventing flows of liquids from reach water-courses;
   (b) build bunds or embankments to retain such pollution, or remove polluting liquids by pump or vacuum, tanker; and
   (c) get help from neighbours with suitable equipment, and/or plant hire firms;
   (d) telephone the following numbers in order to get help:

   1

   2

   3

   4

   (e) in case of human emergency telephone for ambulance — 999 or local doctor telephone ....

10–14 In the aftermath of any incident, statements may be required formally by the Environment Agency. Irrespective of such statements, take the trouble to record as much detail as possible of the incident. This will include details of:

(i) date and time when the matter was first noticed;
(ii) the probable cause;
(iii) actions taken by various staff and contractors;
(iv) time of arrival of EA / emergency services;
(v) actions then taken including sampling, statements, clean up;
(vi) take photographs;
(vii) examine watercourses for dead fish. Remove and retain where possible.

All this may seem very tedious and the degree of handwriting and photograph taking may seem unnecessary. But the process is designed to prevent pollution from occurring in the first instance, with the almost inevitable and extremely uncomfortable consequences. Should the worst happen, damage may be reduced by prompt action being taken by any staff available, even when the person in charge is away from the farm. They will know what to do, where to get help, who to contact and, providing they are properly briefed, they will understand fully the reasons for so doing. Finally, the recording system will provide your solicitor, should it prove necessary, with a first hand, contemporaneous account of events and the (good) work done to contain the damage. It will be of great benefit to him and therefore to his client, should there be a prosecution. For the ability to mitigate an offence thoroughly is extremely important, since, as has been shown earlier, most offences of pollution carry with them strict liability.

Sources of Advice

Advice comes in many guises. It can be practical or legal, or probably both. **10–15**
It can be taken or ignored or distilled and made use of. It is important, therefore, that the most appropriate source of advice for the job in hand is chosen.

There are three phases where advice is normally necessary, as in the case with planning considerations. That is to say at the earliest opportunity when considering how best to deal with a potential waste problem. Secondly, when a problem has been created or has emerged and which needs dealing with. Finally, when a pollution incident has occurred. In regard to the last point, one of our difficulties as advisers ourselves is that clients come to us generally very late in the day. If only farmers could be persuaded to make contact with their adviser at the earliest opportunity, then it would make the job of the adviser very much more simple. More options are generally open at that time and usually costs are kept down. This is not always appreciated by the client, who may be suffering from the "ostrich" syndrome. (Head in the sand, ignore the problem, it will go away).

One of the resolutions which every farmer with livestock should set himself relates to the setting up of a farm waste plan. (See this chapter). MAFF have organised trials on a free basis for farmers and there are now many consultants in the field who will provide the necessary service. These include ADAS, members of BIAC (The British Institute of Agricultural Consultants) and individual farm advisers.

General advice comes from many sources including those above, local firms of land agents and surveyors, farming trade organisations such as the Country Landowners Association, the National Farmers Union, the Tenant Farmers Association, and the Farmers Union of Wales.

The regulators themselves have a dual role. Their first duty is that of enforcement and prosecution where necessary. However, they also give advice and recommendations which, unfortunately, is not binding upon themselves. In other words should a breach of the law or a pollution incident take place, despite taking their advice, that does not prevent a prosecution.

There are also advisory leaflets from the Environment Agency, from the Environmental Health Officers Association and from the Health and Safety Executive.

Solicitors will advise on legal aspects and some firms specialise in environmental law.

10–16 Product manufacturers are also likely to advise but some caution needs to be taken from such sources. Clearly, they are motivated by the need to sell their equipment and may not be entirely unbiased in their recommendations. Nor are they likely to take such a wide overview, as for example an independent consultant during the farm waste management plan phase.

For the serious student there are of course university courses leading to degrees in environmental management, courses through agricultural colleges and text books to study.

Appendices

The three Codes of Good Agricultural Practice are contained at Appendices 1, 2 and 3. The Code for Water was published in July 1991 and is undergoing a process of revision. The Code for the Protection of Air, 1992, is also being revised and the Code for the Protection of Soil was produced in 1993. The Codes are reproduced here specifically for the sound practical advice which they provide. However, readers should note that the Codes refer to some outdated legislation and they should return to the main text for the up-to-date position.

Appendix 1

Code of Good Agricultural Practice for the Protection of Water

Ministry of Agriculture, Fisheries and Food

Welsh Office Agriculture Department

July 1991

Contents

1. Introduction

About this Code

1. This Code of Good Agricultural Practice for the Protection of Water is a practical guide to help farmers and growers avoid causing water pollution. It replaces the previous Code published in 1985. It is intended that this Code will become, by the Autumn of 1991, a Statutory Code under Section 116 of the Water Act 1989. This will mean that, if you do not keep to this Code, it will not be an offence but it could be taken into account in any legal action. Following the Code is not a defence against a charge of causing pollution.

2. The Code describes the main risks of causing water pollution from different agricultural sources. It does not include specialised horticulture or fish farming. In each section, good agricultural practice is set down in a way which minimises the risk of polluting water while allowing economic agricultural practice to continue. This Code was written using the latest information available.

3. Any new practices not covered in the Code should follow the general principles set out in it.

Codes on the protection of air and soil are being prepared.

Laws controlling pollution

4. The Water Act 1989 tries to prevent water pollution happening and allows people to be prosecuted if they pollute. The National Rivers Authority (NRA) is responsible for most of this work.

5. Under Section 107 of the Water Act 1989 it is an offence to cause or knowingly permit a discharge of poisonous, noxious or polluting matter or solid waste matter into any "controlled waters" without the proper authority.

6. "Controlled waters" include groundwater and all coastal or inland waters, including lakes, ponds, rivers, streams, canals and ditches. "Proper authority" is usually a consent to discharge from the NRA under Section 108 of the Water Act.

7. Farmers, employees and contractors can be prosecuted for causing pollution. You could be fined up to £20,000 in a Magistrates Court or get an unlimited fine in the Crown Court. A person found guilty of causing pollution may also have to pay for any damage caused and for NRA costs.

8. The Water Act 1989 has several sections designed to prevent water pollution.

Section 110 of the Water Act 1989 and the resulting Control of Pollution (Silage, Slurry and Agricultural Fuel Oil) Regulations 1991, aim to prevent pollution by silage effluent, slurry, dirty water, and fuel oil by setting standards for keeping and handling these substances. Facilities that you already had before 1 March 1991 are usually exempt from these rules, but the NRA can ask you to improve them if there is a significant risk of causing pollution. New, substantially enlarged, or substantially reconstructed facilities must meet the standards set out in the Regulations. You must tell the NRA at least 14 days before you use such facilities. You must follow the Regulations, but doing so is not a defence against a charge of causing pollution. It may, however, go in your favour when the Court is deciding on sentence.

9. Under section 115 of the Water Act the NRA can do work to prevent or clear up pollution and get back the cost from the person responsible.

10. Under section 118 of the Water Act the NRA can ask for information to help them prevent water pollution.

11. The Environmental Protection Act 1990 updates the UK's pollution control systems. It brings in a system of integrated pollution control for the disposal of wastes to land, water and air. The parts of the Act that have most bearing on this Code are Part I, which establishes integrated pollution control and gives Local Authorities new powers to control air pollution from a range of prescribed processes; Part II, which improves the rules for waste disposal; and Part III, which covers statutory nuisances and clean air.

12. The Town and Country Planning (Assessment of Environmental Effects) Regulations 1988 set out the requirements for the Environmental Assessment (EA) of certain major developments for which planning permission is needed. The local planning authority (or, if the matter is referred, the Secretary of State) will decide on the need for EA. Further details on the planning legislation are given in paragraph 46.

Water pollution problems

13. Each year there are a lot of cases of reported water pollution. In 1987–1989 non-agricultural sources, primarily industry and sewage accounted for 83% of all reported cases with agriculture causing the remainder. In the same period most serious cases of pollution caused by agriculture came from slurry (28%), silage effluent (25%) and dirty water (19%).

14. A lot of point source agricultural pollution, that is pollution that comes from one building, store or field, happens when farm waste with a high Biochemical Oxygen Demand (BOD) (see Table 1) gets into a watercourse and is broken down by micro-organisms. This process takes oxygen out of the water. In bad cases all river life can be killed.

Table 1 Examples of typical BOD levels (mg/litre)

	BOD
Treated domestic sewage	20–60
Raw domestic sewage	300–400
Vegetable washings	500–3,000
Dilute dairy parlour and yard washings (dirty water)	1,000–2,000
Liquid waste draining from slurry stores	1,000–12,000
Liquid sewage sludge	10,000–20,000
Cattle slurry	10,000–20,000
Pig slurry	20,000–30,000
Silage effluent	30,000–80,000
Brewer's grain effluent	30,000–50,000
Milk	140,000

Pollution can also be caused by fuel oil, a pesticide, or ammonia in slurry, which could poison or damage river life or may make groundwater unfit to use.

15. Agriculture can also cause diffuse pollution of waters by nitrate, other nutrients and pesticides. Unlike point source pollution, diffuse pollution comes from many fields and it is not caused by a single event or action.

Diffuse pollution of watercourses or groundwater could mean that Environmental Quality Standards are not met. For example, water may not meet drinking water standards, or adding nutrients could make algae grow in surface waters.

16. Polluting materials, such as animal slurry, contain micro-organisms which could harm humans and livestock. Any surface or groundwater polluted with such waste could be contaminated with these organisms. A recent problem is contamination with the parasite, *Cryptosporidium*, which can make humans ill and is difficult to detect and remove when water is being treated.

NOTES:

Biochemical Oxygen Demand

Biochemical Oxygen Demand (BOD) is used to show the risk of causing pollution from organic wastes. BOD is a measure (in mg/l) of the amount of oxygen needed by micro-organisms to break down organic material.

Groundwater

Groundwater is the water held underground in rock formations. These formations are called aquifers.

Watercourses

In this Code, watercourses include all surface waters whether coastal waters, estuaries, lakes, ponds, rivers, streams, canals and field ditches.

Farmer responsibilities

17. All farm staff and contractors on the farm who handle, store, use, spread or dispose of any substances that could pollute water should know about the causes and results of water pollution. They should know how to operate and maintain the equipment they use and know what to do in an emergency.

18. You should find out about drainage systems on your land and in buildings, especially where pipes, channels and outfalls are. You should also find out the position of nearby boreholes, springs and wells, including private water supplies, from the NRA and the Local Authority if appropriate.

Regular checks should be made to make sure that watercourses are not polluted. Checks should be done more often at times when the risk of causing pollution is highest, such as when slurry, silage effluent or dirty water is being applied to land.

All storage facilities should be regularly checked for leaks and damage.

Emergency action

19. If water becomes polluted tell the NRA at once and take immediate steps

to stop the pollution. All NRA regions have 24 hour cover to answer reports of pollution.

20. Farmers should have a plan to deal with water pollution if it happens. You should know the telephone numbers of the NRA and people who own land or use water downstream. You should also know the details of equipment you can use to prevent causing pollution, before the NRA arrive. For example, you should know what equipment you have on the farm which you could use to plug land drains, dam ditches and hold oil spillages, say by placing wooden boards across the surface of a watercourse.

Advice

21. Farmers can get free general advice on preventing pollution from ADAS. You can get detailed design and planning services from ADAS, consultants and equipment suppliers.

2. Principles of Storing and Applying Livestock Wastes and Other Organic Wastes to Land

Planning stages

22. The most economical and environmentally friendly way of disposing of animal manure, slurry, and dirty water is normally to apply it onto agricultural land. You should plan how and when to apply all livestock wastes to the land, to make the risk of water pollution as low as possible and get the most from the nutrients. Before you apply livestock or other organic waste to the land, you should plan as follows:

- **The first stage.** Pick out any land on the farm where waste should not be spread at any time, (paragraphs 25–26).
- **The second stage.** Work out how much land you need to take the total nitrogen in all the waste that has to be spread on the farm (paragraphs 27–28). If there is not enough land, make arrangements to spread the excess material on suitable land elsewhere.
- **The third stage.** Pick out land where waste should not be spread at certain times, or where the spreading rate should be limited (paragraphs 29–34).
- **The fourth stage.** Work out the largest amount of waste you will have to store before it is spread. If storage facilities you already have are too small then you will need more storage space (paragraphs 35–37).
- If you need more storage **the fifth stage** is to choose and design a suitable storage system to meet the needs of the farm (paragraphs 38–46).

23. The rest of this section gives more advice on each of these stages. In some situations, however, you might need to vary these guidelines in order to reduce the risk of pollution as much as possible. You might need to get professional help to plan how you will manage livestock wastes on the farm.

24. The information in this section can be used to:

- Help you decide when and where to spread waste.
- Work out the storage you need on the farm to avoid the risk of pollution.
- Decide whether the 4 months storage specified in the Control of Pollution (Silage, Slurry and Agricultural Fuel Oil) Regulations 1991 is needed, and sufficient.

NOTES:

Surface run-off

The speed at which liquid soaks into the soil is important in working out the risk of run-off. Water ponding on the soil surface shows that the liquid is being applied faster than it can soak into the soil. There is a greater risk of run-off on sloping land. Application should be stopped or the rate reduced depending on the circumstances. On some sites, even a small amount of rain will cause run-off.

Land drains

Fields with effective land drainage systems cause a particular risk. The danger is that a liquid applied to the surface will find its way into the drains and the watercourse. This risk applies to any drained field whatever its slope or how near it is to a watercourse. Most lowland clays have had a drainage system put in at some time and pipes may still work even if a modern system has not been put in.

Groundwater contamination

Applying waste to land can pollute water underground. The risk applies in any field where permeable soils lie directly on top of rock formations that hold water, especially where the watertable is shallow or the rock has cracks in it (for example shallow soils over limestone).

FIRST STAGE

Areas where waste should not be spread at any time

25. Before you apply livestock wastes and other organic wastes to the land, you should pick out any land where waste should not be spread at any time. Leave an untreated strip at least 10 metres wide next to all watercourses. An uncultivated buffer strip will help reduce the risk of causing pollution. Irrigation systems should work so that there is no chance of their spray coming within 10 metres of a watercourse or of wind blowing material into a watercourse.

26. To reduce the risk of polluting groundwater, livestock wastes and other organic wastes should not be applied within 50 metres of a spring, well or borehole that supplies water for human consumption, or is to be used in farm dairies. In some cases a bigger distance may be needed.

You might not be able to spread waste on some areas of the farm because of the nuisance that could be caused by smell or because of management agreements.

SECOND STAGE

Matching land area to nitrogen in waste

27. The next stage is to match nutrient from the waste to the area of land you apply it to. As a general guide there should be enough land where waste can be spread to make sure that the amount of "total nitrogen" in livestock wastes and other organic wastes that are applied is less than 250 kg/ha/yr (kilograms each hectare each year). This figure does not include manure deposited while livestock is grazing. Lower amounts may be appropriate in sensitive catchments such as Nitrate Sensitive Areas.

For new units, the amount of land needed to achieve this should be available from the outset. Existing units currently applying organic wastes at rates which exceed this amount should take steps to change their practice so that they can meet this limit.

The "available nitrogen" in organic wastes applied to the land should not be more than the crop needs. You should take this "available nitrogen" into account when you are working out how much fertiliser you need.

28. If you would be putting on more than the recommended amount of nitrogen that should be spread on the area of land available, you should arrange to spread it on suitable land somewhere else. (See Appendix III for examples of land area needed for different livestock).

NOTES:

"Total nitrogen" and "available nitrogen"

10% to 90% of the "total nitrogen" in livestock and other organic waste can be taken up by plants in the first few weeks after spreading. This is the "available nitrogen". The amount of "available nitrogen" depends on the type of manure.

Detailed fertiliser recommendations including the contribution from animal manures are given in MAFF Reference Book RB 209.

THIRD STAGE

Estimating the risk of pollution from spreading

29. The third stage of planning is to judge the risk of causing pollution from a field that could have waste spread on it, and the number of months in the year when this risk applies.

Crops may limit the time when waste can be applied because of the chance of damaging them. The risk of damaging the soil might also prevent the waste from being spread during the winter months by machinery that is pulled by a tractor.

30. VERY HIGH RISK AREAS—DO NOT APPLY ANY WASTE WHEN CERTAIN CONDITIONS APPLY

As well as the areas mentioned in paragraphs 25–26, do not apply livestock wastes or other organic wastes at the times of the year when there are the following conditions:

- Fields likely to flood in the month after the waste is applied.
- Fields that are frozen hard.

- Fields next to a watercourse, spring or borehole where the surface is severely compacted.
- Fields next to a watercourse, spring or borehole that are waterlogged.
- Fields next to a watercourse, spring or borehole that have a steep slope and the soil is at field capacity.
- Fields next to a watercourse, spring or borehole that have a moderate slope, a slowly permeable soil and the soil is at field capacity.
- Fields that are pipe or mole drained and the soil is cracked down to the drains or backfill.
- Fields that have been pipe or mole drained in the last 12 months.
- Fields that have been subsoiled over a pipe or mole drainage system in the last 12 months.
- Fields where the soil depth over fissured rock is less than 30 cm and the soil is cracked.

31. HIGH RISK AREAS—DO NOT APPLY MORE THAN THE RECOMMENDED AMOUNTS

On areas not ruled out by paragraphs 25, 26 and 30 and under the following conditions, do not put on more than the amounts of livestock wastes or other organic wastes recommended below:

- Fields next to a watercourse, spring or borehole that have a moderate slope and the soil is at field capacity.
- Fields next to a watercourse, spring or borehole with a slowly permeable soil and the soil is at field capacity.
- Fields where the soil depth over fissured rock is less than 30cm.

32. You should not apply more than 50m³/ha (4500 gallons/acre) of slurry or 50 tonnes/ha (20 tons per acre) of manure at one time. Leave at least 3 weeks between each application to stop the surface sealing and to let the soil recover.

To reduce the chance of pollution in these situations, the amount of diluted liquid livestock waste applied by pumped irrigation systems should not be more than:

- An application rate of 50m³/ha (4500 gallons/acre) for travelling irrigators.
- A precipitation rate of 5mm/hour (0.2 inches/hour) with sprinklers moved regularly to suit the conditions.

Maximum application amounts for other wastes are given in the appropriate Sections of this Code.

33. ALL OTHER SITUATIONS—APPLY WITH CARE

On sites where there is a lower risk of causing pollution, you can apply higher amounts provided you always take into account the pollution risk and the nutrient content (see paragraphs 27–28).

You should not go over the nutrient loading given in paragraph 27 in any period of 12 months. For slurry that has not been diluted this nutrient loading may need an application rate of less than 50m³/ha (4500 gallons/acre) in a year. Poultry manures will usually reach this loading at 5–15 tonnes/ha (2–6 tons/acre) depending on nitrogen content.

34. Pay careful attention on ALL SITES to make sure that spreading does not cause ponding or run-off. Watercourses should be checked frequently during and after spreading.

NOTES:

Field

The rules on site risk could apply to less than the whole field when:

- only part of the field is a high risk and the rest of the field is a lower risk;
- the field is large and part of the field is a long way from the watercourse.

Frozen hard

This term is used when the soil is frozen for more than 12 hours. Days when soil is frozen overnight but thaws out during the day do not count.

Field capacity

Field capacity is when the soil is fully wetted and more rain would cause water loss by drainage.

FOURTH STAGE

Choosing the size of storage facilities

35. To choose the size of store you need on the farm, work out for each month the amount of waste produced and the amount that can safely be spread. Add up any monthly surpluses which cannot be spread. The biggest total of waste which cannot be spread gives the size of store you need. In many cases, dirty water and slurry may be estimated and handled separately. If the type of store you choose cannot be emptied in stages, then you will also have to take the animal housing period into account.

The amount of waste produced depends on:

- Number and type of livestock
- Volume of dirty water and rainwater going into the store
- Amount of bedding used.

Typical volumes of waste produced by livestock are given in Appendix IV. Typical amounts of bedding material used are given in Appendix V.

The size of store you need should be compared to the storage you already have. If the store you have is not big enough, more storage should be provided.

36. Clean rainwater from roofs and open concrete should not run into the store, unless the areas are small, storage capacity is adequate, or the water is needed to dilute the waste to make it easier to handle.

37. Dirty water that runs off from open soiled yards, manure stores or from cleaning buildings and equipment can either be collected in the slurry store or dealt with by a separate system (see Section 4). If such waste is included in a slurry store, work out the extra storage you need from the area of yards and stores involved using appropriate rainfall figures. (Paragraph 109).

NOTES:

Slurry

The Control of Pollution (Silage, Slurry and Agricultural Fuel Oil) Regulations 1991 define slurry as:

"(a) excreta produced by livestock whilst in a yard or building; or

(b) mixture consisting wholly or mainly of such excreta, bedding, rainwater and washings from a building or yard used by livestock or any combination of these; of a consistency that allows it to be pumped or discharged by gravity at any stage in the handling process."

Dirty water

Unlike the Regulations, this Code separates materials covered by the definition of slurry given above into slurry and dirty water. Dirty water is a waste, generally less than 3% dry matter made up of water contaminated by manure, crop seepage, milk or other dairy products or cleaning materials.

FIFTH STAGE

Choosing a storage system

38. The best way of handling and storing waste depends on its consistency. This depends on the type of livestock, how they are housed, the amount and the type of bedding material and whether the waste is diluted with dirty water.

The system you choose will also depend on winter rainfall. In areas with a high rainfall, storage systems that have a large surface area will need extra storage capacity. With storage systems that produce liquid waste continuously the amount will depend on rainfall.

39. Slurry contains dung, urine and water with only small amounts of bedding. It flows by gravity and can be collected in slatted-floor systems, below ground tanks, or reception pits. You can store it for a long time in an above ground slurry store, or in an earth banked structure.

Separating the slurry mechanically will give a liquid that can be pumped through an irrigation system.

40. Semi-solid slurry is a mixture of dung, urine and bedding. You can store semi-solid slurry in earth-banked structures. Cattle slurries that contain straw bedding can be stored in weeping-wall stores.

The time when you can empty these stores could be limited, by when the machinery is available or by not being able to get to the store contents until they have dried out. Liquid waste collected from such stores is highly polluting and must be contained before you spread it on suitable land.

41. Manure may contain large amounts of bedding, can usually be stacked and should be stored in a suitable store. For short-term storage the manure can be put into heaps in a field as long as the heaps can be put where there is no risk of causing water pollution by seepage and run-off.

42. The type of store also depends on other things. If you are thinking about an earth banked storage system the site you choose must be suitable. The machinery you have to empty the store, labour, and the cost of facilities are also important.

Designing, building and choosing the site of storage facilities

43. All storage facilities for waste should be designed and constructed to BS 5502: Part 50: 1989, to stand up to the load of the stored material and safely contain any polluting material.

New, substantially enlarged or substantially reconstructed storage facilities for slurry and dirty water must keep to the Control of Pollution (Silage, Slurry and Agricultural Fuel Oil) Regulations 1991. Do not put stores within 10 metres of a watercourse or field drain.

44. Design each storage facility to suit the conditions and needs of the particular site. Design details are given in the Construction Industry Research and Information Association (CIRIA) Report No 126 "*Farm Waste Storage—Guidelines on Construction.*" You will probably need to get professional help on designing the store from a suitably qualified person.

The building work must be supervised by experienced people to make sure that the standards set by the designer are met.

45. The person who supplies or designs the store and the equipment should give you a manual on how to use the system properly, safety procedures, and how to maintain the store and its equipment.

46. The position of the storage facilities should take into account how easy it is to fill, whether you can get to the store to empty it, its appearance, and the possibility of smell causing a nuisance.

Under the Town and Country Planning General Development Order 1988, you will need planning permission before you can put up any new buildings or convert certain buildings you already have, to house livestock, store slurry, manure or sewage sludge, if they are within 400 metres of protected buildings such as houses and schools. Agricultural dwellings and buildings are not protected buildings.

You may need to prepare an Environmental Statement before applying for planning permission for some major developments, such as large new pig and poultry units.

Information on the legislation is also given in the Code of Good Agricultural Practice for the Protection of Air (which is being prepared).

It is important to speak to the appropriate body before you build facilities in an Environmentally Sensitive Area, a National Park, on Sites of Special Scientific Interest or on archaeological sites.

3. Slurries

Introduction

47. This section is a guide to good practice to minimise the risk of causing water pollution from slurries. It includes how to handle and store slurry in above ground circular stores, weeping wall stores and earth banked structures.

Animal slurry stored and spread on farms causes a lot of pollution. Many pollution incidents happen because stores are not designed, built, maintained or used properly.

48. Slurry will be produced from dairy, beef or pig housing which does not use much straw or bedding material. The slurry could range from a semi-solid with about 12% dry matter to a liquid with 3–4% dry matter, depending on the type of stock and how diluted the slurry is. The best way to store and handle the slurry before it is applied to the land depends partly on the type of slurry being produced.

STORAGE

General rules

49. A facility for storing slurry should be designed to collect and hold slurry safely for a specific length of time. A guide to designing and building slurry storage tanks is given in British Standard (BS) 5502: Part 50: 1989. Design details are given in the Construction Industry Research and Information Association (CIRIA) Report No 126 "*Farm Waste Storage—Guidelines on Construction*".

50. Under the Control of Pollution (Silage, Slurry and Agricultural Fuel Oil)

Regulations 1991 slurry must be kept in a reception pit or slurry storage tank, unless it is kept temporarily in a tanker. The slurry storage tank includes a lagoon, pit or above ground circular store used for the storage of slurry. The Regulations lay down certain rules for most new, substantially enlarged or substantially reconstructed stores, reception pits and channels, which include:

- No part of the storage facility can be within 10 metres of a watercourse or field drain that the slurry could go into if it escaped.
- Floors must not let liquid pass through, i.e., they must be impermeable.
- The base and walls must be protected against corrosion as in BS 5502: Part 50: 1989.
- If the walls of the store let liquid pass through, the base must go beyond the walls and have collection channels draining into a tank.
- The walls and floors must be able to stand up to the loads in BS 5502: Part 50: 1989.
- The storage tank must have a life of at least 20 years if it is maintained properly.
- Reception pits must be able to hold at least 2 days slurry production.
- The storage tank must be big enough to hold at least 4 months slurry unless you have a safe year-round disposal system.
- The size of the store must take into account any rain that falls directly onto or drains into the store while the slurry is being stored.
- The local NRA office must be told in writing at least 14 days before you use such facilities.

Stores that you already have do not have to meet these standards, but the NRA can require improvements if there is a significant risk of causing pollution.

51. The store should be arranged so that the contents can be easily emptied for spreading without spilling them.

Slurry stores should be designed and built by people who are competent to do these jobs. To avoid pollution, more than 4 months storage may be needed on some farms.

Under-floor storage and transfer channels

52. The base and walls of the channels or pits should be impermeable to stop polluted liquids getting out, or to prevent water getting in if they are built below ground.

53. Slurry can be removed through a sluice gate to a reception pit outside the store before emptying. Alternatively slurry can be mixed or recirculated before emptying direct from the under-floor store.

Design channels to empty their contents into a reception pit or tank so that the slurry cannot overflow.

If slurry is emptied from channels to a reception pit through a sluice gate, the pit must be big enough to hold the largest amount of slurry that could be emptied into it when the sluice is opened.

SAFETY NOTE: MIXING OR RECIRCULATING SLURRY CAN GIVE OFF DANGEROUS GASES THAT CAN BE LETHAL TO BOTH HUMANS AND LIVESTOCK. NEVER PUT SILAGE EFFLUENT INTO UNDER-FLOOR SLURRY STORES.

NOTES:

Under-floor storage

Pig slurry is commonly stored below the slatted floor of the housing facility for 4–8 weeks. If extra storage is needed it should be outside the pig house. Cattle slurry can also be collected and stored under-floor as long as it does not have too much bedding or waste feed in it. Building methods include reinforced and rendered concrete block walls on a concrete base, reinforced concrete made on site, or ready made sections.

Transfer channels

Slurry with little or no bedding in it can be transported from the collection place to a storage facility or reception pit, using transfer channels.

For cattle slurry, these channels are normally 1 metre wide and 1 metre deep with a level base and a 150 millimetre lip at the emptying end of the channel to keep a layer of liquid in the base for lubrication. The longest channel is typically 25 metres.

Below ground tanks and reception pits

54. Below ground tanks should be big enough to suit the circumstances and emptying method. Reception pits should be able to hold 2 days slurry and dirty water that is collected.

55. Tanks that are emptied or desludged by a tractor-drawn slurry tanker should be put where the tractor can easily get to them.

SAFETY NOTE: COVER OR FENCE OFF BELOW GROUND TANKS AND RECEPTION PITS TO KEEP TO THE HEALTH AND SAFETY AT WORK ETC., ACT. TANKS MIGHT CONTAIN LETHAL GASES AND SO YOU SHOULD NOT GO INTO THEM. CLEARLY DISPLAY A WARNING SIGN ON THE TANK.

NOTES:

Below ground tanks

Below ground tanks are often used to store small amounts of dilute slurry, run-off from farmyard manure stores or parlour washings for a short time. They are usually too expensive for storing slurry for a long time, but can be used as reception pits to collect slurry before it is pumped to an above ground slurry store.

Below ground tanks are usually built from either rendered reinforced blocks, reinforced concrete made on site, ready made concrete panels, steel panels or glassfibre reinforced plastic.

ABOVE GROUND CIRCULAR STORES

56. If liquid slurry is kept in above ground circular stores you can spread the waste at any time as long as the soil, crop and weather conditions are suitable.

These stores are suitable for storing slurry that is easy to pump, including the liquid that comes from mechanical separation. They are not suitable for slurries that contain a lot of long straw bedding, sand bedding or waste feed.

NOTES:

Above ground circular stores

Stores are normally made from curved steel panels or concrete sections. Steel panels should be coated to protect them against corrosion. As storage depth can be up to 6 metres, they generally take up less space than other storage systems.

Steel stores can be designed to be extended, that is the concrete base and lower panels are strong enough to carry the extra loads if more panels are added to increase the height and size of the store.

A typical system has a reception pit next to the main store (Figure 2). A grid covers the reception pit so that slurry can drop through and long fibres are scraped to one side. Slurry may also get to the reception pit through underground channels.

A purpose built pump moves slurry from the reception pit to the store, a tanker or irrigation system for spreading. These pumps are often fitted with an outlet so that the contents of the reception pit can be recirculated.

The store contents can be mixed by recirculating them through moveable single or multiple outlets in the store, by using the filling pump. Mixing with a fixed or portable propeller or aeration system for separated slurry is better for stores with a large diameter.

Design of the above ground circular store

57. The Regulations require the reception pit for new stores to hold at least two days production of slurry.

A space of 300 millimetres (freeboard) between the level of the slurry and the top of the store must be left when working out the size of the store.

58. Cattle slurry may need to be diluted so it is easier to handle by letting parlour washings or a limited amount of fouled yard area drain into the reception pit. Take this extra liquid into account when working out the size of the store.

59. When the site is chosen, make sure that it gives a stable base for the store. The store base should be designed to suit the size of the store and site conditions.

60. The Regulations say that the discharge pipe between the main store and the reception pit must be fitted with two valves in line, which are locked shut when they are not being used.

61. There should be equipment to make sure that the store contents can be mixed to break up any crusts on the surface and move any sediment, before it is emptied.

62. There should be a ladder and platform that meets Health & Safety requirements, to inspect the store contents and to supervise mixing.

Using and maintaining the above ground circular store

63. Keep long bedding or feed out of the store by scraping it to one side, so you can dispose of it separately. Use enough bedding to keep animals clean.

64. Thoroughly mix slurry in the reception pit with the pump, before you put

it into the store. You might need to add extra liquid in dry weather.

65. You should check the store contents regularly. Mix the contents either when there are signs of crusting and build up of sediment or just before you empty the store. If you mix the contents by recirculation do not leave the pump running unattended with the valves between the store and the pit open.

NOTE: POSSIBLE NUISANCE CAUSED BY SMELL: Mixing the contents will give off smells. A system where mixing is not done so often will reduce the number of times when this happens.

66. Do not overfill tanks or let them overflow. Always leave a space (freeboard) between the level of slurry and the top of the store to allow for rainfall.

67. Check the store regularly for any signs of leaking. Put faults right, getting professional help if you need it.

Completely empty the store once a year. Clean the store down and check for any signs of corrosion or damage.

WEEPING WALL SLURRY STORES

68. Weeping wall slurry stores are suitable for cattle slurry with a lot of straw bedding in it.

NOTES:

Weeping wall slurry stores

Weeping wall stores are built above ground level on a concrete base. Excess liquid drains through narrow gaps in the walls, and is collected and spread onto land. This liquid has a high risk of causing pollution.

The contents of the store gradually dries out and becomes similar in consistency to farmyard manure. The side panels of the store can be taken out to empty these solids.

Walls are typically 2 to 3 metres high. Building methods include:

- Narrow upright pre-cast concrete panels, supported by steel work on the outside.
- Self supporting concrete panel sections, with slots down them.
- Horizontal timber railway sleepers supported between steel uprights.

In all cases, slots are 25 to 35 millimetres wide.

Design of the weeping wall slurry store

69. Store contents are not usually emptied during the winter housing period because panels cannot be opened safely until the contents have dried out enough, typically from early summer onwards. If the panels are opened too soon this could cause a serious pollution risk.

The size of store needed will usually be worked out from how long the winter housing will be, taking into account the volume of dung, urine and bedding but not rainfall, as this drains into the collection tank.

Under the Regulations, a space (freeboard) of 300 millimetres between the level of the slurry and the top of the walls must be allowed when working out the size of the store.

70. Rain that falls on to the store and about 10% of the slurry going into it, will drain out during storage. The size of the storage tank should take into account the rainfall (see paragraph 109), the surface area of the store and how often the tank can be emptied without causing a pollution risk. New, substantially enlarged or substantially reconstructed tanks are subject to the Regulations (paragraph 50). These require among other things, 4 months storage capacity unless you have a safe year round disposal system.

71. The method used to fill the store should be able to deal with strawy material. If there is a ramp for a tractor scraper it should have a suitable slope and raised sides. It can extend into the store if necessary.

Any rainwater that runs off from higher yards should be piped straight into the collection tank and should not be able to go into the store.

72. The Regulations require that the concrete base of the store must not let liquid pass through it, *i.e.* be impermeable. It should also be level and must extend outside the walls to form the base of a collection channel outside the store.

73. The walls should completely surround the store. Normally all 4 sides have slots, although if the store is built into a slope one wall could be solid.

74. Slots in walls should end about 100 millimetres above the floor. This will keep a layer of liquid on the floor so that slurry can flow away from the filling point.

Gaps next to the filling point should be sealed up or made as small as possible.

75. The store should have panels that can be taken out to empty the contents. These panels should not be next to the filling point. There should be a suitable hard area for loaders and spreaders to get to the store to empty it.

76. Liquid waste draining through the gaps in the walls should be collected in the drainage channel outside the store and drained into a suitable tank.

Using and maintaining the weeping wall slurry store

77. There should be enough straw bedding in the slurry to make sure that diluted slurry does not run out through the slots.

78. Check collection channels regularly to make sure that they are not overflowing or blocked. Check the contents of the liquid collection tank frequently and empty them when necessary. SAFETY NOTE: BEWARE OF DANGEROUS GASES). The spreading method, the time of application and where you spread the slurry should take into account the fact that the liquid has a high BOD and high nutrient content (See paragraphs 25–34).

79. Do not take access panels out to empty the store unless the contents are dry enough so that they will not flow out by gravity Panels should be removed carefully, section by section.

80. Check the walls, floor and liquid collection channels regularly for leaks, corrosion and structural damage. Put any faults right with professional help if necessary.

EARTH BANKED STORES

81. A lot of serious pollution incidents are caused by earth banked stores that are too small, badly built or in an unsuitable place. Such stores cannot be built properly in a lot of places, because of unsuitable soil.

To meet the conditions set out in the Control of Pollution (Silage, Slurry and Agricultural Fuel Oil) Regulations 1991 for new, substantially enlarged or substantially reconstructed stores (see paragraph 50), it is important that:

- The site is suitable for this kind of store.
- The structure is designed by a qualified person to suit the particular site and does not let liquids get in or out (i.e., is impermeable).
- The embankment is dug and built properly so that the structure is stable.
- A space (freeboard) of 750 millimetres is left between the level of the slurry and the top of the embankments when working out store size.

If you are thinking about using this type of store, talk to the NRA first.

NOTES:

Earth banked stores

Earth banked structures can be used to store slurry that contains bedding, dilute slurry, separated liquids from mechanical separators, or dirty water. Depending on the consistency of its contents they can either have the liquid taken out and be emptied as a solid or mixed and emptied as a liquid. Such stores are commonly called "compounds" when the contain solids or semi-solids or "lagoons" if they contain more liquid waste.

A series of lagoons may be used to settle dirty water before it is pumped through an irrigation system.

Store can be built below, above, or part below/part above ground. Typical depth from the base to the top of the embankment is 3 to 4 metres.

Working out a size

82. The store should be big enough to store all dung, urine and used bedding produced during the storage period (see appendices IV and V), plus any dirty water or other liquid waste that is going to be stored.

Work out the size of the store for dirty water from yard areas, appropriate rainfall figures for the she and the number of months storage needed (see paragraph 109).

The rainfall falling onto the store during the storage period must also be taken into account.

Layout of the earth banked store

83. If slurry and bedding is scraped over a ramp or edge of a concrete area it should go in the compound at its deepest point. This will keep some liquid in the base, below the filling point, helping the slurry to flow away and fill the whole store.

84. A strainer placed at the deepest part of the compound will let any extra liquids be removed.

85. If the machinery to be used to empty the store will work from the top of the banks, there must be a way of getting to the banks and the banks must be wide enough for the machinery to be used safely, taking into account the weight of the machine. The width of the compound should suit the reach of the machines which will be used. If machinery is going to go into the compound to empty it, there can be a concrete strip or pad in the base.

Lagoons for liquid storage

86. To stop solids building up in a lagoon for liquid storage, you often need to mix the store contents before you empty them. If you will be using tractor driven mixing equipment there should be a safe way of getting to the lagoon.

87. If a series of lagoons is used to settle dirty water, there should not be any overflow pipes through embankments unless they empty into a lagoon next to it that is about the same size, or into a pump tank at a similar level. "T"—pipes will prevent floating solids moving from lagoon to lagoon.

Vehicles should be able to get to lagoons to desludge them.

Design of the earth banked store

88. The designer should check that the soil and site is suitable by digging trial holes, but not under where the embankment is going to be. The designer should give you all details including the building method, the internal and external angles of the banks and the width and foundation details of the embankment.

89. If a site is permeable, that is it lets liquid pass through, soil that contains clay can be imported to build or line the embankments. Using a liner that does not let liquid pass through may be possible. If in doubt, consult the NRA before installing a liner. These liners are not strong enough to stand up to emptying by loaders, and should not therefore be used to contain solid or semi-solid materials.

90. The details the designer gives you will usually include the following practices:

- Moving land drains so that they are at least 10 metres clear of the proposed store.
- Removing plants and topsoil before the building work starts.
- Building the embankment by putting layers of suitable graded soil on top of each other to a given depth over the full width and packing it tight using suitable equipment.
- Building banks high enough to allow for them to settle.
- Covering the exposed surfaces of the embankment with a layer of topsoil to a given depth and sowing grass to prevent erosion.

SAFETY NOTE: ALL STRUCTURES MUST BE SURROUNDED BY A FENCE WHICH MEETS THE HEALTH AND SAFETY STANDARDS

Using and maintaining the earth banked store

91. Keep a space (freeboard) of at least 750 millimetres between the level of waste and the top of the banks in stores built, substantially enlarged or substantially reconstructed after the Regulations were brought in (March 1991). Stores built before then might use a smaller space (freeboard) where a reduction in capacity would lead to a risk of pollution through spreading under unsuitable conditions. If this is the case, you must take great care. The space (freeboard) should never be less than 300 millimetres.

92. Liquids that come out of the store through a strainer will have a high BOD and nutrient content. You should not spread them at times, rates, or in places where runoff and pollution could happen (paragraphs 25–34).

93. If you are going to handle slurry as a liquid, mix it thoroughly before you empty it to prevent solids building up. Make sure you do not wash away the banks or damage any liner during mixing.

Load tankers or spreaders carefully to reduce the chance of spilling slurry.

94. Keep plants growing on embankments short so that the embankments can be inspected regularly. Do not let trees grow on or next to embankments. If cracks appear or the banks settle these should be put right straight away. Examine embankments after heavy rain.

Tell the NRA if there are any signs of liquid seeping out or the embankment slipping. Ask the designer or other suitably qualified person about any repairs and emergency measures that are needed.

TREATING SLURRY

95. You can treat slurry in a number of ways before or during storage and before it is spread. These include mechanical separation, anaerobic digestion (breaking down the slurry without oxygen) and aerobic treatment (treating the slurry using oxygen).

Waste treated by anaerobic digestion or aerobic treatment will normally have a lower BOD, but it cannot be emptied into a watercourse. Treated slurry is usually spread back to land. You will normally need to store it to avoid causing pollution.

96. Anaerobic digestion or aerobic treatment can reduce the risk of a nuisance caused by the smell coming from slurries. These treatment methods are not described here but are covered in detail in the Code of Good Agricultural Practice for the Protection of Air (being prepared).

NOTES:

Mechanical separation

Mechanical separation takes coarse solids and fibre out of slurry. The liquid fraction will have 1 to 6% dry matter and so have the following possible advantages:

- Crusts or sediment are less likely to form during storage and the volume of the liquid that needs to be stored is reduced by about 20%.
- Liquids are easily pumped and can be spread by a travelling irrigator. 70 to 80% of the plant nutrients from the slurry will be in the liquid fraction.
- You can apply it to growing crops with less risk of smothering them or of solids building up.
- If you want to use aerobic treatment the power needed to do this is reduced.
- Separated solids are either spread on the land as solid manures or composted and sold as a soil conditioner if you can find a market for it.
- Separation adds an extra treatment, more equipment and costs. You will still need storage facilities for liquid. There are a variety of separator types. These can use perforated screens, perforated belts, or the principle of the centrifuge.
- Slurry that needs to be separated is collected to one point in a tank. You might need to dilute and mix cattle slurries or slurries containing bedding before separating them. A pump is used to move liquids from the tank to the separator. The separator is often up on a platform so solids can fall into a heap or trailer and liquids can flow down to a store.

Mechanical separation

97. Mechanical separation takes solids out of slurry, giving a liquid fraction that can be easily pumped and a solid fraction.

Designing the mechanical separation system

98. Any reception pit that collects slurry before it is separated should be big enough to hold at least 2 day's slurry production.

The separator should be able to handle the amount of slurry produced on site, in a short working day. There should be some way of protecting the separator against frost.

There should be another way of handling slurry in an emergency, in case of power cuts, or when the separator needs to be serviced.

99. If possible, all pipes and pumps should be placed so that if any slurry is spilt it will go back into the reception pit. The layout, level and slope of the storage area for solids should make sure that any seepage is held safely and will drain back into the reception pit.

There should be enough space to store separated liquids and solids so you do not have to apply them to the land when this might cause pollution (paragraphs 22–37).

Using and maintaining separators

100. Inspect and maintain all parts of the separation system, in particular pumps, pipework and valves that carry liquids, to reduce the risk of causing water pollution. Examine all storage systems at regular intervals and keep them in good condition.

WAYS OF APPLYING SLURRY TO THE LAND

101. Paragraphs 22–34 in Section 2, cover the general rules of applying slurry, and give application rates for spreading slurry in different situations.

The risk of run-off is greater if slurry is spread on bare soil, rather than cropped land.

In all cases, the machinery that applies the slurry should suit the type of slurry being handled. It should be able to apply the slurry evenly at rates down to 25m³/ha (2250 gallons/acre). Avoid spilling slurry while you are filling, moving or unloading the machinery.

Use travelling irrigators for diluted or separated slurries in the way described in paragraphs 126–129 and 132.

102. If you inject the slurry into the ground, it will reduce the nuisance caused by the smell and the loss of nitrogen to the air, in the form of ammonia. There will be more available nitrogen for the crop to take up. Injecting the slurry may reduce the risk of run-off from the surface as long as the rate at which the slurry is applied suits the site. The times and places when slurry can be injected successfully can often be limited by the condition of the soil and the crop. To reduce the risk of causing pollution:

- Follow the spreading guidelines in paragraphs 25–34.
- Inject across slopes rather than up and down.
- Avoid injecting into porous back-fill over drainage systems.
- Avoid injecting into subsoil below the crop's active roots.

103. Make sure the slurry that is applied to the land does not pond, run-off or move through the soil to a drainage system or to groundwater. Inspect watercourses frequently during and after spreading.

NOTE: POSSIBLE NUISANCE CAUSED BY SMELL: Spreaders or irrigators that spread the slurry without throwing it up into the air and produce large drops, will help reduce the chance of causing a nuisance by the smell when slurry is spread. Applying the slurry straight onto the surface or injecting it into the soil can reduce this problem even more. This subject is covered in detail in the Code of Good Agricultural Practice for the Protection of Air (being prepared).

Dirty Water

Introduction

104. This section is a guide to good practice to minimise water pollution caused by dirty water. It includes ways of applying dirty water to the land using different irrigation systems. Methods of storage are described in Section 3.

105. Dirty water is waste, generally less that 3% dry matter, made up of water contaminated by manure, urine, crop seepage, milk, other dairy products or cleaning materials. ALTHOUGH IT IS COVERED SEPARATELY IN THIS CODE, IT IS DEFINED AS SLURRY IN THE CONTROL OF POLLUTION (SILAGE, SLURRY AND AGRICULTURAL FUEL OIL) REGULATIONS 1991.

New, substantially enlarged or substantially reconstructed tanks or stores for dirty water must meet the standards set in these Regulations which include a requirement for 4 months storage unless you have a safe year-round disposal system. Storage facilities you already had before March 1991 do not usually have to meet these standards, but the NRA may require you to make improvements if there is a significant risk of causing pollution.

106. Dirty water comes from cleaning work and run-off from open concrete areas that are dirtied by manure or silage. Liquid that drains from manure or slurry stores is often collected in dirty water handling systems and is covered in this section of the Code. This liquid can be a lot more polluting than yard run-off or cleaning water.

The biochemical oxygen demand (or BOD) and the amount of plant nutrients in dirty water can vary a lot. All dirty water is a lot more polluting than raw domestic sewage. Information is given in Table 1, paragraph 14, for different sources of dirty water.

NEVER LET DIRTY WATER FLOW INTO A WATERCOURSE

107. Dirty water causes a lot of agricultural water pollution incidents. You must collect, store and dispose of it carefully. The main ways of disposing of it are to irrigate it back to the land or spread it by tanker.

Amounts

108. The system used to store, handle and dispose of dirty water must be designed to cope with the amount and type of dirty water coming from your farm.

Water used to clean milking parlours, pig accommodation and other similar areas will be polluted. Appendix VI gives an idea of the volumes of water that might be used. If possible you should check the actual amount used.

109. Water that runs off open stockyards, silos, manure and slurry stores will be polluted. Work out volumes from the area and rainfall figures. Figures for a "return period" of 5 years are often used when working out the design.

If possible, collect all dirty water to a single point before storing and disposing of it. Collect water polluted with dairy chemicals or milk in the dirty water system and do not let it get to a watercourse.

Separating clean water

110. Clean water from roofs, nearby fields or clean concrete, running onto dirty concrete will increase the amount of dirty water which you need to store and dispose of carefully. Avoid this extra risk of pollution and cost by directing the clean water into a ditch, watercourse or soakaway, wherever possible.

NOTES:

Rainfall figures

Historical records of rainfall are used to predict the most rain that is likely to fall in a given time. To design dirty water pumping systems, you might need figures for rain lasting for short periods of time (1–3 hours) and medium periods of time (24 hours). How often such an event will occur on average is called the "return period". Figures for a return period of 5 years are normally used for design calculations.

You can get these figures from the Meteorological Office at Bracknell (Tel: 01344 420242 Extension 6838 or 6864).

CHOOSING A SYSTEM TO DISPOSE OF DIRTY WATER

To land

111. If an unroofed area or the amount of dirty water is small, you can collect and store it with the slurry if the store is big enough. On many sites, however, it is better to use a separate system for dirty water.

112. "Low rate" irrigation systems (see paragraphs 119–124) use suitable tanks or lagoons to collect the liquids and let them settle. They use an electric pump, small bore pipe and sprinklers or a small travelling irrigator to spread the liquid onto the land.

If the area where the liquid is spread is suitable such systems can handle dirty water every day. In some cases you will need to store dirty water to avoid spreading it on the land when there is a risk of causing pollution.

113. "High rate" irrigation systems use large bore pipelines, high flow rates and application rates. These systems are not normally used in winter because of the risk of run-off. Storage of the dirty water for a long period would be needed in most places.

114. You can use a tanker to spread all types of dirty water back to the land. You might need to store the waste to avoid damaging the soil and reduce the risk of run-off. Because it takes a lot of work, this system is only practical for small amounts of liquid.

115. A blind ditch or soakaway cannot be used for materials such as drainage from a slurry store or manure store. They are only likely to be successful with small amounts of liquid on soils that water can pass through easily. They are **not** suitable on most sites. Ask the NRA if you have any doubts about a system you have or if you are thinking of using a new blind ditch or soakaway.

Treatment systems

116. In some cases you might be able to treat the dirty water before you discharge it, spread it to land, or put it into a public sewer. Treatment systems aim to reduce the pollution from dilute wastes by settling them and using the activity of bacteria. YOU WILL NEED TO GET WRITTEN CONSENT TO DISCHARGE FROM THE NATIONAL RIVERS AUTHORITY, BEFORE YOU CAN PUT ANY WASTE INTO A WATERCOURSE. A CHARGE WILL BE MADE FOR THIS CONSENT. Simple treatment systems are unlikely to meet the standards needed.

117. Barrier ditch systems try to treat the wastes by letting the liquid settle in a large barriered section for 90 days, followed by aerobic treatment in a free flowing section of ditch at least 300 metres long.

Although this method was popular at one time, you cannot rely on barrier ditches to reach the standards of treatment needed before the NRA will issue a consent for direct discharge to a watercourse. This system is not now usually acceptable.

Discharging to a sewer

118. If they are able to treat the extra pollution load, a Water Service Company might allow livestock farms in suitable locations to discharge dilute waste into a public sewer. The Water Service Company will make a charge which depends on the strength and amount of waste.

LOW RATE IRRIGATION

The suitability of a site

119. Although low rate irrigation is a good way of disposing of dirty water safely, not all farms can use this system all the year round.

As long as there is a suitable electricity supply, you can pump the dirty water a long way from the farm buildings to the area it is going to be spread on. **It is important to judge whether fields are suitable for low rate irrigation.** Avoid spreading in the "non-spreading" and "very high risk" situations described in paragraphs 25, 26 and 30.

If there is not enough suitable field area for spreading in winter you will need storage facilities for dirty water or another way of disposing of the waste.

NOTES:

Low Rate Irrigation Systems

"Low rate" irrigation systems normally use settlement tanks or lagoons to collect dirty water before it is pumped to land through small bore plastic pipes. Sprinklers are used to apply the liquid at rates of up to 5 millimetres an hour (0.2 inches per hour). Travelling irrigators with low application rates can also be used. These are typically pulled along with a trailing hose connected at the centre of the run.

Design of the system

120. If you can dispose of the dirty water all-year-round, a below ground tank should be provided to collect the dirty water. Unless the pump has a chopping facility or a mechanical separator is used, the tank should have 2 to 4 compartments to remove solids that can settle. These compartments should be joined by overflow "H" pipes.

A tanker should be able to get to the tank to desludge it. The end compartment and the pump output should be big enough to make sure that there is no overflow when a lot of rain falls in a short time (paragraph 109). An emergency overflow should lead to extra storage, or if you have permission from the NRA, into a blind ditch. New, substantially enlarged or substantially reconstructed tanks must meet the Control of Pollution (Silage, Slurry and Agricultural Fuel Oil) Regulations 1991 (paragraph 50).

SAFETY NOTE: COVER OR FENCE OFF TANKS TO MEET THE HEALTH AND SAFETY AT WORK ETC., ACT 1974. TANKS MIGHT CONTAIN LETHAL OR EXPLOSIVE GASES SO DO NOT GO INTO THEM. DISPLAY A CLEAR WARNING NOTICE ON THE TANK.

121. Earth banked lagoons may be used to settle liquids or to store dirty water, if the site is suitable and the embankments are built properly. (paragraphs 81–90).

122. When it is running continuously, the pump should be able to cope with the largest amount of rain that could fall in a day (paragraph 109). It should give enough pressure (head) to pump the liquid through the system to the area where it is being applied. This pressure will depend on friction in the pipe, lift, and sprinkler or irrigator operating pressure.

The pump should start automatically unless there is a large lagoon where water levels in the store rise slowly with rainfall. There should be a warning device that you can see or hear easily to warn you that the system has shut down or failed.

123. Pipes to fields should be made out of a material that does not corrode. If the pipe is buried, it should be deep enough to protect it from frost and machinery.

The main pipe should have outlet points (hydrants) so that the liquid can be spread in at least two suitable fields.

124. The sprinklers should be able to apply the liquid at a rate of no more than 5 millimetres an hour (0.2 inches an hour) and you should be able to move them easily.

A mobile irrigator should be able to apply 50m^3/ha (4500 gallons/acre), that is 5 millimetres (0.2 inches) or less on each run. Irrigators should have an automatic shut down to stop them applying too much liquid at the end of a run.

MANAGING IRRIGATION SYSTEMS

Introduction

125. Pollution can often happen because sprinklers or irrigators are not moved often enough, the application rate is too high or they are used on unsuitable land.

This section applies mainly to using irrigation systems for disposing of dirty water. The rules also apply to travelling irrigators used for diluted or separated slurries.

General management

126. A person should be in charge of the system to make sure that the equipment is maintained and that the fields used for spreading are frequently inspected.

127. How often the sprinklers need to be moved and the safe application rate of mobile irrigators depend on soil type and conditions, the slope of the land, weather conditions and the type of liquid being pumped.

Do not spread dirty water on non-spreading areas (paragraphs 25–26), or on land in the "very high risk" category (paragraph 30). Take extra care when you are irrigating bare soil or fields that are drained.

128. Move sprinklers regularly. Check the land you are irrigating for any signs of run-off and ponding on the surface or worms being killed. Move sprinklers or re-set travelling irrigators to a lower application rate if there are any signs of these problems.

If you use sprinklers to apply liquids with a high nutrient content, move them frequently to limit application rates.

NOTE: POSSIBLE NUISANCE CAUSED BY SMELL: Applying dirty water and slurry by sprinklers or irrigators can cause smells. Reduce this problem by paying attention to wind direction and where the liquids are being spread. More details are given in the Code of Good Agricultural Practice for the Protection of Air (being prepared).

When frost lasts for a long time systems cannot be used, and you will have to make other arrangements to handle the small amount of dirty water produced in these weather conditions.

129. Check watercourses frequently during and after spreading to make sure that there is no pollution.

Maintenance

130. Inspect tanks or lagoons frequently. Desludge sections where solids settle, using a vacuum tanker. Apply this sludge to the land, taking care to avoid causing pollution.

SAFETY NOTE: TANKS MIGHT CONTAIN LETHAL OR EXPLOSIVE GASES. DO NOT GO INTO THEM.

131. Check pumps, filters and control gear regularly to make sure they are working properly. Maintain them according to the supplier's instructions.

Check the warning devices, that show that the system might have shut down, several times a day to make sure that the pump is working.

Check sprinklers regularly to make sure that they are turning properly. Check travelling irrigators to make sure that they are winding-in correctly and that the automatic cut-off is working.

Travelling irrigators

132. Paragraphs 126–129 also apply to travelling irrigators. Set the speed at which they travel to give an application rate that does not cause ponding or run-off on the surface and does not apply too much nutrient. You should not apply more than 50m^3/ha (4500 gallons/acre) in "high risk" situations (paragraphs 31–32).

On sloping land, set the irrigator to run across the slopes.

The irrigator should shut off automatically at the end of each run. If the amount of liquid that can be stored is limited you should start the irrigator on a new run as soon as possible.

5. Solid Manure

Introduction

133. This section deals with solid animal manures stored on farms. Although solid manures are less likely than slurries to cause pollution, they can make a lot of liquid waste if they are heaped outside. This liquid has a high BOD and there is a high risk of it causing pollution. You should contain it if there is a risk to watercourses or groundwater.

134. Liquid waste from manure stored on yards is treated as slurry under the Control of Pollution (Silage, Slurry and Agricultural Fuel Oil) Regulations 1991. It has to be collected and stored as described in these Regulations.

135. Only put the manure in a temporary field heap if you can put it where there is no risk of run-off polluting water. Do not put heaps over field drains, within 10 metres of a watercourse or 50 metres of a spring, well or borehole that supplies water for human consumption, or is to be used in farm dairies.

Manure stores

136. Stores specially built for solid manure will take away the risk of pollution through run-off and will make it easier to handle and load the stored material.

137. When you are estimating the volume of waste you need to store, take into account the amount of bedding. Fresh manure taken from livestock housing every day can fill a space of up to 2 m^3/tonne (70 ft^3 a ton). The volume can decrease by quite a lot while it is being stored. (A guide to typical amounts is given in appendices IV and V.)

138. Permanent stores should have a base that does not let liquid pass through it. This base should slope so that liquids run-off into a collection channel across the front of the store which, along with channels at the side of the store, contain the liquid waste.

Collection channels should be outside the walls of the store if the walls let liquid pass through them.

139. Liquid waste should go into a below ground tank built as in paragraphs 50, 54 and 55. Either empty the tank regularly by tanker and spread the waste onto the land or connect the tank to a suitable pumped disposal system.

When you are choosing the size of the tank, take into account the rain that is likely to fall and the way you will empty it to make sure that the tank does not overflow and cause pollution.

NOTES:

Solid manures

These include: material from traditional covered straw yards, manure with a lot of straw in it and solids from mechanical slurry separators. Most poultry battery, broiler and deep litter systems produce solid manure. These organic wastes will generally contain enough bedding material, or have enough dry matter to be stacked.

Manure stores

Stores usually have a concrete base that can take the weight of tractors and spreaders. This base has one, two or three walls. These walls are typically 2–3 metres high. Ways of building the walls include ready-made concrete panels, reinforced concrete, reinforced block work, or good quality railway sleepers supported by suitable upright RSJs. The height of the store is normally limited to 3 metres. The width of the store is typically 10 to 15 metres. Liquid waste is collected in a below ground tank.

Applying the waste to the land

140. Check the waste in the tanks frequently and empty them when necessary. (SAFETY NOTE: TANKS MAY CONTAIN LETHAL OR EXPLOSIVE GASES. DO NOT GO INTO THEM). How, where and when you spread the waste should take into account that these liquids have a high BOD and nutrient content. You should apply them according to paragraphs 25–34.

141. Although the risk of causing pollution by spreading solid manures is low, surface run-off can happen if rain falls after waste has been applied. To reduce this risk you should not spread solid manures on non-spreading areas (paragraphs 25–26, or on land in the "very high risk" category (paragraph 30). You should not go over the recommended rates in "high risk" situations (paragraphs 31–32). Take particular care not to apply poultry manure at a rate above the nutrient loading guideline in paragraph 27.

142. Make sure that spreading manure does not cause pollution. Check watercourses frequently during and after spreading.

6. Other Organic Wastes

Introduction

143. This section covers the other main organic wastes that are applied to agricultural land. The risks of polluting watercourses and groundwater are similar to the risk from livestock wastes. You must not empty any organic waste into a watercourse without consent from the NRA. Waste must not be emptied into a sewer without an authorisation from the Water Service Company.

The Control of Pollution Act 1974 (Part I) largely controls non-agricultural wastes. Under the Act you need a licence to dispose of waste. It is an offence to apply waste on land unless the site is licensed. The Act does not control waste from farms.

The Collection and Disposal of Waste Regulations 1988 allow the deposit of waste from off-farm sources on agricultural land, without licensing, provided it fertilises or otherwise beneficially conditions that land. The Waste Disposal Authority must be provided with certain details, such as a description of the waste and the amount to be deposited. It is strongly advisable to consult the Waste Disposal Authority before accepting any waste of this type.

When Part II of the Environmental Protection Act 1990 comes into force it will replace and update these standards. The Act reorganises the system for collecting and disposing of waste, makes it your legal duty to take care when you are handling waste and strengthens the licensing system for disposing of waste.

Paragraphs 25–34 apply to spreading all organic wastes, but the maximum application rates are lower for some types.

Sewage sludges

144. The Sludge (Use in Agriculture) Regulations 1989 apply to spreading sewage sludge onto agricultural land. They aim to prevent substances that could be potentially toxic from building up in soil and to prevent possible spread of disease. They are supported by a Code of Practice.

Sewage sludges contain nitrogen and phosphorus, but little potassium. When applying sludge to land, the amount you apply should not contain more than 250 kg/ha/year of "total nitrogen". When you apply both livestock manures and sewage sludge this limit is the combined nitrogen in both materials. You should take the amount of "available nitrogen" into account when you are working out how much inorganic fertiliser the crop needs (see para. 28 for explanation of "total" and "available nitrogen").

145. You can get liquid sludge in raw and digested forms. Raw sludge contains micro-organisms that could be harmful. Do not apply it to crops that could be eaten raw.

You might need to store liquid sludge before you apply it. You must have enough storage space.

The rules for avoiding water pollution when sewage sludge is applied to the land are the same as for slurry (paragraphs 25–34). You should not apply it in on non-spreading areas (paragraphs 25–26), or on land in the "very high risk" category (paragraph 30). You should not apply more than 50 m^3/ha (4500 gallons/acre) at one time in high risk situations (paragraphs 31–32).

146. Solid sewage sludge cake is usually only stored in a field heap for a few weeks. You should not place heaps over land drains, within 10 metres of a watercourse, or within 50 metres of a spring, well or borehole that supplies water which is for human consumption or to be used in farm dairies.

You should not apply sewage sludge cake on non-spreading areas (paragraphs 25–26), or on land in the "very high risk" category (paragraph 30). You should not apply more than 50 tonnes/ha (20 tons/acre) in high risk situations (paragraphs 31–32).

Milk and dairy waste

147. At certain times of the year, you might want to dispose of milk that you cannot sell. This could happen because quota has been exceeded, because the milk cannot be collected due to bad weather or because the milk is contaminated.

Milk has an extremely high BOD and so there is a very high risk of it causing pollution if it reaches water. If possible, feed surplus milk to livestock. Alternatively it can be added to stored slurry or applied directly to land. If you add it to a slurry store, you should treat it as slurry when you apply it to land.

SAFETY NOTE: MIXING MILK AND SLURRY CAN GIVE OFF LETHAL OR EXPLOSIVE GASES.

A veterinary surgeon should be consulted on animal health aspects before you spread milk onto grazing land or feed it to animals.

Do not spread milk on non-spreading areas (paragraphs 25–26), or on land in the "very high risk" category (paragraph 30). On other sites, dilute the milk with the same amount of water before you apply it. You should not apply more than 50 m^3/ha (4500 gallons/acre) of diluted milk.

Similar rules apply to disposing of surplus whey or other waste liquid dairy products.

Effluent from by-products used to feed animals

148. Feeds such as wet brewers' grains and sugar beet pulp will produce effluent when you store or ensile them. Store this effluent safely, and apply it to land as in paragraph 175.

Wastes from vegetable processing

149. WATER THAT HAS BEEN USED TO WASH VEGETABLES MUST NOT BE EMPTIED INTO A WATERCOURSE UNLESS YOU HAVE A CONSENT TO DISCHARGE FROM THE NRA. This water will usually have a relatively low BOD and a medium amount of solids in it. Water you have used for peeling vegetables will have higher levels of both. Water that has been used for peeling and washing vegetables will need to be biologically treated to meet the standards set before you can discharge it to a watercourse.

Under the Disposal of Waste (Control of Beet Rhizomania Disease) Order 1988 it is illegal to apply any solid or liquid waste resulting from processing any raw potatoes, beets, carrots, celery or celeriac, leeks, swedes or turnips that have been imported from outside Great Britain onto land, unless it has been approved for that purpose. Application for land approval or any questions should be sent to the local Ministry of Agriculture, Fisheries and Food plant health and seeds inspector (PHSI).

If you apply untreated washings from vegetables to the land follow the same rules as for disposing of dirty water (see Section 4).

Wastes from animal processing

150. Under the Meat (Sterilisation and Staining) Regulations 1982 it is illegal to spread any untreated abattoir waste on agricultural land, except for blood and contents of the intestines that you use as a fertiliser.

You need permission from the Waste Disposal Authority responsible for the abattoir before you can use this waste. Under the Control of Pollution Act 1974 (Part I) the farm also needs to be licensed, unless the waste meets the requirements of the Collection and Disposal of Waste Regulations, 1988. These Regulations let you apply waste to fertilise or beneficially condition agricultural land provided you have notified the local Waste Disposal Authority before depositing the waste.

151. Under the Diseases of Animals (Waste Food) Order 1973 you must not let livestock get to unprocessed waste food, including blood. To meet these standards you must not let livestock or poultry get into fields where this waste has been spread until none of it is left on plants or the ground surface.

152. You should not spread the contents of animals intestines on non-spreading areas (paragraphs 25–26), or on land in the "very high risk" category (paragraph 30). In high risk situations (paragraphs 31–32) you should not apply more than 50 m^3/ha (4500 gallons/acre).

153. You should not spread blood on areas mentioned in paragraphs 25, 26 and 30. In all other situations, you should dilute blood with at least the same amount of water before you spread it. You should not apply more than 25 m^3/ha (2250 gallons/acre) of undiluted blood.

154. You should choose sites where you can apply these materials to avoid causing public nuisance. Make sure that applying them does not cause ponding or run-off. Inspect watercourses during and after application.

Silage Effluent

Introduction

155. This section is a guide to good practice to minimise water pollution caused by silage effluent.

Effluent from crops stored in an enclosed pit or silo is one of the most concentrated and harmful pollutants on the farm (paragraph 14). Even small amounts in a watercourse can cause a lot of damage to the environment, such as fish being killed, for a long way downstream. A lot of serious pollution incidents happen each year, because people do not contain or dispose of silage effluent properly.

156. The main causes of pollution are silos or waste collection facilities that are not designed or maintained properly. Silage effluent is very corrosive and can damage concrete and steel. It can easily escape through silo floors, collection channels or tanks that are damaged, cracked or which let liquid through them.

Silage effluent cannot be treated to be discharged into a watercourse. You should store it safely and spread it onto the land or use it for animal feed.

Regulations

157. The Control of Pollution (Silage, Slurry and Agricultural Fuel Oil) Regulations 1991 require you to make silage:

- either in your existing silo;
- or in a new silo or one that has been substantially enlarged or substantially reconstructed after 1 March 1991;
- or in wrapped and sealed or bagged bales;
- or in a tower silo that meets the appropriate British Standard;
- or if you have made the majority of your silage by another method over the last 3 years between 1 March 1988 and 1 March 1991, providing you tell the NRA you are doing so before 1 September 1991.

  New, substantially extended, or substantially reconstructed silos, have to meet the Regulations. The requirements include:

- Liquid should not be able to pass through the silo base i.e., it should be impermeable. The base should have channels around it to collect effluent. The base and any drains should be able to resist corrosion by silage effluent.
- If the silo has walls, the base should go beyond the walls and have channels to collect effluent.
- The collection channels should lead to a tank which is able to resist acid. It should be able to hold at least 20 litres of effluent for each $1m^3$ of silo space, if the silo holds less than $1500m^3$. Other rules apply to larger silos.
- No part of the silo, tank or channels should be within 10 metres of a watercourse or field drain, which silage effluent could get into if it escaped.
- Any silo walls should be able to resist corrosion and be built to stand up to the loading given in British Standard 5502: Part 22: 1987.
- If the base of the tank is below ground, the tank should be able to resist acid attack for 20 years without maintenance.

Silos you already had before 1 March 1991 are not normally covered by these rules, although the NRA can require you to make improvements if there is a significant risk of causing pollution.

Amounts of effluent

158. The amount of effluent depends on how wet the material is in the silo. Effluent comes out fastest within two days of putting the material in the silo. The flow of effluent is affected by the depth of silage, the drainage inside the silo and the additives you use.

159. Rainwater that falls onto the silo will add to the amount of effluent. Putting a roof on silos will reduce this problem.

Design of the silo

160. The base and walls of the silo should be professionally designed to suit the conditions of the site. The building work should be supervised to make sure the silo is structurally sound and effluent cannot escape.

Design details are given in the Construction Industry Research and Information Association (CIRIA) Report No. 126 "*Farm Waste Storage—Guidelines on Construction*".

161. Move any land drains that are under the site so that they are at least 10 metres away from the silo. Check for old drainage systems.

162. Concrete floors need to be designed and laid properly to make sure that liquid cannot pass through them.

New materials and ways of building the floor such as hot rolled asphalt, have been developed which may be better at protecting against corrosion. These materials must be the correct type and the floor must be laid properly.

163. Floors should slope at about 1 in 50 towards drains inside the silo that run along the length of the floor. These drains reduce the pressure the liquid puts on the silo walls. The silo floor should slope from back to front with a fall of 1 in 75. There should also be a drain across the front of the silo.

164. The floor slab in walled silos should go beyond the outer edge of the walls, and channels made to hold any effluent that escapes. If there are no walls, the base must have a drain around the edge.

Drains and channels should empty into a tank of suitable size, normally below ground. Tanks should be made from materials that are protected from corrosion and are often made out of one piece of that material without any joints.

165. Effluent can be pumped from a small below ground tank to a larger store above ground. You can mix waste with slurry in such a store, as long as the store can resist the corrosion from neat silage effluent, and it is well ventilated.

NOTE: POSSIBLE NUISANCE CAUSED BY SMELL—Mixing effluent with slurry could increase the risk of causing a nuisance because of the smell.

SAFETY NOTE—DO NOT ADD SILAGE EFFLUENT TO SLURRY IN ENCLOSED BELOW GROUND TANKS OR TANKS INSIDE BUILDINGS AS IT GIVES OFF LETHAL GASES.

166. If floors are cracked or corroded, it might be possible to mend them in a number of ways, including covering with hot rolled asphalt. If this method is used, the existing floor slab you are covering must give a stable base.

167. Silo walls should be built to stand up to the loads given in BS 5502: Part 22: 1987. Walls can be made of any suitable material that is protected against corrosion.

All tower silos must meet the British Standard 5061: 1974(a).

Control measures

168. Anyone who makes and handles silage should know that silage effluent is highly polluting.

169. Clean and inspect walls and floors when the silo is empty, and mend any cracks, corrosion or other faults before you make silage again.

170. If you cut the crop in dry weather and let it wilt until it has a suitable dry matter content (at least 25% for clamp silos) this will significantly reduce the amount of effluent.

If the crop cannot wilt because of wet weather or you put fresh grass in a silo, you can use additives to get good quality silage. Take extra care in such situations to make sure you can cope with the amount of effluent produced.

SAFETY NOTE: SOME TYPES OF SILO WALLS MIGHT NEED THE STORED MATERIAL TO HAVE MORE THAN 20% DRY MATTER.

171. You can put straw bales in a layer on the silo floor to soak up liquid. Alternatively, you could mix absorbent materials with the grass when you put it into the silo. Although these methods may reduce the total amount of effluent produced, using straw may in fact increase the speed with which it runs out.

172. Check collection channels and the area around the floor slab regularly for leaks or blockages.

Check the level of effluent in the tank and empty it regularly. It must never overflow. A visible or audible warning device may help.

SAFETY NOTE: TANKS MAY CONTAIN LETHAL OR EXPLOSIVE GASES. DO NOT GO INTO THEM. LOCK TANK COVERS WHEN YOU ARE NOT USING THEM. DISPLAY A CLEAR WARNING NOTICE NEAR THE TANK.

Baled silage

173. Let material you are going to bale wilt until it contains at least 25% dry matter, to prevent effluent from being produced inside the package.

174. Under the Control of Pollution (Silage, Slurry and Agricultural Fuel Oil) Regulations 1991, wrapped or sealed silage bales have to be stored at least 10 metres away from any watercourse or field drain into which effluent could enter if it escaped from the bales.

When you feed the silage, you must not take the bags or wrapping off the bales within 10 metres of a watercourse or field drain into which silage effluent could enter. If there is any effluent inside the packaging, you must dispose of it safely.

Applying effluent to land

175. Do not apply effluent to non-spreading areas (paragraphs 25–26) or on land in the "very high risk" category (paragraph 30). Dilute silage effluent with the same amount of water before you apply it to the land. Do not apply more than 50 m^3/ha (4500 gallon/acre) of this diluted effluent.

NOTE: NUISANCE CAUSED BY SMELL. Take this into account when you are choosing the site for spreading the effluent.

Feeding effluent to livestock

176. Silage effluent contains a fairly low amount of dry matter but has some feed value. It is unlikely that dairy cows will drink all the effluent made each day. Therefore, you will need to spread the effluent that is left over onto the land, or store it safely to be used in the future. Any new storage facilities must meet the Regulations.

Silage additives

177. Most silage additives are extremely polluting. They should be stored and handled at least 10m from a watercourse or field drain. Care should be taken to make sure that no additive or used container gets into a watercourse.

8. Fertilisers

Introduction

178. This section deals with the inorganic and man-made fertilisers which you store and use on the farm. You must consider the risk of polluting water by fertiliser leaking from a store, field runoff or by being applied directly to surface water. Avoiding unnecessary nitrate leaching is important when you are planning fertiliser use (see Section 13).

179. The risk of solid fertiliser causing pollution while it is being stored is relatively low but pollution incidents, when they happen, can be serious. You should not store bags within 10 metres of a watercourse or field drain. Handle them carefully to avoid damage. Gather up any spilt material.

You need to be especially careful to avoid spilling stored liquid fertiliser and causing water pollution.

Storing and handling liquids

180. Place storage facilities as far away as possible from any watercourse, ditch or drainage system. Ask the NRA if you do not know whether a site is suitable.

181. The storage tank should be designed to suit the type and amount of liquid that is going to be stored. It should be made from a material that is resistant to corrosion from liquid fertiliser. The base should be designed to support the weight of the full store. There should be a hard area so that large delivery vehicles can get to the store.

182. Mild steel tanks should be welded from plates of adequate thickness that are protected against corrosion on the outside by a suitable coating. If you are storing nitrogen fertilisers, you can prevent corrosion inside the tank either by first using a phosphate containing compound fertiliser which will form a protective layer on the inside of the tank or by adding a small amount of phosphate to the nitrogen fertiliser.

Glass-fibre reinforced plastic (GRP) tanks should be fixed to the base and put where the chance of damage from a vehicle hitting the tank is as low as possible. Protective barriers might need to be put at the filling and emptying points of the tank.

183. You can use a flexible liner, which is supported and protected by a suitable structure, to store liquid fertiliser. **Do not use unprotected or unsupported flexible containers for either temporary or permanent stores.**

184. Pipes, valves and connections for filling and emptying stores should be made out of materials that do not corrode and should be placed to avoid damage. Lock any valves where the fertiliser could empty under gravity when they are not being used.

185. Keep the storage tank and any connected pipes and valves clean and in good condition. Inspect them each year for any signs of leaking or corrosion. Paint the outside of steel tanks regularly. Treat any damage to the surface of GRP tanks with a coat of resin.

186. Good handling procedures will keep low the risk of spilling fertiliser either when you are filling stores from road tankers or filling the field applicator or bowser. Do not overfill tanks.

Leave space for the contents to expand. Anyone using fertilisers should know about these procedures, the possibility of causing pollution from spillage, and emergency action you have to take.

NOTES:

Liquid fertilisers

The term "liquid fertilisers" as used in this code includes clear solutions and suspensions.

Applying fertilisers

187. Take special care when applying any inorganic fertiliser on fields where there is a risk of runoff to surface water. The risk is greatest when the field is waterlogged or frozen hard. Do not apply nitrogen fertiliser between 1 September and 1 February unless a crop needs it during this time.

188. Avoid applying fertiliser to a watercourse. Full width distributors will not generally cause any problems if you use them carefully. Spinning disc and oscillating spout machines are more difficult to operate so that the full application rate is spread right up to the edge of the field. This can cause some fertiliser to go into a watercourse. You can adjust some newer machines by fitting headland discs or tilting the tractor linkage to avoid this happening. Otherwise the machine should be driven further away from the watercourse, leaving an area next to the water where the application rate is lower. Use liquid fertiliser applicators in a way that avoids the wind blowing droplets into watercourses.

Keep machinery that spreads fertiliser in good condition and adjust it following the maker's instructions.

9. Fuel Oil

Introduction

189. This section covers agricultural fuel oil stored on farms. Oil spills on farms cause a number of pollution incidents each year.

Regulations

190. The Control of Pollution (Silage, Slurry and Agricultural Fuel Oil) Regulations 1991, cover storing of more than 1500 litres (330 gallons) of agricultural fuel oil on farms. The Regulations do not cover domestic fuel oil that is stored separately. Most fuel stores you already have can be used without being altered, although the National Rivers Authority (NRA) can ask you to make improvements if there is a significant risk of causing pollution.

The Regulations require among other things that new, above ground fuel tanks or areas for storing fuel drums must:

- Be surrounded by walls and a base that liquid cannot pass through i.e., is impermeable, to form a bund, which is large enough to hold a specific amount of fuel.
- Have no part of the bund or storage area within 10 metres of a watercourse or field drain which fuel oil could get into if it escaped.
- Have the bund and the base of the storage area built to last for 20 years with reasonable maintenance.
- Be arranged so that all parts of the tank and any taps or valves permanently fixed to the tank, empty vertically downwards inside the bund and are locked shut when they are not being used.
- If a flexible pipe is used for filling vehicles this pipe must be fitted with a tap or valve which closes automatically, at its far end.

There are different sizes for bunds where fuel is stored in drums, barrels, a single tank or several tanks. For example, with a single tank the bund should be big enough to hold the tank's contents plus an additional 10%. See the Regulations for full details.

Design of storage facilities

191. Tanks are normally above ground and built from welded mild steel plate. The supporting structure is often built from masonry pillars or walls and/or steelwork.

192. A suitable standard for new tanks for fuel oil is British Standard 799: Part 5: 1987. This standard gives details of plate thickness, supports, filling pipes, vents and other tank fittings you need.

193. Place the tank away from any foul or surface water drains, and where the delivery driver can see the filling gauge. The tank should be protected from being hit by vehicles.

194. Below ground tanks should not be used if leaks could pollute groundwater or where water in the soil could corrode the tank. If the store has to be underground, you should ask the NRA first, and the tank should be inside a masonry or concrete chamber.

Under the Regulations all other newly installed tanks must have a bund of the size laid down. There should not be an outlet or drain from the bund. The floor of the bund should slope towards a small sump. There should be some way (for example, a hand pump) to remove water or fuel oil from the sump before you dispose of it safely.

195. You should be able to lock any drain cock closed. There should be room for a container (for example a bucket) underneath it. The tank should have an anti-siphon device fitted to the filling pipe if its inlet is lower than the highest fuel level in the tank. Fuel lines to equipment such as grain driers should have hand valves fitted next to the tank.

Outlet valves should be marked to show when they are open and closed.

There should be a way to measure the fuel level in the tank. If there is a sight tube, it should be protected from damage, and not be made of glass.

SAFETY NOTE: YOU SHOULD PUT THE TANK ON A SUITABLE SITE AND TAKE OTHER PRECAUTIONS TO REDUCE THE RISK OF FIRE. ASK YOUR LOCAL FIRE SERVICE.

196. Mobile fuel tanks should be built to a similar standard as that described in BS 799: 1987. They should be designed so that they are protected from accidental damage. The tank should have a contents gauge. It should be stable enough to travel on roads and have suitable brakes. Keep all connections and valves where fuel could empty by gravity locked when you are not using them.

Using and maintaining the store

197. You should provide sand or another suitable absorbent material next to the storage area to soak up any spillages.

198. Where possible, a member of farm staff should be present when fuel is delivered.

199. Keep all valves inside the bund closed and locked when you are not using them. This includes valves on fuel lines to boilers or grain driers. Store flexible hoses for refuelling vehicles with the hose outlet in the bund. Avoid overfilling vehicle tanks.

200. Check for leaks at all times and repair them as soon as they appear. Take water or oil out of the bund and dispose of it safely. Water will often contain some oil. Large amounts of oil can be removed from water using a blanket that is specially made to absorb oil. Water that is only slightly polluted can be spread on land that has not got any crops on it. Avoid non-spreading and very high risk situations (paragraphs 25, 26 and 30).

201. Inspect tanks regularly and repaint them on the outside to prevent corrosion. Inspect bunds and keep them in good condition.

202. Use mobile tanks with care, especially when you are refuelling machines such as irrigation pumps next to watercourses. Check the fuel systems and tanks of all tractors and diesel engined equipment used in a fixed position for leaks.

10. Sheep Dip

Introduction

203. Some cases of pollution are caused each year by handling and disposing of sheep dips carelessly. This can cause the death of fish and other water life. It can also pollute water supplies. This section covers using both permanent and mobile dips.

204. Install dipping facilities as far away as practical from any watercourse, spring, well or borehole. The same rules apply to the position of mobile facilities while they are being used. If there is any doubt about whether a position is suitable ask the National Rivers Authority (NRA).

Designing facilities

205. Ready made dipping baths made from one piece of material are preferable. They should not have a drain hole.

206. You might need to repair or replace dip baths you already have. If the bath has a drain hole, you should seal it. If you are replacing the bath you should consider if there is a better place to put it on the farm (paragraph 204).

207. There should be "draining-off pens" for sheep to stand in after dipping. The floor of the pen should be impervious (for example concrete) and be on a slope of at least 1 in 60 so that surplus dip drains back to the dip bath.

Dipping

208. You should only use licensed dip concentrates. Only buy enough dip concentrate to meet your immediate needs. You should store dip concentrates so that if any is accidentally spilt it is safely contained.

You should follow the instructions on the label for using and disposing of the dip. You should neither overfill the dip bath nor let it overflow when you are dipping the sheep. Fit splash boards if they are needed.

209. You should keep sheep in draining-off pens for 5 to 10 minutes after dipping them. The drain-back system for dip must work properly. You should check regularly any traps the dip settles in and clear them if necessary. Never let freshly dipped sheep walk into a watercourse.

Disposing of used dip

210. Dispose of used dip wash as soon as possible after dipping. Never empty it into a watercourse.

Soakaways are not suitable in most places as they could pollute groundwater. Ask the NRA if there is any doubt about the risk of polluting groundwater by using an existing soakaway. Do not build new soakaways for sheep dip.

211. Spread used dip onto land at low application rates if you have a suitable area. You should cooperate with mobile dipping contractors to dispose of used dip safely. Do **not** spread dip on non-spreading areas (paragraphs 25–26), or on land in the "very high risk" category (paragraph 30). Ask the NRA if there is any doubt whether an area is suitable for dip to be spread on.

You should not apply more than 5.0m^3 of used dip on each hectare (450 gallons/acre). If you are using a vacuum tanker, you will have to dilute used dip before you can spread it. You might need to dilute one part dip to three parts or more of water, as most tankers cannot apply less than 20m^3/ha (1800 gallons/acre).

CAUTION

Some sheep dip chemicals are poisonous to birds including domestic geese and hens. You should not let birds and other livestock drink the dip. Do not let livestock graze on land for at least one month after used dip has been spread.

212. If you cannot find a suitable area of land on the farm, you should store used dip in a suitable holding tank till it is collected by an approved waste disposal contractor. You can get details of local contractors from the local Waste Disposal Authority.

Containers and unwanted concentrate

213. You should never re-use empty containers for any purpose. Containers should be cleaned when the dip is being prepared so that you use the rinsing liquid to dilute the dip. After cleaning, you should crush or put holes in the containers so they cannot be used again. Containers that are clean and have been crushed or had holes put in them will be accepted at licensed disposal sites where they will be regarded as non-hazardous industrial waste. Most local Waste Disposal Authorities will collect them if they are asked but there may be a charge. For details of other ways of disposing of containers see paragraphs 240–246.

214. Unwanted concentrate must be disposed of by a specialist waste disposal contractor. In some circumstances suppliers may be prepared to take back unopened containers.

11. Pesticides

Introduction

215. Water pollution incidents happen every year because farmers do not store, prepare, apply or dispose of pesticides properly. Many pesticides harm water life. There is also concern over levels of pesticide residues found in water sources.

216. The use of pesticides is controlled by Part III of the Food and Environment Protection Act (FEPA) 1985 and, in particular, the Control of Pesticides Regulations 1986 (COPR), and the Control of Substances Hazardous to Health Regulations (COSHH) 1988, made under the Health and Safety at Work etc., Act 1974 (HSW Act).

Everyone who uses pesticides should know the rules set out in these laws. Practical points are covered in the *MAFF/HSE Code of Practice for the Safe Use of Pesticides on Farms and Holdings* (1990), which you can get from HMSO bookshops price £5.00.

217. Under FEPA everyone who uses pesticides on a farm or holding must be trained to use them safely and efficiently. They should know what emergency action to take if there is a spillage. People who use pesticides for agriculture may need to have recognised certificates of competence.

Storing pesticides

218. Any new pesticides store that is built should meet the highest standards of design and construction. You might need to improve buildings that you use or want to use to store pesticides. You should not build pesticide stores where there is a risk of polluting watercourses or groundwater. Get advice from the National Rivers Authority (NRA), the local planning and fire authorities, the crime prevention officer, and the Health and Safety Executive before you build or substantially alter a pesticide store.

219. You can store small amounts of pesticide in a suitable chest, bin, vault or cabinet. This container should be impact and fire resistant, and have a built-in sump big enough to contain the amount of pesticide stored in case the packages leak.

220. A store should have enough storage space, be soundly built from fire resistant materials and be equipped and organised to store the intended contents.

221. The store should be able to contain the contents safely if they leak or are spilt. The floor should not let liquids pass through it, i.e. be impermeable and either be below ground level to form a sump, or there should be a door sill and walls that do not let liquid pass through and can contain spillage. This facility should be able to hold the store contents plus at least an extra 10%.

222. Liquids such as dilute sprayer-tank washings can be stored in a separate below ground tank or sump of adequate capacity outside the store. This can also double as an emergency store for contaminated water if there is a fire.

223. YOU CAN GET MORE DETAILS ON HOW TO STORE APPROVED PESTICIDES IN HSE GUIDANCE NOTE CS19, "*Storage of Approved Pesticides: Guidance for Farmers and other Professional Users*". British Standard BS 5502: Part 81: 1989—"*Code of Practice for Design and Construction of Chemical Stores*"—also applies.

Spillage

224. Avoid spilling pesticides while you are handling and storing them. If you do spill pesticide take quick action to limit the effects and to warn others, including the NRA, who may be affected.

Applying pesticides

225. Never apply pesticides where they could drift onto water unless they are specifically approved to be used in or near water. Ask the NRA if you want to use a pesticide in or near water, and get their agreement if you want to use a herbicide to control weeds in water.

226. To make the danger of pesticides drifting into water as low as possible use the right spraying techniques (for example to produce the correct droplet size, and to avoid unnecessary spraying of field margins and boundary areas close to watercourses). Also take into account the weather conditions, in particular wind speed and direction. These points are covered in the Pesticide Code (Paragraph 216).

Laws on disposal of waste pesticides

227. The FEPA and the HSW Act, the Control of Pollution Act 1974 (COPA), the Water Act 1989 and their regulations apply to the disposal of waste pesticides and containers (in the case of COPA, until Part II of the Environmental Protection Act 1990 comes into force). People who use pesticides should know about their legal responsibilities and duty to dispose of any waste they produce properly.

228. Under Part One of COPA, it is normally an offence to leave or dispose of waste which is poisonous, noxious or polluting, on any land where it is likely to damage the environment. Waste Disposal Authorities are responsible for giving disposal licences under the Act to dispose of waste on land in their area. They can give general advice on disposing of waste including, where appropriate, details of specialist disposal contractors working in the area.

229. Under the Water Act 1989, it is an offence to cause or knowingly permit a discharge of poisonous, noxious or polluting matter to enter any controlled waters without the proper authority (see paragraphs 5 and 6).

230. You need a Trade Effluent Consent from the local Water Service Company (WSC) before you can empty waste into a sewer. To empty wastes containing substances prescribed under the Water Act 1989 into a sewer you also need approval from the Secretary of State, advised by the Her Majesty's Inspectorate of Pollution (HMIP), before the WSC can give you a Consent.

231. If any poisonous, noxious or polluting material has gone or is likely to go into any controlled waters other than by an authorised discharge, the NRA may do work to prevent or put right the pollution. The person responsible for the pollution may have to pay the costs of doing this work, including the cost of restocking rivers.

NOTES:

Substances prescribed under the Water Act 1989

The substances currently prescribed are as follows:

Mercury and its compounds
Cadmium and its compounds
gamma hexachlorocyclohexane
DDT
Pentachlorophenol and its compounds
Hexachlorobenzene
Hexachlorobutadiene
Aldrin
Dieldrin
Endrin
Polychlorinated biphenyls

Dichlorvos
1,2-Dichloroethane
Trichlorobenzene
Atrazine
Simazine
Tributyltin compounds
Triphenyltin compounds
Trifluralin
Fenitrothion
Azinphos-methyl
Malathion
Endosulfan

More substances could be added to the list from time to time.

Waste pesticide

232. If you buy and use pesticides you will produce some waste. First of all, therefore, and to satisfy COSHH you need to consider whether you have to use a pesticide in the particular circumstances.

233. If you need to use a pesticide, estimate how much you need to buy. Think about how you will dispose of the waste, any problems the pesticide could cause, the shelf-life of the pesticide and how you can store it safely.

234. You should try to produce as little waste as possible. For example, you can cut down the amount of waste washings when you clean out equipment if you use an efficient flushing system, instead of filling the spray tank with water and pumping it through the equipment.

Disposal of waste concentrates

235. From time to time you will need to dispose of pesticides, for example because you have more than you need, they are out of date regarding shelf-life, they are not approved, have had approval withdrawn or if material has been spilt or the containers are damaged.

236. It is not economical to store pesticides you cannot use. It is illegal to store them if the approval has been taken away. In some cases, you might be able to send unwanted, unused containers back to the supplier. Otherwise, you will probably need to use a specialist waste disposal contractor. Never dilute and dispose of waste concentrates in the way described in paragraph 239.

Disposal of dilute wastes and washings

237. Fill and wash equipment in an area chosen and built for that purpose.

Spillages should not be able to escape from the area. All spraying will produce some liquid waste. You will need to dispose of pesticides in a way that is environmentally acceptable (see paragraph 239).

238. When you have finished spraying, you should clean, wash and rinse all the equipment you have used. The washing facilities should be designed so that back syphoning of pesticides into the water supply cannot occur. If suitable, the contaminated water can be used later to make a further batch of the dilute pesticide.

239. Otherwise, you will need to dispose of it. The preferred ways are as follows:

- applying the contaminated water to the treated crop if this is within the terms of the product approval, although this could reduce the efficiency of the last application of pesticide;
- applying to untreated crop areas if this is within the terms of the product approval and there are no watercourses nearby; or,
- storing the waste in a suitable container until a reputable specialist waste disposal contractor collects it.

Other ways, that need prior approval from the NRA or the local WSC, include the following:

- using equipment designed to treat liquid waste that contains pesticides, as long as you can store the treated waste and use it again or dispose of it in a way approved by the NRA or local WSC. In England and Wales, HMIP must agree before substances prescribed under the Water Act 1989 can be emptied into a public sewer;
- spraying it onto an area of uncropped land, (not stubble or fallow) of little wildlife value, that supports only poor vegetation and without hedges, trees, or bushes on it or nearby. The area of land must be able to absorb the liquid that will be applied to it without any run off, puddles or risk to wildlife, watercourses, groundwater, septic tanks, field drains or sewerage systems. It must be signposted and fenced off to keep people and livestock out;
- subject to a consent from the local WSC and HMIP for substances prescribed under the Water Act 1989, emptying the liquid into a public sewer;
- using a soakaway that is designed and built properly. Soakaways are not suitable in most places because of the risk of polluting groundwater. Ask the NRA if you are unsure about the risk of polluting groundwater by using an existing soakaway. You should not build new soakaways unless you have permission from the NRA.

Disposal of containers

240. Never use empty pesticide containers again except, if in good condition, to hold an identical pesticide from a container that is damaged or leaks. Containers, except those mentioned in paragraph 242 below, should be cleaned before you dispose of them. Clean them by the instructions on the label or, if there are no instructions, rinse them repeatedly. If possible, you should clean the containers when you are preparing a working strength spray dilution so you can use the rinsing liquid to dilute the spray.

241. You should crush or make holes in the cleaned containers so that they cannot be used again. Try not to damage their labels. The crushed and holed containers should be stored in a secure compound, preferably not a pesticide store, until you can dispose of them. If you are not preparing a spray dilution you should collect the rinsings in a suitable container, label and store it in a safe place until you can dispose of it elsewhere.

242. You should not rinse or clean containers that hydrogen cyanide gassing powders or aluminium, magnesium or zinc phosphides were supplied or kept in because they give off dangerous gases if they get damp. You should fill them with dry earth, sand or other inert material. Put holes in containers just before you dispose of them. Never put containers that are "empty" or have been filled with harmless material in a building. You can bury the treated containers as described in paragraph 244.

243. Clean containers that have been crushed or had holes put in them will generally be accepted at licensed disposal sites, depending on their conditions for accepting such waste (see paragraphs 227–231 of this Code).

244. You can bury containers you have cleaned or treated as described in paragraphs 240–242 on agricultural land that you own or occupy. Chose the burial site carefully so that there is no risk of polluting surface or groundwater. Bury the containers at least 0.8 metres below the surface and below the level of any land drains. Mark the area so that you can find it easily in the future. Keep a record of the type and amount of the materials buried there.

245. The disposal of certain containers and packaging is described in paragraphs 243–244. In some cases, you can burn lightly contaminated containers to dispose of them. Such burning is subject to national clean air laws. It could cause a statutory nuisance and the local authority could take action under Part III of the Environmental Protection Act 1990. Before you burn such material, ask the pesticide supplier about any dangers and seek advice from the Environmental Health Department of the local authority. Fumes and smoke could cause a serious health risk.

246. When you are burning waste packaging you should make sure that:

- it is done in an open space at least 15 metres from a public highway and where smoke is not likely to drift over people or livestock or move towards any public highway, housing or business property;
- the containers are open and you put them on the fire a few at a time;
- you watch the fire;
- you put the fire out before you leave it.

Bury any residues from the fire as in paragraph 244. Do not burn products classed "Highly flammable"; pyrotechnic devices, such as smokes; and atomisable fluids, such as aerosols.

Disposal of other contaminated materials

247. You will also need to dispose of packaging and other wastes, including protective clothing that you have used to deal with spillages. Disposal of such wastes on the property is unlikely to be acceptable. If you have this kind of waste get advice on a suitable authorised way to dispose of it (see paragraph 228 of this Code).

248. Dispose of used rodenticide or other pesticide baits and carcases in the way the instructions on the product label tell you. If you are allowed to bury them and the label does not give any special instructions you should dispose of them in the way set out in paragraph 244.

249. You should hire a specialist disposal contractor to dispose of containers which cannot be cleaned thoroughly, solid waste from the clean-up of spillages, loose pesticides, heavily contaminated equipment and protective clothing, materials used to soak up liquid spillages and the like (see paragraph 228 of this Code).

12. Disposing of Animal Carcases

Introduction

250. There are a number of ways to dispose of animals that die on the farm. The best way is to send them to a licensed knackerman, licensed landfill site or licensed incinerator. Disposal methods on the farm such as burial, incineration or burning in the open air could cause water or air pollution. The Code of Good Agricultural Practice for the Protection of Air (which is being prepared) covers air pollution.

251. Under The Control of Pollution Act 1974 Part I (shortly to be superseded by the provisions of Part II of the Environmental Protection Act 1990) it is normally an offence to apply any waste onto land that is likely to damage the environment. It is an offence under the Dogs Act 1906 to leave carcases unburied where dogs can gain access.

252. Never dispose of carcases in or near watercourses, boreholes or springs. Apart from being prosecuted for causing water pollution, you could also spread disease to animals on neighbouring farms.

Notifiable diseases

253. If you think that a notifiable disease has caused ill health or death you must report it to the Divisional Veterinary Officer at the local Animal Health Office of the Ministry of Agriculture, Fisheries and Food or Welsh Office Agriculture Department. Carcases should be available to be examined by post mortem in these cases. Always consider the possibility of anthrax if death is sudden and unexplained.

Burying carcases on the farm

254. If you do not suspect a notifiable disease or it has been ruled out as a possible cause, and other ways of disposing of the carcase are not practical, you can bury the carcase on the farm as long as the following rules are. The site must:

- be at least 250 metres away from any well, borehole or spring that supplies water for human consumption or to be used in farm dairies;
- be at least 30 metres from any other spring or watercourse, and at least 10 metres from any field drain;
- have at least one metre of subsoil below the bottom of the burial pit, allowing a hole deep enough for at least one metre of soil to cover the carcase;
- When first dug, the bottom of the hole must be free of standing water.

Ask the National Rivers Authority (NRA) if you do not know whether a burial site is suitable. If you have a lot of carcases to dispose of on a regular basis, talk to the NRA first.

255. Do not let dogs and foxes get to the carcase. Cover the carcase with topsoil straightaway. Do not bury carcases in a manure store.

256. Small carcases and waste from a birth may be put in a lined pit without a base covered with a substantial top that has a manhole cover. Rules for the position of this type of pit and depth of soil are in Paragraph 254.

257. Keep records and a field plan of the burial site and dates of burial.

NOTES:

Lined Disposal Pit

Pits are usually built out of precast concrete rings and are typically 1.2 m diameter × 2.7 m deep. The top can also be made from precast concrete with a metal manhole cover that is locked when it is not being used.

These pits work best if you start filling them in spring or summer and use a bacterial starter such as sewage sludge. It will help if you slit the dead animals stomach so the contents of the intestines come out. Add a few gallons of water each week to keep the contents moist.

LIME MUST NOT BE ADDED BECAUSE IT SLOWS DOWN DECOMPOSITION.

13. Nitrate

Introduction

258. This section of the Code covers the nitrogen lost as nitrate from farmland and the way you can cut down this loss at little or no extra cost. In some cases, better farming methods will reduce both the cost and the amount of nitrate lost by leaching (that is the nitrate washed away by water draining from the soil).

259. Nitrate leaching causes nitrogen to be lost from soils. Nitrate is lost to surface waters by run-off or through land drains and to groundwater. The amount of nitrogen lost depends on weather, soil and farming system.

260. There is concern over the increasing amount of nitrate in many of our drinking water sources, particularly groundwaters. There is also concern over the amount of nitrogen reaching our rivers, estuaries and seas. The Pilot Nitrate Scheme was set up during 1989/90 to look at ways of cutting down the amount of nitrate lost from a range of mainly agricultural water catchments.

261. In some catchments, action beyond the Good Agricultural Practice described in this Code will be needed to keep water below 50 mg/l nitrate which is the most nitrate allowed in drinking water.

Section 112 and Schedule 11 of the Water Act 1989 cover the designation of Nitrate Sensitive Areas where the Government considers it appropriate to control the amount of nitrate going into water from agricultural land. The National Rivers Authority (NRA) are responsible for suggesting areas for designation by the Government.

NOTES:

Nitrate

Nitrate, NO^-_3, is the main nitrogen containing anion occurring in soil. It is very soluble and moves freely in water through the soil profile.

Ploughing up grass

262. A lot of nitrate is released if permanent grassland is ploughed up and changed to arable. Nitrate will be lost by leaching for several years. This practice should be avoided if possible.

If permanent grassland needs reseeding do it with as little cultivation as possible and make sure that grass covers the field by early October.

263. If grass leys are grown in rotation with arable crops, sow the first crop as soon as possible after the grass has been ploughed up. Following winter cereal crops should be drilled early.

When you are reseeding leys, do it with as little cultivation as possible and try to get the crop to cover the land by early October.

Organic manures

264. Animal manure and other organic wastes such as sewage sludge contain different amounts and forms of nitrogen. When you apply them to the soil, the soluble nitrogen is turned into nitrate in a few weeks. The rest of the nitrogen takes longer to break down and be converted to nitrate.

265. Because of the different forms of nitrogen and the different rates at which they can be used by the crop, the risk of losing nitrate by leaching is higher than from inorganic fertilisers. To avoid losing too much from leaching do not apply more than 250 kg/ha of total nitrogen in organic manure in any 12 months. You should not apply more available nitrogen than the crop needs. (For the definition of total and available. Nitrogen see paragraph 28).

266. Apply organic manures which have a lot of available nitrogen when they can be used by the crop. This type of manure includes cow slurry, pig slurry, poultry manures and liquid sewage sludges. To cut down the risk of nitrate leaching, application to arable land in the autumn or early winter should be avoided whenever practicable.

267. You can apply organic manures that do not contain much nitrogen that can easily be converted to nitrate, at any time. These included farmyard manure and sewage sludge cake.

Inorganic nitrogen fertiliser

268. To keep the amount of nitrate lost from the soil as low as possible, carefully work out the amount of inorganic nitrogen fertiliser you need. Do not use more than the economic optimum in each field. Work out how much nitrogen is in the soil and how much the crop needs. Take into account the type of soil, previous cropping and the use of animal manure and other organic wastes when you are working out how much nitrogen a crop can get from the soil itself.

Do not apply extra fertiliser to be on the safe side. Applying above the economic optimum will increase the amount of nitrate lost by leaching. Recommendations are given in MAFF Reference Book 209 *"Fertiliser Recommendations for Agricultural and Horticultural Crops"*.

269. The time you apply the fertiliser is just as important. Apply the fertiliser when the crop can make best use of the nitrogen. Do not apply fertiliser to crops in the autumn unless there is good evidence that the crop can use it. Do not apply to cereals that are sown in the autumn. Cut down the amount of fertiliser you apply to grass from mid-season onwards. Cut down the amount of nitrogen you apply to grass if the growth will not be used fully or if the growth is limited by drought. Do not apply more fertiliser to the seedbed of crops that are sown in the spring than the amount that will be used by the crop at that time.

270. Records of the amounts and dates of applications of fertilisers, livestock wastes and other organic wastes will help you to work out how much nitrogen fertiliser is needed.

271. Spread nitrogen fertiliser accurately, at the right rate, and without overlapping or applying it to uncropped areas, hedges and watercourses. Adjust all fertiliser spreaders carefully to apply the amount you want. Get the spread pattern tested regularly.

Crop cover

272. If the soil is bare and at field capacity, there is a big risk of losing nitrate. If you grow a crop in the autumn and early winter it will reduce the amount of nitrate in the soil, and so the amount that could be lost by leaching.

273. Sowing crops in the autumn so they are growing by early September will reduce the amount of nitrate lost by leaching. Sow crops as early as possible. Sowing crops after mid October will have little effect in reducing the amount of nitrate lost through leaching in the winter.

When the decision on which crop to grow is evenly balanced, crops sown in early autumn should be grown rather than those which are sown in the late autumn or spring.

If possible cover or catch crops should be sown in fields that would otherwise be bare over the autumn and winter.

NOTES:

Field capacity

Field capacity is when the soil is fully wetted and more rain would cause water loss by drainage.

Crop residues

274. Crop residues that do not contain much nitrogen such as cereal straw will help reduce the amount of nitrate leached if you mix them into the soil in autumn, especially if you also sow a crop.

Crop residues that contain a lot of nitrogen such as those from most non-cereal and vegetable crops can release nitrogen quickly. You should not mix these into the soil until just before you sow the next crop.

Autumn cultivations

275. To delay the build up of nitrate in the soil in the autumn, put off cultivating the land for as long as possible without delaying when the next crop is sown.

Cultivation after the early harvest of a crop, such as vining peas or oilseed rape, which leave a residue that contains a lot of nitrogen can often be put off without affecting when the following winter cereal is sown.

You can often leave residues of crops that are grown on sandy soil and harvested late such as maize and sugar beet undisturbed until just before you sow the following spring's crop.

Managing grassland

276. The risk of losing nitrate from grassland that is intensively grazed is high, especially if grazed with cattle throughout the autumn. If the intensity of grazing is reduced, particularly in the autumn, the amount of nitrate lost will be cut down.

Irrigation

277. Good irrigation will generally reduce the amount of nitrate lost by leaching by making sure that the crop makes good use of the fertiliser you apply. If you apply too much water, or you apply it unevenly, the amount of nitrate lost could he high. Use a reliable scheduling system to help avoid this. The system should not need the soil to be returned to field capacity during the growing season.

. . .

Appendix III

LAND AREA NEEDED FOR SPREADING WASTES FROM DIFFERENT LIVESTOCK

1 Dairy cow (6 month housed)	0.16 ha
1 Beef bullock (6 month housed)	0.10 ha
1 Pig place (20–90 kg)	0.04 ha
1 Sow and litters (to 4 weeks)	0.07 ha
1000 laying hen places	2.3 ha
1000 broiler places	1.4 ha

Typical figures to meet the recommended maximum loading of 250 kg/ha/yr of total nitrogen in applied organic manures (Paragraph 27).

Appendix IV

AMOUNT OF EXCRETA PRODUCED BY LIVESTOCK

Type of livestock	Body weight (kg)	Moisture content %	Typical volume (litres/day)
1 dairy cow	450–650	90	57.0
1 beef bullock	200–450	90	27.0
1 dry sow	90–120	90	4.0
1 lactating sow + litter	90–120	90	12.0
1 pig, dry meal feed	45–75	90	4.0
1 pig, liquid fed (water: meal ratio 2.5:1)	45–75	90	4.0
1 pig, liquid fed (water: meal ratio 4:1)	45–75	94	7.0
1 pig, whey fed	45–75	97	14.0
1 fattening lamb	45	89	2.2
1 mature sheep	60–80	89	4.0
1000 laying hens	2000	70	115.0
1000 laying hens (air dried)	2000	30	49.0
1000 broilers + litter	1000	30	36.0
1000 turkeys + litter	5000	30	124.0

Appendix V

TYPICAL AMOUNTS OF BEDDING MATERIAL USED BY EACH ANIMAL IN LIVESTOCK HOUSING SYSTEMS

Livestock	Housing system	Litter used	Typical amount used in 180 days (kg)
Dairy cows	Cubicles	Chopped straw	120
		Sawdust, wood wastes	150
Dairy cows	Loose housing	Straw	530

Livestock	Housing system	Litter used	Typical amount used per year (kg)
Pigs	Pens	Straw	102
Poultry	Deep litter	Wood shavings Straw chopped 38–50 mm	1.0
Broilers	Deep litter	Wood shavings Chopped straw Chopped paper	0.5 (per bird per crop)

Appendix VI

AMOUNT OF CLEANING WATER USED

Livestock Type	Cleaning system	Amounts in litres Range	Typical
Dairy cows	Cleaning milking parlour equipment, washing udders, etc., without a power hose	per animal/day 14–22	18
	With a power hose	27–45	35
Pigs	Cleaning out pens after each batch (10 pigs per pen)	per batch 16–24	18

. . . . .

Appendix 2

Code of Good Agricultural Practice for the Protection of Air

Ministry of Agriculture, Fisheries and Food

Welsh Office Agriculture Department

1992

Contents

PART A GENERAL INFORMATION

1. Introduction

About this Code

1. This Code of Good Agricultural Practice for the Protection of Air is a practical guide to help farmers and growers avoid causing air pollution from odours, ammonia and smoke, or from greenhouse gases which cause global warming. It will help you dispose of your wastes in ways which reduce the risk of causing nuisance or annoyance from air pollution.

It is not a statutory code. Following this Code will not provide a defence such as "best practicable means" (paragraph 10) if you cause air pollution. Nor will it protect you from legal action although it should lessen the chance that this will happen. If you are in any doubt about what the law requires contact the local authority Environmental Health Department.

2. The Code describes the main causes of air pollution from different agricultural activities. In each Section, good agricultural practice is set down in a way which takes account of the need to avoid causing pollution or nuisance while allowing economic farming to continue. The Code was written using the latest information available. Any new practices not covered should follow the general principles laid down in the Code.

3. This Code does not give advice on noise, spray drift from pesticides or air pollution caused by dust. You should read the Code of Good Agricultural Practice for the Protection of Water if there is also a risk of causing water pollution from any particular agricultural activity.

Air pollution problems

4. Agricultural activities which involve housed livestock, storing wastes or spreading livestock wastes are those most likely to cause odour problems. Advice on minimising odour nuisance is given in Sections 2 to 8 of this Code.

5. Dark smoke or smoke nuisance from agriculture and horticulture can be caused by the burning of crop residues, packaging, plastics, tyres, waste oil or animal carcases in the open or in unsuitable equipment. Advice on how to minimise the need to burn these materials and on how to avoid producing dark smoke or causing smoke nuisance when burning is given in Sections 9 to 17 of this Code.

6. Agricultural activities can give off various gases which help to cause atmospheric problems. Advice on how to minimise the amount of gases given off is given in this Code. Ammonia, which contributes to making soils acid is covered in Sections 2 to 8, along with odours. Section 18 covers greenhouse gases which contribute to global warming—carbon dioxide, methane, nitrous oxide and chlorofluorocarbons (CFCs).

Laws controlling air pollution—general

7. The local authority Environmental Health Department is responsible for enforcing legislation on odour nuisance and smoke. Under Part III, Section 79, of the Environmental Protection Act 1990, local authorities have a duty to inspect their areas to detect any statutory nuisances and to take reasonably practicable steps to investigate complaints of statutory nuisance which are made to them.

8. Section 79 of the Act defines statutory nuisances as including:

- Any premises in such a state as to be prejudicial to health or a nuisance.
- Smoke emitted from premises so as to be prejudicial to health or a nuisance.
- Any dust, steam, smell or other effluvia arising on industrial, trade or business premises and being prejudicial to health or a nuisance.
- Any animal kept in such a place or manner as to be prejudicial to health or a nuisance.
- Any other matter declared by any enactment to be a statutory nuisance.

9. Where a local authority Environmental Health Department is satisfied that a statutory nuisance exists, or is likely to occur or recur, it has a duty to serve an abatement notice under Part III, Section 80 of the Act requiring:

- The abatement of the nuisance or prohibiting or restricting its occurrence or recurrence.
- The execution of such works and the taking of such other steps as may be necessary for any of those purposes.

A person served with an abatement notice may appeal to a Magistrates' Court within 21 days of being served with the notice.

Apart from action taken by a local authority, any person aggrieved by a statutory nuisance can take proceedings in a Magistrates' Court.

10. It is an offence to contravene or fail to comply with an abatement notice without reasonable excuse. You could be fined up to £20,000 in a Magistrates' Court if you commit an offence under this part of the Act. It is usually a defence to show that you have used the "best practicable means" (which is defined to have regard amongst other things to local conditions and circumstances, to the current state of technical knowledge and to the financial implications) to prevent or counteract the nuisance. Since the law relating to statutory nuisances is not straightforward, you would be well advised to consult a suitably experienced lawyer if difficulties arise, and should certainly do so if you are served with an abatement notice.

Laws controlling planning consents

11. Legislation governing planning consent for developments also includes provisions which relate to the avoidance of nuisances.

The Town and Country Planning General Development Order 1988 (the GDO) sets out certain types of development which may be carried out on agricultural land without planning permission. However, you will need planning permission for certain new facilities (such as livestock buildings, slurry storage and sewage sludge facilities), and for extensions or alterations to similar structures, where these will be within a distance of 400 metres from the boundary of any protected buildings (such as houses or schools). This rule has been introduced to reduce the number of potential odour problems coming from new livestock buildings or waste storage facilities being built close to housing developments.

12. For livestock buildings, slurry stores and sewage sludge facilities which do not require planning permission under the GDO, a prior notification system is now in force. You must notify the local planning authority of such developments. The local planning authority must then decide within 28 days whether it wishes to approve details of the siting, design and external appearance of the proposed development. Where prior approval is required the development must not begin until such approval has been obtained.

13. The Town and Country Planning (Assessment of Environmental Effects) Regulations 1988 require an environmental assessment to be carried out for certain types of major project which are likely to have significant effects on the environment.

In the case of agriculture, environmental assessments are likely to be required for new pig units (more than 400 sows or 5000 fattening pigs) and new poultry units (more than 100,000 broilers or 50,000 layers or other poultry including turkeys). Under current planning regulations, new units of this size will almost certainly need planning permission. You should talk to the local planning authority about the need for an environmental assessment before you send in a planning application. This may involve preparing an environmental statement covering the possible environmental effects of a project eg, emissions of offensive odours, and the measures to be taken to reduce these effects.

Laws controlling dark smoke

14. The Clean Air Acts 1956 and 1968 prohibit the emission of dark smoke from chimneys of buildings or from trade premises. Land on which an agricultural or a horticultural business is carried on is considered to be a trade premise.

15. The Clean Air (Emission of Dark Smoke) (Exemption) Regulations 1969, provide for the exemption of the burning of certain matter from Section 1 of the Clean Air Act 1968, which applies to trade premises. In certain circumstances the regulations allow the burning of carcases of animals or poultry and containers contaminated by any pesticide, provided, amongst other things, there is no other reasonably safe and practicable method of disposing of the matter other than burning (paragraphs 155, 169 and 192).

16. Under the Clean Air Act 1968 (subject to the exemptions given in paragraph 15) the occupier of the premises and any person who causes or permits the emission of dark smoke is guilty of an offence. Everyone who is involved in agriculture and horticulture should take all practicable steps to prevent the emission of dark smoke.

Laws: smoke control areas

17. In some cases a farm may fall within a "smoke control area" as declared by local authorities under the Clean Air Act 1956. It is an offence to emit smoke from the chimney of any building caused by the burning of an unauthorised fuel in these areas. You should ask your local authority about any local smoke control areas.

Laws: prescribed processes

18. Part I of the Environmental Protection Act 1990 establishes a new pollution control system for certain "prescribed processes". The Environmental Protection (Prescribed Processes and Substances) Regulations 1991 set out the processes which pose a particular risk of air pollution and are subject to special controls. Those prescribed processes of particular interest to farmers are given in the list (see box overleaf). Under the Act, Her Majesty's Inspectorate of Pollution (HMIP) and local authorities have powers to control pollution over a range of processes. Those activities which are affected need an authorisation. This would normally be from the local authority for farm scale processes.

The requirements for the local authority air pollution control system mean that:

- You must not operate a prescribed process designated for local authority control without their authorisation. The process must be operated using BATNEEC (Best Available Techniques (including technology) No Entailing Excessive Cost).

The Secretary of State for the Environment's Process Guidance Notes (available from HMSO) for all the main processes include detailed descriptions of the techniques to be applied in order to meet the BATNEEC objective.

- If you operate a prescribed process you must submit a detailed application to the local authority, for authorisation. You have to pay a fee with the application for authorisation as well as an annual charge for the authorisation to continue in effect.

If you carry out a prescribed process which is exempted from local authority control because of size or volume, you should aim wherever practicable to meet the standards set out in the appropriate Process Guidance Note, to reduce the possibility of nuisance.

NOTES:

Prescribed Processes

Prescribed processes include many of interest to farmers such as:

- general waste incineration processes under 1 tonne an hour;
- waste oil burners;
- straw combustion processes between 0.4 and 3 MW net rated thermal input;
- wood combustion processes between 0.4 and 3 MW net rated thermal input;
- poultry litter combustion processes between 0.4 and 3 MW net rated thermal input;
- animal carcase incineration under 1 tonne an hour;
- treatment and processing of animal or vegetable matter including:
  - fur breeding;
  - animal feed compounding;
  - production of compost for mushrooms.

Some processes covered in the Process Guidance Notes, for example, any process under the heading of "treatment and processing of animal or vegetable matter", are exempt from controls when carried out on a farm and when they do not involve manufacture of goods for sale. Others may be exempt below a certain size of operation, for example animal carcase incineration below 50 kg/hr.

Advice

19. Farmers can get free general advice on preventing pollution from the Agricultural Development and Advisory Service (ADAS). You can also get information from local authority Environmental Health Departments and Waste Disposal Authorities. Detailed design and planning services are available from ADAS, other independent consultants and equipment suppliers.

PART B ODOURS AND AMMONIA

2. General Principles

Introduction

20. This Section describes the main causes of complaints about odours, outlines the sources of odours and how they can be measured. It also defines good agricultural practice to minimise odour problems. Ammonia is included in this Section because methods of controlling odour generally reduce the release of ammonia.

Causes of odour problems

21. Complaints from the public about odours caused by agriculture and industry are recorded and reported every year by the Institution of Environmental Health Officers. Numbers of agricultural odour complaints can be looked at in two ways: by animal type or by source point.

22. The number of complaints varies considerably with the type of animal. In the years 1987/88 to 1989/90 pigs were on average the cause of 650 justifiable complaints annually (47%), poultry 339 (25%), cattle 298 (22%) and horses kept for riding 95 (7%).

23. In the same years the spreading of slurry or manure was on average the major source of justifiable complaints about odours from agriculture at 613 annually (44%), followed by farm buildings 350 (25%), slurry or manure stores 289 (21%), animal feed products (swill boiling) 74 (5%) and silage clamps 56 (4%).

24. Most farm odours come from several sources. For example, odours from buildings are mainly caused by the breakdown of faeces and urine. Other sources of odour are from waste food spilt onto floors, the scent glands of animals, and the animals' feed.

25. When slurries, silage effluent and solid manures are spread on land, they may also be a source of odour, either during or after the spreading takes place.

Ammonia

26. Livestock production is the major source of ammonia in the atmosphere, mainly arising from livestock buildings, waste stores and spreading wastes on land. Loss of nitrogen as ammonia reduces the potential value of the waste as a fertiliser. Following deposition to land as a gas or as ammonium salts in rainfall, ammonia can have effects on natural vegetation. These include direct damage to plants and changes in the sort of plants present in heathland due to the enrichment of the soil with nitrogen and acidification of soils. Acidification may cause long term damage to trees.

Minimising odours by good agricultural practice

27. It is not possible to avoid all odours from agriculture, because often the right techniques do not exist. Even where there is a solution, the cost may sometimes be too high. This is recognised by the legislation which refers to "best practicable means", which takes financial implications into account.

However, by using good agricultural practice and appropriate control systems, you can minimise odour problems from both new and existing installations. The aim is to minimise the escape of odours beyond the farm boundary, and where practical, stop it entirely. This is done by firstly reducing the amount of odour coming from the source and then allowing air movement and distance to reduce any problem, by diluting the odour.

28. You should carry out good agricultural practice as described in the following Sections of this Code:

- Section 3 describes good agricultural practice to minimise odour nuisance from housed cattle, pigs and poultry.
- Section 4 describes good agricultural practice to minimise odour nuisance during the storing and handling of slurry or manure.

- Section 6 describes good agricultural practice to minimise odour nuisance from the spreading of livestock wastes on agricultural land.

In situations that could be particularly sensitive, you may need to go beyond good agricultural practice and use more rigorous treatment and control measures. Section 7 describes methods of treating livestock wastes to give further odour reductions during storage and spreading. Before investing in any of these you may need to get the advice of an independent consultant.

29. If an odour complaint has been made to the local authority Environmental Health Department and they decide the complaint is justifiable, then you should take the following steps:

Firstly, discuss the matter with the Environmental Health Department and find out the cause and source of the odour causing the complaint.

Secondly, compare the management practices and systems which you use for housing livestock, handling and storing manure or slurry, and spreading livestock wastes, with those set out in Sections 3, 4 and 6 of this Code. Make any changes that are needed.

Thirdly, evaluate the improvements. At this stage, the amount of odour given off may have reduced enough to solve the problem.

If the improvement has not been enough, get advice on the techniques you need to use to reduce odour still further. Keep the local authority Environmental Health Department informed of proposals at all stages of the process.

NOTES:

Odour Measurements

Agricultural odours are caused by a large number of chemical compounds. No single compound has been identified which can be measured and used to assess odour.

"Olfactometry" is the method used to measure smells. It normally relies on using the human nose as a detector. It is based on the assessments of a group of people, called a "panel", under controlled laboratory conditions. Samples of odorous air are collected on site and transported to the laboratory.

Odour threshold value is most commonly used to measure an odour. It is the number of volumes of odour free air needed to dilute an odour until it is smelt by 50% of the panel members. The odour threshold value is commonly expressed as an odour concentration (odour units per cubic metre (m^3)).

Background odour concentrations measured in rural areas are typically 30 odour units per m^3. There are few if any situations where farm odour concentrations at source; are more than 5,000 odour units per m^3 air, whereas industrial odours may have to be diluted over a million times to reach the odour threshold value.

3. Housed Livestock Systems

Introduction

30. This Section describes good agricultural practice to avoid odour nuisance from housed cattle, pigs and poultry. It also covers silage making.

31. It is essential to maintain a high standard of hygiene and cleanliness. If you don't, all other measures to control odours are likely to fail.

General points of good practice

32. There are a number of general points of good practice which should be followed:

- Whenever possible, collect and transfer slurry every day to a suitable store. Dung from non-bedded, concreted areas, should also be dealt with in this way.
- Keep concrete areas around buildings clean and free from any build-up of slurry or manure.
- Remove and dispose of all dead animals, birds and foetal remains as soon as possible. (For safe methods of disposal see Section 14 of this Code, and Section 12 of the Code of Good Agricultural Practice for the Protection of Water).
- Maintain drains and repair broken or badly laid concrete to prevent effluents from ponding.
- Where bedding is used, use enough to keep animals clean. Stock covered in manure can add to the amount of odours produced. Store bedding materials in a dry condition to avoid moulds and dust forming and the loss of capacity to absorb liquids.
- Manage drinking systems to avoid overflow and spillage.

Cleaning buildings

33. Livestock buildings need to be cleaned regularly.

If livestock are produced in batches, thoroughly clean and disinfect buildings after each batch of stock is removed. Remove thick deposits of dust from the surfaces inside the building and in particular from all ledges, ventilation shafts and cowls.

If livestock are not produced in batches, thoroughly clean and disinfect individual pens as they become empty.

Clean out grit and sediment from slurry channels, collection systems and stores. Thick sediments encourage micro-organisms to grow. This produces odours.

Open concrete areas

34. Keep areas of concrete which livestock use to the minimum necessary as these areas will be fouled by manure. Pipe or channel waste water rather than letting it flow across open concrete. Information on the disposal of dirty water from buildings and yards is given in Section 4 of the Code of Good Agricultural Practice for the Protection of Water.

Cattle

35. The space allowances and amount of bedding for cattle should meet the MAFF Code of Recommendations for the Welfare of Cattle. For dairy cows loose housed in yards, good management is essential to maintain a balance between stocking density and the amount of litter you use.

36. Providing cubicles of suitable dimensions for the size of the cows is crucial for maintaining the cleanliness of the animals. Keep cubicles well maintained. Unless you use mats, you should keep bedding clean and topped up daily.

Scrape cubicle passages and other heavily soiled areas regularly, typically twice daily.

37. Dairy and parlour buildings need to be washed and cleaned frequently. Where disinfectants are used make sure you have the correct type and quantity of disinfectant and the right volume of wash water. If you use high pressure hoses take care to avoid splashing manure onto walls, ceilings and milking equipment.

NOTE: COLLECT CONTAMINATED WASH WATER AND DISPOSE OF IT IN A WAY THAT WILL NOT CAUSE WATER POLLUTION.

Pigs—general

38. The space allowances for lying areas should meet the recommendations set out in the MAFF Code of Recommendations for the Welfare of Pigs. Suitable extra space should be given for exercise and dunging.

39. Odour problems are minimised if pens are kept clean. Dirty pens can be caused by a number of factors including poor management and building design. Overstocking or understocking, poor ventilation design, wrong pen shape, poor floor surfaces, incorrect construction of pen divisions as well as badly sited feeding and watering facilities, can all contribute to dirty pens.

Pigs—solid manure systems

40. Bedded systems often don't absorb all the effluent produced. Appropriately placed drainage and suitably sized and constructed collection tanks should be part of such systems. Effluent should not be allowed to flow across open concrete.

41. Wherever possible you should clean non-bedded, concreted dunging areas every day.

Pigs—slurry systems

42. Less odour comes from fresh slurry and therefore you should remove slurry from buildings while it is fresh if this is practicable.

43. Clean slats give off less odour. Well designed and installed slats should be self-cleaning and minimise the risk of injury to the pig.

Poultry—general

44. Increasing stocking density increases odour production. Follow the recommended space allowance in the MAFF Code of Recommendations for the Welfare of Domestic Fowls. The type of feed, the humidity in the building and the amount of litter, if used, all contribute to the amount of odour produced. To reduce odour maintain any manure stored within the house in a dry condition.

Poultry—caged laying birds

45. Frequently removing the manure which is collected on belts beneath cages to a store or spreader outside the building helps to reduce odour. How often you need to remove the manure will vary from daily to twice weekly depending on the system design. Do not add water to poultry manure as this can result in strong, unpleasant odours.

Prevent leaking drinkers spilling water onto manure belts or into manure stores.

46. If the manure is stored beneath the caged area, air drying the manure will reduce odour formation. One way of achieving this is to separate the manure store from the birds with a slotted floor. The manure is scraped each day to fall through the slots into a storage area beneath the floor. If the ventilation air leaves the building by going through the slotted floor this increases air drying of the stored manure.

Poultry—deep litter systems

47. The drier the litter is in poultry houses for broilers, growers, breeders or layers, the lower the risk of odour from the buildings. In many cases keeping the litter dry will be enough to avoid problems. The following points will help to achieve this:

- Buildings should be adequately insulated with suitable materials which have a vapour barrier to prevent deterioration of the insulation.
- A well designed ventilation system should be provided.
- Direct fired gas or oil heaters put extra moisture into the house. Indirect heating systems avoid this problem.
- Drinkers should be designed to minimise spillage. If suitable for the type of stock, nipple and drip cups (or similar system) are preferable to hanging bowl drinkers, as they minimise water spillage. The drinking system must be maintained at the correct height by frequently adjusting them to bird eye level to avoid spillage and wet litter.
- The number of birds in the space available should be in line with the MAFF Code of the Recommendations for the Welfare of Domestic Fowls. This will prevent over-loading the litter. Litter should be 10-15cm deep which should be enough to absorb the manure load.
- Feeds which contain certain oils and animal fats which are poorly absorbed by the birds can result in the manure being greasy, causing capping of the litter and odour production. Rations should be adjusted to minimise this problem if it occurs.

Ventilation of livestock buildings

48. Ventilation systems in livestock buildings have two functions: firstly to control temperature and humidity and limit the concentration of poisonous gases, and secondly to make sure that clean air is evenly distributed under a wide range of weather conditions.

Poor ventilation can result in humid conditions which give rise to the production of unpleasant odours, high levels of ammonia and poor animal health. Maitain ventilation fans and check that they are running at the correct airflow for the numbers and weight of animals present.

49. The position and design of ventilation outlets will affect the dilution of odours from buildings. For new buildings you should get advice on the most favourable ventilator outlet position for your site conditions. The higher the outler is, the more the odour will be diluted by air movement. Ventilation outlets positioned along the sides of buildings below a slatted floor and immediately over a slurry collection channel can produce very strong odours.

Biological treatment of odorous air

50. Odorous air can be treated by passing it through an air cleaning device such as a film or mist of water in an air scrubber. Many systems use a material with a large surface area, which micro-organisms can become attached to. Many odorous compounds are nutrients for the micro-organisms which clean the liquid, so it can be recycled. An alternative biofilter system uses a moist mixture of peat and heather or lightly packed soil.

At the moment, costs of buying and running these air cleaning devices are likely to be too high to be considered as a practical method of controlling odour from most livestock buildings.

Feeding and food stores

51. Odours can be absorbed by dust particles and then carried in the air. Finely ground feeds and long feed drops (into bins or onto floors) increase amounts of dust. Using liquid-feeding systems or pelleted feed can reduce dust and may help to reduce odours.

52. Keep foods such as milk by-products (whey, skimmed milk), yeasts and molasses which can produce strong odours in properly constructed covered tanks or silos. The delivery area should be concreted and all spillage and wash water should be piped into the foul-drainage system.

SAFETY NOTE: DO NOT ALLOW EFFLUENT FROM SWILL OR WHEY TANKS AND FROM ENSILED PRODUCTS TO ENTER SLURRY CHANNELS AS THIS MAY CAUSE LETHAL GASES AND ODOURS TO BE RELEASED.

53. The collection and treatment of swill by cooking is controlled by the Diseases of Animals (Waste Food) Order 1973. Premises have to be approved and licensed by MAFF. Processing of swill often causes odour complaints.

Using automatically controlled systems which avoid excess steam injection can reduce odours and save fuel. Enclosed treatment systems stop nearly all escaping steam and greatly reduce odours from cooking. Odours can also be reduced by maintaining the treatment equipment properly and by avoiding spilling the feed. Letting swill cool before feeding it to the pigs may help to reduce odours.

Silage

54. Controlling odours from silage clamps, once these have been opened for daily use, can be difficult because of the large surface area exposed. Well-made silage smells a lot less than silage which is badly made.

55. You should take the following precautions to control odours from silos and during the handling and disposal of silage effluent:

- Do not let silage effluent flow across open concrete; it should be collected in a channel and taken to a suitable storage tank.
- Apply silage effluent with a slurry spreader suitable for the area which effluent will be spread on (see Section 6). Do not spread silage effluent on fields where it is likely to cause odour problems. Do not apply silage effluent to land where it could cause water pollution (see Section 7 of the Code of Good Agricultural Practice for the Protection of Water).
- Do not add silage effluent to slurry stores if the store or the land the slurry will be spread on could cause odour problems.

SAFETY NOTE: ADDING SILAGE EFFLUENT TO SLURRY PRODUCES LETHAL GASES AND STRONG ODOURS VERY QUICKLY. NEVER ADD SILAGE EFFLUENT TO SLURRY IN CONFINED SPACES OR IN BUILDINGS.

56. The design and construction of new, substantially enlarged or substantially reconstructed silos and effluent tanks must comply with the Control of Pollution (Silage, Slurry and Agricultural Fuel Oil) Regulations 1991.

57. Consider making baled and wrapped or bagged silage where silos could cause an odour nuisance. Baled silage has the advantage of being enclosed until you use it and only a small quantity is exposed at any time. Careful use of this technique can help to limit the amount of odour released.

Effect of housing on ammonia emissions

58. Approximately 35% of ammonia emissions from agriculture in the UK are from livestock buildings. Measurements have shown that ammonia losses are increased if the walls and floors are constantly covered with layers of faeces or urine. The depth is less important than the surface area. Removing slurry frequently by flushing or scraping and washing floors will help control ammonia emissions from cattle and pig buildings.

59. For poultry, the rapid air drying of droppings in laying houses and the maintenance of dry, crumbly litter in broiler houses will reduce ammonia loss.

4. Storing Slurry and Manure

Introduction

60. This Section describes good agricultural practice for the design and management of manure and slurry stores in order to reduce potential odour nuisance.

61. Storage of manures and slurries is also one of the most important ways of avoiding water pollution at times of the year when spreading them to land is likely to cause pollution. A detailed description of the design and management of slurry and manure storage facilities is given in Sections 2 and 3 of the Code of Good Agricultural Practice for the Protection of Water.

Solid manure storage

62. To minimise odours from manure stores, you should encourage natural composting to take place within the store by helping air to penetrate into the bulk of the manure. Make sure that there is enough bedding in the mix to allow air to penetrate.

63. The design of the store is also important. If the store has walls, preferably they should be constructed so that there is a series of gaps at least 25mm wide to allow air into the manure. It is also preferable to have low, long, narrow stores, no more than 10–15m wide and no taller than 3m high. A series of stores will mean that one store can be filled and left to compost for a period of time while a second is filled.

64. You should provide a way of safely collecting and containing any run-off from the store, to avoid causing water pollution (see the Code of Good Agricultural Practice for the Protection of Water).

Storage of slurry and dilute effluents

65. The design and construction of new, substantially enlarged or substantially reconstructed slurry stores must comply with the Control of Pollution (Silage, Slurry and Agricultural Fuel Oil) Regulations 1991. The Code of Good Agricultural Practice for the Protection of Water gives advice on the design, construction and management of stores for slurry and dirty water. General points of good management to avoid odour nuisance are described below. Siting of stores in order to avoid odour nuisance is covered in Section 8 of this Code.

66. Do not add feeds such as milk or whey or silage effluent to slurry or dirty water if there is a high risk of causing odour problems because of the location of the slurry store, or from spreading the waste. Where practicable, you should contain silage effluent in a separate collection tank.

SAFETY NOTE: THE ADDITION OF SILAGE EFFLUENT OR WHEY TO SLURRY CAN RELEASE LETHAL GASES. NEVER ADD THESE MATERIALS TO SLURRY IN CONFINED SPACES OR BUILDINGS.

67. If slurry is frequently agitated in store there will be a frequent release of odours. If possible, above ground circular stores located where there is a high risk of causing odour problems should be equipped with an efficient agitation system which can break up any crust or remove any sediment. This will then need to be used only when the tank is going to be emptied.

68. If slurry is stored in a lagoon or an above ground tank, it can be easier to manage if it has been mechanically separated (see Section 7). Mechanical separation removes coarse solids from the slurry leaving a liquid that can be easily pumped. This liquid can be stored without having to mix it frequently, which can reduce the amount of odour released.

69. If cattle slurry contains a lot of straw bedding material, a self-draining, weeping walled store can be used.

The contents of the store are removed for spreading once they are dry enough. Usually, these solids are only emptied once a year. The liquids draining from the store pose a potential odour problem. They should be spread in a place and using equipment which will minimise the risk of odour problems and water pollution (see Section 6).

Storage of poultry manure

70. Poultry excreta has a dry matter content of 20 to 24%. It is best to handle it as a semi-solid. It should not be diluted with water, as this can result in strong unpleasant odours.

Laying-hen manure which is collected on belts can be air dried in the poultry house as described in paragraph 46.

71. Broiler litter, when well managed in the house, should have a dry matter content of at least 65%. To avoid it becoming wet and causing odour problems you should, where practical, store it under cover, on a base which will not let liquids pass through, until you spread it on the land. Do not burn it under uncontrolled conditions in the open (see Section 16 of this Code).

72. If you use field heaps, they should be put as far away as practical from residential housing, and not within 10m of a watercourse, ditch or field drain. Narrow "A"-shaped heaps shed rainwater more easily and prevent manure from becoming very wet.

5. Producing Compost for Mushrooms

Introduction

73. Producing compost for mushroom growing involves mixing ingredients, mainly straw and manure, and adding water. The process can give rise to odours. This Section gives advice on the legislation which applies, and on practices which will minimise odour emission.

Laws

74. Production of compost on which mushrooms will be grown is a "prescribed process" and requires an authorisation from the local authority Environmental Health Department, under Part I of the Environmental Protection Act 1990 (see paragraph 18). This will be based on the Secretary of State's Guidance Note on production of compost for mushrooms. The Note sets out controls and alternative technologies for new and existing processes.

However, any process for the manufacture of compost other than for sale, carried out on a farm or agricultural holding, is exempt from the above legislation. That is to say if compost is produced and used at the same location and by the same grower for growing mushrooms, or produced at one location and transferred to another location for use by the same grower, the process is exempt.

Processes at locations which are exempt are still subject to Part III of the Environmental Protection Act 1990 which relates to statutory nuisances (paragraphs 7–10).

Good practice

75. In order to minimise the production of odours you should adopt the measures outlined in paragraphs 76–78. A good standard of general management is important. Keep the composting yard and surrounding areas clean and avoid the ponding of liquids which could give rise to odours.

76. If poultry manure or other manure is stored prior to composting, follow the guidelines given in paragraphs 70–72, in order to prevent it becoming too wet. If practical, very wet and potentially odorous material should not be accepted or stored at a composting site.

77. To avoid producing odours, encourage as much air as possible to penetrate into the material which is being processed. To do this you may have to limit the width and height of windrows or heaps and carefully manage the amount of water applied. Turn compost frequently to minimise anaerobic conditions which will cause odours to be produced.

78. Run-off and leachate which is contained in storage tanks should be aerated by suitable equipment. Spray heads that are used to moisten the compost with leachate should work at low pressures and produce large droplets to reduce drift and possible odour problems.

NOTE: DO NOT LET LEACHATE ENTER WATERCOURSES. GUIDANCE ON HOW TO AVOID WATER POLLUTION IS GIVEN IN THE CODE OF GOOD AGRICULTURAL PRACTICE FOR THE PROTECTION OF WATER.

6. Land Spreading of Livestock Wastes

Introduction

79. This Section describes factors which affect the amount of odour emitted by spreading livestock wastes on land. It

describes good agricultural practice and the choice of spreading machinery to minimise odour nuisance.

80. Odours released during spreading of livestock wastes to land cause about 44% of all complaints of odours from agriculture. Odours from spreading manures and slurries can be smelt a long distance from the field, depending on the weather, type of waste, and method of spreading.

Factors which affect levels of odour emitted and its dispersal

81. Generally, the highest odour emissions occur while spreading of waste is actually taking place. With conventional splash plate spreaders, the odour concentration can be 7 to 15 times greater during spreading than immediately afterwards. Odour emission during the next 8 to 12 hours may also be high enough to cause a nuisance.

82. A number of factors affect the amount of odour emitted during and after spreading slurry or manure. These include the type of livestock (pig slurry tends to be most odorous), whether the waste contains waste milk or silage effluent (these increase the amount of odour released) and the method and length of storage. The type of spreading equipment used and rate of application to land are also very important (paragraphs 87 and 92-100).

83. The weather conditions which are least suitable for spreading are high humidities and very light winds or clear, still nights. These conditions prevent odour from dispersing, and so increase the risk of causing a nuisance.

The best spreading conditions are where air mixes to a great height above the ground, which are typically sunny, windy days, followed by cloudy, windy nights. These conditions cause odours to be diluted quickly.

84. The location of the fields where the slurry or manure will be applied, the direction and strength of the wind, and distance from houses are extremely important to get enough dilution and dispersal of the odour and so avoid problems.

Losses of ammonia during land spreading

85. Approximately 35% of ammonia emissions from agriculture in the UK result from spreading livestock wastes on land. Most of the loss of ammonia to the atmosphere from manures and slurries takes place as the material is being spread on land and during the following 12 hours. Any attempt to reduce and control losses must take place as soon as possible after spreading. Injecting, or rapidly incorporating the waste into the soil will have a significant effect in reducing emissions.

Precautions when spreading manure and slurry

86. Use a weather forecast to help choose suitable conditions for spreading (paragraph 83). Check wind direction in relation to nearby houses before spreading. Avoid spreading in fields close to and upwind of houses unless slurry is band spread, injected or has been treated to effectively reduce its odour.

87. Avoid applying more than 50 m^3/ha (4500 gallons to the acre), or 50 tonnes/ha (20 tonnes per acre) at one time if odour could be a problem. Always apply slurry and manure in a way that avoids the risk of causing water pollution. See Section 2 of the Code of Good Agricultural Practice for the Protection of Water for detailed information on assessing the risk of causing water pollution and the land area needed for different classes of stock.

88. On bare land, lightly cultivate the land after surface spreading to mix in the material as soon as possible.

89. When spreading slurry use a spreader which is suitable for the location of the fields it will be used in (paragraphs 94–100).

Avoid over-filling tankers or spreaders. Do not spill manure or slurry on roads. This may be an offence under the Highways Act, 1980. Clean the outside of spreading machinery regularly.

90. Unless slurry is band spread, injected or has been treated to reduce odour effectively, avoid spreading at weekends, bank holidays or in the evening.

Precautions when spreading sewage sludge

91. Spreading of sewage sludge is controlled by the Sludge (Use in Agriculture) Regulations 1989. Follow the

Code of Practice for Agricultural Use of Sewage Sludge. Care should be taken to choose application sites so that odour nuisance is not caused. In general, the factors which affect odour nuisance are the same as those for slurry and manure.

Choosing slurry spreading equipment

92. Choosing suitable slurry spreading equipment is, in many cases, the most important decision to be made when planning a waste handling system to minimise odour problems.

93. Volatile odorous compounds in slurries are released when the slurry is directed onto a splash plate or similar device. This causes the jet of slurry to shatter into very small drops and releases odorous compounds directly into the air.

Often, it is this concentrated release of odour which causes problems. One tanker may spread three or four loads an hour, causing a series of such events.

94. Choose the type of slurry spreader that is suitable for the fields it will be used in. If the fields which the slurry will be spread on are away from houses, then you can use a tanker with a conventional splash plate spreading device. Tankers which give a low trajectory and large droplets are best.

95. When the fields are close to and upwind of houses, choose a machine which has reliable information on its ability to control the amount of odour which is emitted.

The band spreaders and injectors described in paragraphs 96–99 below provide a series of choices for controlling odour and ammonia. The costs of buying and running equipment vary in relation to the amount of control achieved. It may be necessary to separate slurry mechanically, or to remove coarse solids to make sure that the spreader works properly.

Alternatively, you could treat the slurry before it is spread to reduce the amount of odour emitted to an acceptable level (see Section 7).

96. Band spreaders discharge slurry at ground level through a series of trailing pipes. Measurements of odour show a reduction of 55 to 60% compared with conventional splash plate spreaders.

97. Shallow channel application uses a mechanism to make grooves 50–70mm deep in the soil, 200–300mm apart. The slurry is directed into the channel immediately behind the cutting blade. As with band spreaders the odour can be reduced by 55 to 60% compared with conventional spreaders.

98. Shallow injection applies slurry at a depth of 50–80mm in grooves 250–300mm apart. The groove is then closed again by press wheels or discs. The amount of odour emitted is about 85% less than from conventional spreaders. Ammonia emissions are reduced by 90 to 95%.

99. Deep injection equipment applies slurry at a depth of 120–300mm in the soil using injector tines, spaced about 500mm apart. The amount of odour emitted is about 85% less than from conventional spreaders. Ammonia emissions are reduced by 90 to 95%.

NOTES:

Band Spreaders

Slurry is pumped to a manifold distributor, often in a rapid succession of pulses to make sure that all pipes are supplied at the same rate. The trailing pipes may hang loosely or can be more rigid with a small metal shoe which rides along on the surface, parting the crop and making sure that waste is applied directly onto the surface of the soil.

Deep injection

A winged time may be used to loosen the soil over a strip about 20cm wide so that slurry is mixed into the soil. However, as with all injection systems the method has limitations: it may not be usable when the soil is heavy, dry, frozen or stony and where there are steep slopes. Deep injection generally requires a more powerful tractor compared with other systems.

100. The following points should help you choose slurry spreading machines to reduce odour emissions. Manufacturers should be able to provide such information. Look for:

- A reduction in the amount of odour emitted during spreading of at least 50% compared with a conventional splash plate distribution device.
- Good control of application rate, so that the machine can give rates ranging from 20m^3/ha (1800 gallons per acre) to 50m^3/ha (4500

gallons per acre), when operating at a suitable speed.

Irrigation of liquid wastes

101. Dilute effluents and separated slurry are usually applied using sprinklers or travelling irrigators. A detailed description of such systems is given in Section 4 of the Code of Good Agricultural Practice for the Protection of Water.

102. Odour problems can arise when silage effluent, waste milk or the liquid from weeping wall stores or manure stores is added to dirty water or separated slurry.

There will be some situations when storage will be needed for the dirty water or separated slurry to avoid causing water pollution. However, storing them for long periods will encourage odours to develop and extra care must be taken to avoid nuisance when such liquids are spread.

103. Application systems should be designed for the particular site. Where there is a risk of causing an odour nuisance choose sprinklers or irrigators providing a low trajectory and operating at a low pressure to produce large droplets.

Spreading solid manures

104. Spreading solid manures, including mixtures of bedding and manure, poultry manure, solids from weeping wall stores, and the solids from mechanical separators, can sometimes produce as much odour as spreading slurry. Because the material is solid, it cannot be applied by injection which would reduce the release of odour.

105. Wherever possible, store manure in a way that will encourage natural composting. This process, when carried out correctly, as outlined in Section 4, reduces the concentration and offensiveness of odour released during spreading.

106. When odorous or partly composted manure has to be applied to land, do not spread it close to houses. Where practicable, you should spread it onto arable land and bury it immediately by ploughing.

7. Treatment of Livestock Wastes

Introduction

107. This Section describes methods of treating livestock wastes to give further reductions in odour emissions during storage and spreading beyond those that would result from the good practice described in Sections 4 and 6 of this Code.

108. Biological treatment of livestock wastes and odour emissions from buildings is a step beyond currently accepted good agricultural practice. However, the use of these techniques may be necessary in exceptional situations.

Aerobic and anaerobic treatment can be expensive, as the costs of buying and running the treatment systems must be added to the cost of collecting, storing and spreading the waste. It is important that you get advice to make sure that the treatment you intend to use works efficiently and is suitable for the specific problem.

109. The type and degree of treatment that is needed depends on how serious the odour problem is. In some cases, the source odour concentration may need to be reduced by as much as 95% before the odour problem is reduced enough. (See para. 29 for definition of odour concentration).

Mechanical separation

110. Mechanical separation can be useful as an aid to improved waste management. There is a range of mechanical separators available for livestock slurries. It is important that the correct machine is chosen for the slurry produced on a particular farm.

111. The process removes coarse solids from farm slurries. The solid portion, 10 to 20% of the original slurry volume, can be stacked and stored in a similar way to farmyard manure. If this solid is produced by a separator which gives high dry matter solids, this portion will compost readily to produce a relatively mild smelling material which is unlikely to cause a nuisance.

112. The separated liquid portion, which is 80 to 90% of the original volume, flows easily and can therefore be pumped to a store and handled by the band spreaders or slurry injectors described in Section 6, without causing blockage problems. After separation, storing the liquid portion is easier because there is less risk of a crust forming and solids settling. Therefore, mixing in store only needs to be carried out occasionally so odours released during storage are reduced.

113. The separated liquid portion of slurry can be applied in the spring to arable crops or grass after silage cuts. This makes good use of the nutrients in the waste. The separated liquid leaves very little solid residue on crops and avoids one of the sources of odour associated with whole slurry.

114. Mechanical separation is usually a necessary treatment before aerobic treatment (aeration) because it is easier to aerate separated liquid than a mixture that contains large particles which need extra power input to keep them in suspension and more oxygen to give odour control.

NOTES:

Choice of mechanical separator

For pig slurry of 2 to 4% dry matter a wedge wire screen or vibrating screen will work satisfactorily. The dry matter content of the separated solids will be 8 to 12%. These solids will self-drain if they are held in a suitable store.

Separators which press, squeeze or screw the slurry against a fabric belt or perforated stainless steel screen will produce a solid with a dry matter ranging from 18 to 30%. These solids can be composted.

Biological treatment—general principles

115. Techniques for treatment of manure, slurries, and other organic effluents using micro-organisms are well developed.

116. Any treatment of slurry by micro-organisms relies on steady flow conditions to encourage their rapid continuous growth. Therefore, it is essential that the daily loading rate of slurry should be kept within the design standards of the particular treatment system. Variations in load will alter the retention time; a very large load may flush out the micro-organisms which will lead to treatment failure.

There are two basic methods of treatment—aerobic (with a good supply of oxygen always present) and anaerobic (without oxygen).

NOTES:

Retention times:

This is the average time that slurry will stay in the container that treatment takes place in. For continuous flow systems, normal retention time in days is the volume of the treatment vessel divided by volume loaded every day.

Aerobic treatment (aeration)

117. Treatment of slurries and farm effluents by aerobic biological treatment systems which are correctly designed and used should be capable of reducing the amount of odour emitted during and after land application by up to 90%.

118. Aerobic treatment is usually only suitable for separated slurry or dilute effluents. Solids in the waste increase the amount of oxygen needed and also increase the energy needed for mixing. The most efficient oxygen transfer occurs when very small bubbles are used. Currently the most successful aerators are "sub-surface" and "venturi jet", whilst "compressed-air sparge systems" are more efficient in deep tanks. Aerators should supply a minimum of 1 kg of dissolved oxygen for each kilowatt hour they use, if they are to be economical. The following conditions should be met:

- A reasonably constant volume of slurry each day to give controlled retention time in the treatment tank.
- A slurry dry matter content of less than 3%.
- Absence of bedding material and animal hair from the slurry.
- A suitable oxygen concentration throughout the treatment tank achieved by effective mixing.

119. Continuous flow aeration systems can successfully treat slurries to reduce odour nuisance with retention times of as little as 2 days. In these systems odour can be controlled at the treatment tank as well as at spreading. Increasing the retention time during treatment will allow you to store the treated slurry for at least a month or more before the odour returns.

120. If a batch system is used much of the odour will be driven out into the air above the treatment tank when treatment starts.

Anaerobic digestion

121. In a properly designed and run system, the odour emitted during and after spreading anaerobically digested slurry will be reduced by up to 80% and it will be less offensive. The digested slurry can be stored for several months after it has been treated before offensive odours return.

122. Anaerobic digestion of livestock slurries involves using micro-organisms to turn the complex organic substances into less complex compounds. This process is done in the absence of oxygen and at temperatures normally between 30 and 35°C. The end products of digestion are biogas (a mixture of 60 to 70% methane and 30 to 40% carbon dioxide) and a stabilised treated slurry. The biogas may be used for heating or generating electricity. It is not necessary to separate the slurry before treatment. Performance of the digester is affected by:

- Temperature—below 25°C the digestion process is very slow.
- Dry matter content—6 to 8% is the optimum.
- Retention time in the digester—the optimum time for pig slurry is 12 days; for cattle and poultry slurry it is 20 days.

Treating odours by additives and other methods

123. Several kinds of additives are available that act in different ways and which are claimed to control odours. The main ones are: oxidising agents, deodorants which react with odorous compounds, masking agents, biological agents, feed additives and miscellaneous chemicals.

These additives vary in their effectiveness. Current evidence shows that they are not generally a long-term solution to reducing odour problems. However, additives may be useful as a short-term emergency treatment for a batch of slurry or a store which is causing a nuisance.

124. Electrolytic methods are also available for treating slurry. This treatment uses copper electrodes immersed in a treatment tank, and is claimed to reduce odour nuisance.

125. Ask manufacturers or suppliers of additives and other methods to provide independent proof of their product's ability to control odours when it is used according to the manufacturer's instructions.

8. Siting of Livestock Buildings, Manure and Slurry Stores

Introduction

126. When you are planning the location of new livestock buildings or waste storage facilities or extensions or alterations to existing structures, it is essential to consider the risk of odours and noise causing nuisance. By law you need to get planning permission for livestock buildings and any structures intended to contain slurry or sewage sludge sited within 400m of the boundary of protected buildings such as houses or schools.

For livestock buildings, slurry stores and sewage sludge facilities which do not require planning permission under the Town and Country Planning General Development Order 1988, a prior notification system is now in force. You must notify the local planning authority of such developments. The local planning authority must then decide within 28 days whether it wishes to approve details of the siting, design and external appearance of the proposed development.

You may need an environmental assessment in support of a planning application for large pig and poultry units. The legislation on this subject is described in paragraphs 11–13 of this Code.

Factors affecting odour problems

127. A number of factors strongly influence the risk of odour problems arising from livestock buildings, manure or slurry stores. These factors include:

- the distance from neighbouring properties and the local topography;
- the number and type of stock;
- the prevailing wind direction in relation to neighbouring properties;
- the management of the livestock and housing system used;
- the type and size of slurry or manure store and the way in which it is managed;
- the type of feed used.

The distance of a site from a potential complainant is very important as odours are diluted in the atmosphere. The longer the distance, the more the odour will be diluted by dispersal. However, distance alone is often not enough to avoid odour nuisance and it is important to take the other factors into account.

128. Good management of livestock housing and manure stores which takes account of the factors outlined in Sections 3 and 4 of this Code will reduce potential odour problems.

129. A number of factors have a large effect on the odour concentration downwind and on the direction of dispersal. Strong wind mixes the air and increases dilution, so exposed sites may aid odour dispersal. The frequency and distribution of wind direction and wind speeds can affect the site chosen, so that odours are carried away from housing. You may need specific advice on weather influences such as wind direction, atmospheric stability and odour dispersal.

130. Woodlands and shelter belts can act as barriers and help odour dispersal. Shelter belts and plantations must be correctly laid out with trees spaced to allow 40 to 50% of the wind to pass through them. Get advice on a suitable layout and the best types of tree to plant.

Siting of existing livestock units

131. A large number of existing livestock units and existing waste storage facilities are situated close to houses and similar properties. It is important to follow the advice given in this Code to help reduce potential odour problems in such cases.

Government guidance to local planning authorities requires them to consider carefully applications for new housing development near existing livestock units. Where farmers are made aware of such proposals, they may wish to draw potential odour problems to the local planning authority's attention.

Siting new livestock units

132. Building new livestock units and their associated storage facilities in close proximity to housing can cause particular problems. Siting of such new units should take account of the factors outlined in paragraphs 127–130. Paying attention to these factors may also help you to obtain local authority planning approval, when necessary, for the siting of new units.

PART C SMOKE POLLUTION

9. General Principles

133. This part of the Code deals with the risk of causing air pollution by smoke from the burning on agricultural and horticultural premises of carcases and waste materials arising from agriculture.

In agriculture, dark smoke and smoke nuisance are most frequently caused by burning waste materials in the open or in unsuitable equipment.

134. Under the Clean Air Acts 1956 or 1968 it is an offence to burn any material which produces dark smoke unless an exemption applies (paragraphs 14–16). Part III of the Environmental Protection Act 1990, which relates to statutory nuisances, also applies (paragraphs 7–10). Certain prescribed processes are subject to specific controls under the Environmental Protection (Prescribed Processes and Substances) Regulations 1991 (paragraph 18).

135. Minimise the need to burn waste materials by:

- Firstly, reducing the use of materials if possible.
- Secondly, recycling materials where appropriate.
- Thirdly, using alternative environmentally acceptable methods of disposal wherever this is practicable, as set out in Sections 11 to 16.

136. Where burning cannot be avoided, Sections 11 to 17 of this Code give advice on methods of burning which avoid producing dark smoke or smoke nuisance.

137. Make regular and frequent assessments of the appearance and odour of smoke produced when burning waste materials in the open. If dark smoke is emitted or if the smoke is likely to cause a nuisance take action immediately to put the problem right.

NOTES:

Dark smoke

Smoke is finely divided particles of matter suspended in the air as a visible cloud. Dark smoke can arise from incomplete combustion of organic compounds.

Dark smoke production will be avoided if the temperature is high enough for ignition and if enough oxygen is available to keep the material burning at this temperature for long enough for combustion to be completed.

Measuring of dark smoke

The darkness of smoke from chimneys can be measured by comparing its shade with a graduated scale. For the purpose of this Code the Ringelmann Chart should be used as described in British Standard 2742—Use of Ringelmann and Miniature Smoke Charts. This scale starts at 0 and increases up to a maximum of 5. Dark smoke is defined as 2 or more on the Ringelmann Chart and represents 40% obscuration.

10. Reducing the Volumes of Waste Materials for Disposal

Reducing waste

138. Using materials, packaging and equipment carefully can extend their useful life and reduce the amount of waste produced. Using suitable machinery and regularly maintaining it will reduce wear and prolong the useful life of items such as tyres.

139. Take waste disposal into account when choosing products to bring on to the holding. Wherever practicable, choose those methods, equipment and husbandry practices which give extended life and produce relatively low amounts of waste for disposal.

Recycling

140. You should recycle wastes on the holding by re-using materials wherever practicable. Some wastes can also be recycled by specialist operators. For this, different waste materials usually need to be sorted out, and stockpiled in good condition for them to be collected or delivered to the operator. Some local authorities and commercial companies also run recycling programmes.

141. Recycling straw by processing it into added value products can also be considered as good practice as long as the processes are controlled to avoid causing water pollution and producing odours and harmful gases.

Ease of disposal

142. If packaging and disposable materials for crop protection, mulching or crop storage are brought onto the holding, you should consider how easy it is to dispose of the waste. If possible choose materials which can be disposed of safely and economically without burning them. Consider using materials which biodegrade after they have been used.

143. Only burn materials which cannot practically be disposed of in any other way, which burn easily and which do not produce dark smoke or poisonous by-products when burnt under suitable conditions.

144. Ask the local Waste Collection and Disposal Authority about facilities for the disposal and collection of difficult wastes.

11. Plastic Materials

Introduction

145. Do not burn plastics in the open on agricultural holdings because this can cause large amounts of dark smoke and poisonous by-products which can be extremely harmful to health.

146. If you burn plastics in an incinerator, the installation may require authorisation by the local authority under Part I of the Environmental Protection Act 1990 (paragraph 185).

Repeated use of plastics

147. Consider reusing plastic materials on the farm or holding. If an item can be used several times before it becomes unserviceable, the quantity of material which needs to be disposed of will be greatly reduced.

148. To maximise recycling take care when handling and using plastics. Use suitable equipment and methods of handling to make sure that the plastic item is not damaged. Carefully reclaim and re-use items such as crop covers for mulching.

Alternative uses

149. If a plastic material cannot be re-used for its original purpose, try hard to make use of it for other things. However, never use containers that have held agricultural chemicals and persistent, poisonous or harmful substances for any other purpose. (See paragraph 171 of the Code of Practice for the Safe Use of Pesticides on Farms and Holdings).

Recycling

150. Recycle polythene materials using specialist recycling companies. Suitable items include:

- silage bags and sheets
- polythene inners from fertiliser "big bags"
- 50 kg fertiliser sacks
- pallet covers
- polythene covers from greenhouses

151. Materials for recycling should be clean and free from soil. Keep different types of items separate. Store the material in one safe place ready to be collected.

Choosing materials

152. When choosing plastic materials to use in crop husbandry, if recycling is not practical, then choose those materials which are biodegradable. Biodegradable plastic materials are likely to be unsuitable for recycling.

153. If plastic items such as plant pots or trays are re-used, their life can be increased by choosing more durable products. This reduces waste. If returnable items are thrown away because of their appearance, using a more durable type of plastic, a different colour or different type of returnable container may enable each unit to be used more times.

154. Save plastics which cannot be recycled and dispose of them to the local authority or commercial licensed landfill sites, or incinerators.

Containers contaminated by pesticides

155. Paragraphs 171–180 of the Code of Practice for the Safe Use of Pesticides on Farms and Holdings gives details of preferred disposal methods and all precautions to take when disposing of or burning these containers. The Code has a statutory basis under Part III of the Food and Environment Protection Act 1985 and should be read by all farmers.

Under the Clean Air (Emission of Dark Smoke) (Exemption) Regulations 1969, dark smoke emitted by the burning of containers which are contaminated by any pesticide or by any toxic substance used for veterinary or agricultural purposes is exempt from the prohibition in Section 1 of the Clean Air Act 1968 **provided that the following conditions are satisfied:**

- there is no other reasonably safe and practicable method of disposing of the matter;
- the burning is carried out in such a manner as to minimise the emission of dark smoke;
- the burning is carried out under the direct and continuous supervision of the occupier of the premises concerned or a person authorised to act on their behalf.

There are few circumstances where other practicable methods of disposal cannot be found. Many specialist contractors now offer well-managed disposal services.

Part III of the Environmental Protection Act 1990, which relates to statutory nuisances, also applies if you do resort to burning (paragraphs 7–10).

12. Tyres and Rubber

Dark smoke risk

156. Rubber tyres produce large amounts of dark smoke and may give off poisonous substances when burnt in the open. Do not burn tyres and other rubber materials on agricultural holdings.

157. Ask tyre suppliers to take away old tyres from the premises when new ones are fitted to agricultural machinery.

Disposal off the farm

158. Dispose of large numbers of tyres to specialist waste removal operators or contractors. Small quantities of tyres may be accepted by licensed local authority sites, but you may need to get special permission from the site operator.

13. Waste Oils

Sources

159. Waste oil comes from the servicing of agricultural machinery. The main types of waste oil are used lubricating oil from engines and oil from hydraulic systems.

Recycling

160. Collect used oil drained from machinery during routine servicing and store it in suitable leak-proof containers. Store surplus oil in a central store and dispose of it to waste oil dealers. Different types of oil should be kept separate.

NOTE: NEVER DISPOSE OF WASTE OIL INTO SOAKAWAYS, WATERCOURSES, DRAINS OR SEWERS AS IT CAN CAUSE SERIOUS WATER POLLUTION.

Waste oil burners

161. You can burn waste oils for heating on farms provided that you obtain approval for the installation of the burner to be used from the local authority Environmental Health Department. Under Part I of the Environmental Protection Act 1990 such burners must comply with the Secretary of State's Guidance Note for waste oil burners less than 0.4 MW and waste oil or recovered oil burners less than 3 MW net rated thermal input (paragraph 18).

NOTE: THE DESIGN AND CONSTRUCTION OF NEW OR SUBSTANTIALLY ENLARGED OR RECONSTRUCTED STORAGE FACILITIES FOR STORING MORE THAN 1500 LITRES (330 GALLONS) OF OIL TO BE BURNT FOR AGRICULTURAL PURPOSES MUST COMPLY WITH THE CONTROL OF POLLUTION (SILAGE, SLURRY AND AGRICULTURAL FUEL OIL) REGULATIONS 1991. THE CODE OF GOOD AGRICULTURAL PRACTICE FOR THE PROTECTION OF WATER GIVES FURTHER ADVICE.

14. Animal Carcases

Introduction

162. There are a number of ways to dispose of animals that die on the farm. The best way is to send them to a licensed knackerman, licensed landfill site or licensed incinerator operator. If a notifiable disease is involved, disposal is subject to the MAFF State Veterinary Service animal health controls.

163. Disposal methods on the farm, such as burial, incineration or burning in the open may cause water or air pollution, particularly if they are not done correctly.

164. The Code of Good Agricultural Practice for the Protection of Water gives advice on how to avoid causing water pollution from burying carcases. Consult the National Rivers Authority if there is any doubt over the suitability of a proposed burial site.

Never dispose of carcases in or near watercourses, boreholes or springs. Apart from being prosecuted for causing water pollution, there is a serious risk of you spreading disease to animals on neighbouring farms.

Notifiable diseases

165. If you think that a notifiable disease has caused ill health or death you must report it to the Divisional Veterinary Officer at the local Animal Health Office of the Ministry of Agriculture, Fisheries and Food or Welsh Office Agriculture Department. Carcases should be available for post-mortem examination in these cases. Always consider the possibility of anthrax if death is sudden or unexplained.

Incineration

166. If animal carcases are burnt on farm it should be done in an incinerator wherever possible. The incinerator used should be fitted with a secondary combustion chamber so that high temperatures can be achieved throughout incineration to give complete combustion of all products. Get advice about siting, choosing, installing and running incinerators, chimneys, associated buildings and carcase storage facilities.

If you intend to install an incinerator designed for or to be operated at loading rates of more than 50 kg/hour you must first get approval for the installation of the appliance in question from the local authority Environmental Health Department under Part I of the Environmental Protection Act 1990. It must comply with the Secretary of State's Guidance Note on animal carcase incineration processes under 1 tonne an hour (paragraph 18).

For units below 50 kg/hour the Clean Air Act 1956 which prohibits the emission of dark smoke from chimneys and Part III of the Environmental Protection Act 1990 which relates to statutory nuisances still apply (paragraphs 14–16 and 7–10).

167. Incinerate dead animals as soon as possible. Do not exceed the design loading rate of the incinerator at any time.

Open burning

168. Using suitable on site incineration equipment is strongly preferred to open burning.

169. Under the Clean Air (Emission of Dark Smoke) (Exemption) Regulations 1969, emission of dark smoke, caused by the burning of carcases of animals or poultry which:

- have died or are reasonably believed to have died because of disease;
- or have been slaughtered because of disease;
- or have been required to be slaughtered under the Animal Health Act 1981;

is exempt from the prohibition in Section 1 of the Clean Air Act 1968, provided that:

- there is no other reasonably safe and practicable method of disposing of the matter;
- and the burning is carried out under the direct and continuous supervision of the occupier of the premises concerned or a person authorised to act on their behalf.

The Environmental Protection Act 1990, Part III, which relates to statutory nuisances, still applies (paragraphs 7–10).

If burning is essential, follow the general precautions on open burning given in paragraph 196. A shallow pit should be dug with cross trenches to provide a good air supply to the base of the fire. Use only dry fuels which are not likely to produce dark smoke and which burn easily. Do not use tyres or liquids as a fuel and do not use the fire to dispose of other materials not recommended for burning. Gas fired equipment may be used to start the fire. Place the primary fuel in the base of the fire and place the carcases on top. Use enough fuel to ensure that the carcases are completely burned. Do not overload the fire with carcases. Burning should begin as early in the day as possible.

15. Fuels Produced on the Farm

Introduction

170. Straw and other crop residues can be used as animal feed, for animal bedding and, where markets exist, for paper pulp and for manufacturing board. Excess amounts of straw can be sold to other agricultural holdings or to straw merchants. Residues can be mixed into the soil. The burning of crop residues will be banned before the 1993 harvest unless specifically exempted by the legislation (paragraph 186).

Straw and wood as fuel

171. Straw is a useful energy source and may provide a cost effective and environmentally acceptable fuel for furnaces that are designed to burn it. Other crop residues, wood and litter from stock can also be used as alternative fuels.

Choosing equipment

172. Straw or wood fuelled furnaces should be properly designed for the purpose and have facilities to give adequate control over combustion in order to prevent the production of dark smoke. If units of over 400 kW (0.4 MW) rated thermal input are used, you must obtain approval for the installation of the appliance in question from the local authority Environmental Health Department under Part I of the Environmental Protection Act 1990. It must comply with the requirements of the Secretary of State's Guidance Notes on either straw combustion processes between 0.4 and 3 MW net rated thermal input or wood combustion processes between 0.4 and 3 MW net rated thermal input, depending on the fuel used (paragraph 18).

Chimney height approval may be required under Section 6 of the Clean Air Act 1968.

173. Equipment with a thermal input of less than 400 kW (0.4 MW) is still subject to the provisions of the Clean Air Act 1956 which prohibits the emission of dark smoke from chimneys (paragraphs 14–16). Part III of the Environmental Protection Act 1990, which relates to statutory nuisances, also applies (paragraphs 7–10).

Using and maintaining equipment

174. Efficient burning of fuel will prevent the production of dark smoke. It is important to choose suitable equipment and operate it correctly. Automatic fuelling equipment that is properly set up and maintained can provide the most stable operating conditions and will automatically provide the heat that is needed at any particular time.

175. Many boilers and heaters have a large chamber and are designed to burn a single charge of fuel. These units should be designed so that the supply of primary and secondary air can be controlled to give efficient burning of the large charge of fuel without producing dark smoke.

176. Do not try to prolong the burning of a large charge of fuel by reducing the air supply. This will give inefficient combustion and cause dark smoke. With large charge boilers, if heat is needed over a long period, they should be used in conjunction with water-based thermal storage systems or the boiler itself should have a large water content so that it stores the heat.

177. To avoid producing dark smoke only burn fuels that the burner is designed for and which are recommended by the manufacturer. Do not burn animal carcases, plastics, tyres or other rubber materials in straw or wood burners. Store fuel for the burner under cover. Always make sure that the fuel is dry. Adjust the primary and secondary air supply to give efficient combustion and minimum dark smoke emission.

178. Get burning equipment cleaned and serviced regularly. Scrape or brush internal heat transfer surfaces to keep them in a clean condition and free from char and other deposits. Do not carry out uncontrolled burning of a charge of fuel in the furnace to remove deposits of char from the internal surfaces of the boiler, as this is likely to produce dark smoke.

Using litter from poultry and other animals as a fuel

179. If litter from poultry or animals is to be used as a fuel in heating appliances for space heating or agricultural processes, specialised equipment designed for this type of fuel should be used. Automatic fuelling should be part of the system. Air supply for primary and secondary combustion should be controlled to give high combustion efficiency.

180. The plant should be operated in a way which minimises the emission of dark smoke. Monitoring the appearance and smell of the flue gases should be carried out at least once a day.

181. If a unit of over 400 kW (0.4 MW) net rated thermal input is used you must get approval for installation of the appliance in question from the local authority Environmental Health Department under Part I of the Environmental Protection Act 1990. It must comply with the requirements of the Secretary of State's Guidance Note on poultry litter combustion processes between 0.4 and 3MW net rated thermal input.

182. Equipment with a thermal input of less than 400 kW (0.4 MW) still comes under the provisions of the Clean Air Act 1956 which prohibits the emission of dark smoke from chimneys (paragraphs 14–16). Part III of the Environmental Protection Act 1990, which relates to statutory nuisances, also applies (paragraphs 7–10).

183. If you wish to install straw, wood or animal litter fuelled heating systems you will normally need professional help to design such an installation.

16. Other Waste Materials

Introduction

184. Under the Clean Air Act 1956 or 1968 it is an offence to burn waste materials if the burning produces dark smoke (paragraphs 14–16). Part III of the Environmental Protection Act 1990, which relates to statutory nuisances, also applies (paragraphs 7–10).

185. If waste materials are to be burnt in an incinerator which is designed or operated at rates of more than 25 kg/hr, you must get approval for the appliance in question from the local authority Environmental Health Department, under Part I of the Environmental Protection Act 1990. It must comply with the Secretary of State's Guidance Note on general waste incineration processes under 1 tonne an hour.

Crop residues

186. The burning of cereal straw and stubble, the residues of field peas and beans harvested dry, linseed and oil seed rape is controlled by the Crop Residues (Restrictions on Burning) (No 2) Regulations 1991. Included in these Regulations are requirements about: the area to be burned, firebreaks, distances from vulnerable objects such as trees, hedges, buildings, days of the week and times for burning, supervision and other safety requirements, notifying relevant authorities and neighbours, and incorporating ash after burning. Guidance Notes on the Regulations were issued to all farmers in England and all cereal producers in Wales in 1991.

187. The Clean Air Act 1968, the Health and Safety at Work, etc. Act 1974, the Highways Act 1980 and the Environmental Protection Act 1990 also apply.

188. After 1992, there will be a general ban on the burning of crop residues. Exemptions will be granted for the burning of residues from lavender, hops, potatoes, herbage seed and reeds. There may be other exemptions in certain circumstances and the above controls (or equivalent) will continue to be used.

Wood waste

189. Wood waste is produced during forestry operations, orchard pruning, demolition of buildings, estate maintenance, and building construction and maintenance.

190. Larger items of timber and waste wood can be used as firewood. Therefore, it is preferable to process these into burnable lengths for domestic use or dispose of them to specialist dealers in this material. Arrangements with contractors for forestry work and woodland clearance should include an agreement for the disposal of any waste wood that is produced.

191. Trimmings from woodland or orchard pruning may be converted to wood chips where practicable. If they have to be burned, follow the guidance in Section 17.

192. Under the Clean Air (Emission of Dark Smoke) (Exemption) Regulations 1969, emission of dark smoke caused by the burning of timber and any other waste matter (other than natural or synthetic rubber, or flock or feathers), which results from the demolition of a building or clearance of a site in connection with any building operation or work of engineering construction (within the meaning of Section 176 of the Factories Act 1961), is exempt from the prohibition in Section 1 of the Clean Air Act 1968, provided that the following conditions are satisfied:

- there is no other reasonably safe and practicable method of disposing of the matter;
- **and** the burning is carried out in such a manner as to minimise the emission of dark smoke;
- **and** the burning is carried out under the direct and continuous supervision of the occupier of the premises concerned or a person authorised to act on their behalf.

If in doubt, get advice from the Environmental Health Department of the local authority before burning any waste.

Paper sacks and other packaging

193. Where practicable, paper sacks and other packaging that are not contaminated by pesticides should be stockpiled and sent for recycling, for example to a board mill. If recycling is not possible, burn paper sacks carefully in small quantities as long as this does not cause a nuisance (paragraphs 7–10).

Litter from poultry and other animal litter

194. Because litter from poultry or other animals varies in its moisture content and composition, it is difficult to burn except under closely controlled conditions. Uncontrolled burning will produce dark smoke and odour. Therefore, do not burn poultry and animal litter in the open.

17. Burning in the Open

Good practice

195. Under the Clean Air Act 1968 it is an offence to burn any material in the open on trade premises if the burning produces dark smoke (paragraphs 14–16). Part III of the Environmental Protection Act 1990, which relates to statutory nuisances, also applies (paragraphs 7–10).

196. If burning in the open is the only practicable method of disposal, take the following precautions to prevent producing dark smoke or causing a nuisance:

- Do not burn plastics, rubber, tyres or other materials known to produce dark smoke.
- Avoid burning if it will cause a nuisance to nearby residential areas.
- Materials should be dry and have a low moisture content. Do not burn green vegetation.
- Keep fires small and continually add combustible material, minimising the depth of the combustion area. Do not pile material high on fires.
- Minimise the quantity of incombustible material which is added to the fire. Wherever possible keep incombustible materials separate from the materials to be burnt.
- For better combustion, agitate the base of the fire to improve the air supply.
- If a fire produces dark smoke, don't add any more material that burns slowly.

Safety precautions

197. Also take the following precautions to minimise fire hazard:

- Build fires well clear of houses, other buildings, overhead cables or flammable materials such as stacks of straw, trees, hedgerows, ripe cereals or stubble.
- Fires must not be lit near a public road. If the fire, or smoke from it, causes injury, interruption or dangers to road users, this may be an offence under the Highways Act 1980.
- Do not burn materials in the open, when it is very windy or in a period of drought.
- Only light fires downwind of public highways, houses, other buildings or inflammable materials, so that the wind will carry any sparks and smoke away from them.
- Tell the local authority Fire Service before starting any substantial burning operations.
- Have a fire extinguisher and a supply of water from a mains supply or bowser on hand in case of an emergency.
- Burning should be carried out under direct and continuous supervision of the occupier of the premises or a person authorised to act on their behalf. The only exception to this should be if there is an emergency elsewhere on the farm requiring immediate attention.
- Put out all fires before you leave them.

18. Greenhouse Gases

Introduction

198. This Section describes the greenhouse gases emitted by agricultural systems and some steps which can help limit the amount of gases that are released.

199. Climate change is one of the biggest environmental problems now facing the world. The sun is the earth's source of heat. Some of the sun's energy is absorbed by the surface of the earth. In turn the earth radiates the energy back into space as infra-red radiation. Some of the gases in our atmosphere can absorb this infra-red radiation, and so prevent it leaving the earth and its atmosphere. This acts as a blanket and makes the earth warmer. This is similar to the effect of glass in a greenhouse, which lets the sunlight in but stops some of the radiated heat from escaping. The gases which cause this effect are therefore called greenhouse gases. Most of these occur naturally in the atmosphere, and produce a natural greenhouse effect which keeps the temperature of the earth about 30°C higher than it would otherwise be.

The greenhouse gases

200. Many gases can absorb infra-red radiation to some extent. The most important greenhouse gases are water vapour, carbon dioxide, methane, nitrous oxide, and chlorofluorocarbons (CFCs). The natural greenhouse effect is essential to life but human activity causes the release of extra greenhouse gases. It is believed that these extra gases will increase the greenhouse effect, causing the earth's surface to warm up even more which could have major effects on the world. Changes in sea level could cover lowlying coasts, and changes in climate and weather could damage agriculture and natural systems. Because some of the greenhouse gases last for a long time in the atmosphere, it is important that any action to reduce emissions of greenhouse gases is taken as early as possible. Negotiations are taking place between governments to reach an international agreement on targets and ways to reduce the amount of greenhouse gases that are being produced. In advance of any international agreements, it is best to take steps now to reduce emissions of greenhouse gases. The UK has set itself a target, if other countries take similar action, of returning UK emissions of carbon dioxide back to 1990 levels by 2000.

Reducing emissions

201. It is impossible to prevent all emissions of greenhouse gases from agriculture. There are, however, some methods that farmers can use to reduce the amount emitted, many of which will also save money.

Carbon dioxide

202. It is important not to confuse the carbon dioxide that is recycled within agriculture and the human and animal food cycle, with the permanent release into the atmosphere of fossilised carbon from fossil fuels and limestone. As crops grow, they absorb carbon dioxide from the atmosphere, but an equal amount is released to the atmosphere when the crop products are used as food for animals or people, so that agriculture cannot be considered a net consumer of carbon dioxide. However, if agricultural products are used as fuels instead of fossil fuels, there is a net reduction in the amount of carbon dioxide generated.

203. As well as by using fossil fuels, agriculture also contributes carbon dioxide from the breakdown of liming materials in the soil. Limestone is made from calcium carbonate which releases fossilised carbon dioxide into the atmosphere as it neutralises acidity in the soil.

204. The most effective way of reducing carbon dioxide emissions is to use energy more efficiently and to exploit alternative non-fossil fuels as sources of energy. Improvements in energy efficiency can reduce farm running costs. The following are important:

- Maintain engines by following the manufacturers recommendations. A 5 to 15% reduction in fuel consumption can be obtained by servicing air cleaners and fuel injectors regularly.
- Choose tractors and machinery that are suitable for the tasks they will be performing. Use the lowest powered tractor capable of doing the required job.
- Do not make unnecessary journeys and cultivation passes.
- Maintain fixed equipment such as grain driers, refrigerated stores and bulk milk tanks in good condition and operate them efficiently.
- Reduce heat loss from heated buildings. Unintentional ventilation of buildings can waste a lot of heat. Effective insulation of walls, roofs, and heating pipes can significantly reduce the amount of heat that is lost.
- Heated glasshouses, mushroom houses and polythene covered structures are major users of energy. Economise on fuel by precise control of the correct temperature regimes, using thermal screens and correct maintenance of boilers and burners.
- Consider the use of energy sources which are not fossil fuels. There are opportunities for using alternative energy sources, such as solar heating, heat pumps, straw burning boilers, biogas from manure digestion, wind and water power. These techniques may be cost effective especially when the amount of energy needed is consistent through the year. Each project needs firstly to be critically assessed for its capital, management and running costs. Further details of some of these possibilities are given in Section 15. There are also potential commercial opportunities to sell the

energy from such sources. Under the Non-Fossil Fuel Obligation, electricity supply companies are required to buy a proportion of their electricity from alternative energy sources.

- Large amounts of fossil fuel are needed to manufacture nitrogen fertilisers. Fertilisers should only be used at the rates suitable for the cropping situation. When calculating application rates, take into account any organic manures or sewage sludge applied to the land. Make sure that fertiliser spreaders are properly maintained and use suitable settings for different types of fertiliser.

Methane

205. The major source of methane loss in UK farming is from ruminant animals and stored slurry. Research is being done on modified diets for livestock that may minimise emissions, although in UK conditions it is unlikely that these will result in significant reductions. Installation of an anaerobic digestion system which makes use of methane produced from slurry (paragraphs 121 and 122) reduces methane losses to air.

Nitrous oxide

206. Nitrous oxide from farms comes from the reaction of nitrogen compounds in manures and soils especially in oxygen-free conditions. The most effective way for farmers to reduce releases of this gas is to avoid excess use of nitrogen fertiliser and manures and make sure that they are not applied to waterlogged soils.

Chlorofluorocarbons (CFCs)

207. Apart from their effect as greenhouse gases, CFCs may also cause the ozone layer around the earth to thin out. This allows more of the sun's ultraviolet-B radiation (UVB) to reach the earth's surface. This could have important economic and health effects as UVB radiation can lead to increased numbers of human eye disorders and skin cancer, as well as damaging crops, farm animals and wildlife.

208. CFCs are used in refrigeration equipment. Keep refrigeration equipment properly maintained to minimise the risk of leaks of refrigerant. Whenever such equipment is serviced, make sure that no refrigerant is lost. Do not allow unused equipment to deteriorate on site. Get a specialised contractor to take away the equipment and safely remove the refrigerant, so that it can be recycled or destroyed.

209. CFCs are also used in halon fire extinguishers which are often kept for usc on electrical fires. When such extinguishers reach the expiry date marked on them or have been partly used, dispose of them through the manufacturer or a specialised contractor so that the halon can be recycled or destroyed.

Appendix 3

Code of Good Agricultural Practice for the Protection of Soil

Ministry of Agriculture, Fisheries and Food

Welsh Office Agriculture Department

1993

Contents

1. Introduction

About this Code

1. This *Code of Good Agricultural Practice for the Protection of Soil* is a practical guide to help farmers and growers avoid causing long-term damage to the soils which they farm. It also provides general guidance on practices which will maintain the ability of soil to support plant growth. It complements advice given in the *Codes of Good Agricultural Practice for the Protection of Water* and of *Air* and the *Code of Practice for the Safe Use of Pesticides*.

2. The Council of Europe, of which the UK is a member, adopted the European Soil Charter in May 1972 and agreed to the Recommendation on Soil Protection in May 1992. These emphasise that soil is a limited natural resource which is easily destroyed, and needs to be protected against damaging farming practices, erosion, pollution and degradation caused by human settlement and civil engineering.

Agriculture has an important role to play in maintaining soils. There is a clear incentive for farmers to protect their soils because that is the basis of their future income.

3. This Code describes the main risks of causing irreversible—or only slowly reversible—physical, chemical or biological changes to soils which would reduce their ability to grow plants for commercial, conservation or recreational purposes and to support living organisms. In each section of the Code, Good Agricultural Practice is defined. It aims to reduce the possibility of such changes occurring. This Code is based on the best information available at the time of writing.

4. The Code provides guidance on protecting the current condition of the soil. It does not include methods of soil management such as land drainage, or methods which deal with short-term damage such as compaction, that can be remedied in a year or two by natural processes or good management practices. However, farmers should avoid such short-term damage, especially if it may encourage other effects. Severe compaction can lead to increased run-off and erosion. The Code concentrates on maintaining soils in a condition that is suitable for a wide range of current and future uses. It is recognised that particular plants or certain uses of soil may justify specific conditions that do not keep to this general aim.

5. The Code is mainly concerned with preventative action to protect the soil, including while it is not being used to grow plants. It also includes remedial actions to cope with contamination incidents such as sea flooding or oil spillage, and following soil disturbance such as mineral workings or laying pipelines.

6. When applying the Code it is important to recognise the properties of a particular soil and to carry out appropriate action. If you do not, you could make matters worse rather than better. The United Kingdom has a wide range of soils. Their physical, chemical and biological properties depend on the materials of which they are made up, the influence of climate and previous management. Details of soils, where they can be found and their properties are shown in the maps and reports published by the Soil Survey and Land Research Centre (previously the Soil Survey of England and Wales).

7. You should manage soils in a way that will maintain their long-term ability to perform their vital functions. You should find out the correct management requirement for the soils on your farm, as set out in this Code. For the areas likely to suffer from erosion, you should draw up a plan of action for future decisions.

NOTES:

The Importance of Soil

Soil is a basic, limited resource that will continue to be essential for many human activities. It includes both topsoil and subsoil to a depth of at least 1 metre. The biological, physical and chemical characteristics of soil need to be protected for it to perform its important functions. These include producing food, raw materials and energy. Soils also provide a filtering and buffering action to protect water and the food chain from potential pollutants; they help to maintain gene pools and wildlife populations; and they often cover historic and archaeological sites and contain artefacts and historical indicators such as pollen.

LAWS ON SOIL PROTECTION

8. This is not a statutory code. Following it will not protect you from legal action, although it should reduce the chance of this happening. Causing pollution of soil is not a specific offence, but there are various laws on contamination and degradation of soils and some of these are outlined below. This is not a detailed description and if you are in any doubt about what the law requires, and how it affects you, you should obtain professional legal advice.

Waste

9. The disposal of industrial, household and commercial waste is regulated by the *Control of Pollution Act 1974* (COPA), the *Environmental Protection Act 1990* (EPA) (whose provisions are in the process of being implemented and will replace COPA), and various regulations such as the *Collection and Disposal of Waste Regulations 1988*. Industrial, household and commercial wastes are defined under this legislation as "controlled wastes" and are subject to a number of provisions including licensing controls. At present waste from premises used for agriculture is not "controlled waste".

The UK is currently working towards implementing the *EC Framework Directive on Waste* (91/156/EEC) by developing waste management Regulations under the *Environmental Protection Act 1990*. These regulations are the responsibility of the Department of Environment (DoE). Should new controls on agriculture prove necessary, the DoE will issue a public consultation paper explaining its proposals before making any change.

Special waste

10. Certain types of waste which are toxic or dangerous, or difficult to treat, keep or dispose of are called "special waste" and are subject to strict controls. The *Control of Pollution (Special Waste) Regulations 1980* regulate the disposal of controlled waste which contains specified substances that make it dangerous to life or give it a flash point of 21°C or less. The 1980 Regulations prescribe a system of consignment notes which are to be used by those who produce, transfer for disposal, or dispose of, special waste. Local authorities, who administer the special waste control procedures, should be notified in advance of its removal from the place of production, and disposers must record the location of the deposit of all special waste on land. These Regulations are under review.

Sewage sludge

11. About 50% of sewage sludge produced in the UK is now recycled and used as an organic fertiliser for agricultural land. Sewage sludge contains heavy metals which can be poisonous to humans, animals, plants or soil micro-organisms if they are present in high concentrations. Applying sludge to agricultural land is regulated throughout the EC by Council Directive 86/278 which is enforced in the UK by the *Sludge (Use in Agriculture) Regulations 1989* and amendments to those regulations.

12. The main provisions of the Regulations are:

- to prevent people from applying sewage sludge to agricultural land when the concentrations of certain heavy metals in the soil (lead, cadmium, mercury, copper, zinc and nickel) are greater than specified limits according to soil pH, see Appendix II;
- to restrict the rate at which heavy metals in sewage sludge are added to soil;
- to prevent animals grazing on agricultural land for three weeks after treated sewage sludge has been applied; and
- to ban farmers from harvesting fruit and other crops which are normally eaten raw for at least 10 months after sewage sludge has been applied.

Other safeguards are recommended in a complementary Code of Practice (DoE) which has been adopted by the Water Companies. These include concentration limits for molybdenum, selenium, arsenic and fluoride (see Appendix II) and special requirements for grassland.

Contaminated land

13. Under Section 143 of the *Environmental Protection Act 1990*, the Government proposed to require local authorities to set up public registers of land subject to contaminative uses. Contaminative uses were defined as "any use of land which may cause it to be contaminated with noxious substances". After consultation the Government withdrew its proposals for registers and established a review of the powers and duties of public bodies in relation to land pollution. The review is being carried out by an inter-departmental Committee who are expected to report to Ministers by early 1994. Meanwhile, local authorities have powers to identify contaminated land and to take action on any threats which it may pose to health. Local authorities are also required to take contamination into consideration in planning decisions.

Minerals

14. The main law controlling the mining of minerals and disposing of mineral wastes is the *Town and Country Planning Act 1990*. Virtually all developments to extract minerals need planning permission. Other conditions for dealing with old mineral permissions which were granted before the 1947 Town and Country Planning Act, are contained in the *Planning and Compensation Act 1991*.

Soil stripping

15. Removing large amounts of surface soil may be regarded as a development as defined by Section 55 of the *Town and Country Planning Act 1990*. If so, you will need planning permission to do this. If you do not get planning permission it is an offence under the *Agricultural Land (Removal of Surface Soil) Act 1953* to remove for sale, more than 5 cubic yards of surface soil from agricultural land in any three month period unless the removal is reasonably necessary for cutting turf or peat. If you are not sure, get advice from the local planning authority (usually the District Council).

Contamination by radioactive substances

16. Radioactive waste is controlled by the *Radioactive Substances Act 1960*. Under this Act, no discharge may take place without permission from the Government.

Ancient monuments and archaeological areas

17. Ancient Monuments and Archaeological Areas are protected by the *Ancient Monuments and Archaeological Areas Act 1979* which prevents any works being carried out on Scheduled Ancient Monuments without the permission of the Secretary of State for National Heritage. This is known as scheduled monument consent (SMC). However, under Section 3 of the Act the Secretary of State has made provision, by way of the *Ancient Monuments (Class Consents) Order 1981*, for agricultural, horticultural and forestry works to be carried out without the need to apply for SMC. The current order covers such works provided they are of the same kind as works previously executed in the same field or location during the period of five years immediately prior to October 1981. This does not include subsoiling, drainage works, the planting or uprooting of trees, hedges or shrubs, or any other works likely to disturb the soil below the maximum depth affected by normal ploughing. There is provision for this permission to be rescinded in individual cases (Section 3) of the 1979 Act. Management agreements may also be offered to occupiers of farmland bearing ancient monuments, and these usually include small grants. For further information you should contact your local English Heritage office.

2. Soil Fertility

Introduction

18. This section deals with chemical and biological processes which affect fertility, including the acidification of soils, maintaining the soil's nutrient reserves and its organic matter content. Loss of fertility due to physical degradation and chemical contamination are covered in later sections of this Code. Only those aspects which take several years to change are covered. Many effects cause short-term reversible change and can be dealt with by good soil management. A well planned rotation of crops can have many benefits for soil fertility. Raising the fertility of soil in natural or semi-natural habitats may reduce the range of plant species living there.

Biological activity

19. Soils contain very many living organisms ranging from microscopic bacteria and fungi to burrowing animals. All play a part in maintaining the natural soil processes which are vital for maintaining the fertility of the soil.

20. Earthworms are one of the most obvious organisms that benefit the soil. Along with other organisms, they are sensitive to certain chemicals and contaminants which you may apply to the soil. These include some pesticides designed to control particular problems but which affect a wide range of organisms. Always choose pesticides carefully according to the purpose for which you need them. Follow the instructions on the label when you use them.

21. Excessive amounts of fertilisers or manures which contain a high proportion of their nitrogen in the form of ammonium, such as ammonium sulphate and certain animal manures or slurries, may reduce the number of earthworms in soil. You can reduce harmful effects on earthworms by not applying slurry on wet, poorly-drained soils. However, the long-term effect may be to increase numbers due to the extra food source provided. If you apply composted materials or well-rotted farmyard manure you will be more likely to increase the number of earthworms in the soil.

22. You can increase earthworms in soil by including grass in your crop rotation, or by regularly applying other bulky organic manures or crop residues. Shallow cultivation may cause less damage to worms than ploughing, and minimum tillage systems help to maintain their burrows which improve the drainage of the soil.

By following these actions to increase the number of earthworms, general biological activity in the soil will also be improved. As a result, the nutrient supply to crops will be increased and the soil structure will be improved.

Acidification

23. Acidification is a natural process which occurs in all soils but which can be increased by man's activities. The extent to which it happens depends on the composition of the soil, deposition from the atmosphere, cropping, nitrogen fertilisers and other management practices. Unless the soil is naturally well-supplied with calcium or magnesium carbonate or is regularly limed, the pH of the soil is reduced until a new balance point is reached. Very acid soils at a pH below 4 will only support a limited range of plant species and are not suitable for agricultural production. Water draining from acid soils may contain chemicals, particularly aluminium, which can have an adverse effect on the quality of surface and groundwaters. In particular, it can harm plants and animals, especially fish, living in streams and lakes.

24. You can maintain or raise the pH value of the cultivated layer of a soil by using liming materials which contain calcium or magnesium carbonate. The pH of soil which has not been cultivated, or of the soil below the depth of cultivation, can only be changed very slowly by applying lime to the surface of the land. For this reason it is important that uncultivated soils, other than peats, growing agricultural crops should not fall below pH 5.5 unless you can use the soil at a lower value. This may be the case in upland areas, woodland and natural habitats (see paragraph 27). If the pH is below this, it can take many years to raise it to an appropriate value. If it is necessary, you should always work lime into the soil before planting perennial crops that are sensitive to acidity (such as fruit trees), taking care to avoid mixing subsoil into the topsoil layer.

25. Have samples of soil analysed regularly to find out how much lime needs to be applied. The amounts you apply should take into account the neutralising value of the particular liming material used. Do not overlime soils and make sure you apply it evenly. The amount of most nutrients which plants can take up will be decreased and plant growth may be reduced. If too much lime is applied, it can take several years for excess lime to be lost from the soil.

26. Not all soils can be maintained at pH 5.5 or above, particularly in the subsoil. Acid sulphate soils occur in limited areas of England and Wales, mainly in peat-covered river valleys or in marine alluvium. Generally, you should leave these soils in their natural state, as drainage and cultivation can cause extreme acidification. If this occurs, liming is often expensive and often fails to achieve a lasting increase in pH. However, very high rates of finely divided liming materials, for example sugar beet factory lime, have been used successfully. Drainage of acid sulphate soils permits oxidation of the naturally-occurring sulphur-containing compounds. This can have a harmful effect on both the quality of the drainage water and the structure of the soil which may make drainage systems ineffective.

27. Some soils may be correctly maintained at a pH below 5.0 to grow and encourage particular species or plant communities in natural and semi-natural habitats. These soils will not be suitable for growing a wider range of species, including most arable crops, unless you raise the pH by liming the soil. Take care to make sure that liming agricultural land does not raise the pH of nearby acid soils or aquatic habitats, which would reduce their conservation value.

28. If you are going to grow crops which prefer acid soils, you can reduce the pH of soil by applying acid-forming materials such as flowers of sulphur. In practice, this is not suitable for large areas and the effect can be difficult to predict. If there is chalk or limestone in the soil it is not a practical option because you would have to apply very large quantities of sulphur to obtain a lasting effect. Obtain professional advice if you are planning such treatment.

NOTES:

Definition of pH

The pH of a soil is a way of expressing how acidic or alkaline it is. It is usually measured using a water extract. A pH of 7 is neutral whereas lower values are said to be acid and values above pH 7 are alkaline. Most agricultural soils (other than peats) are maintained at a pH of between 6.0 and 7.5. Although 5.5 is adequate for grass and some crops, clovers are more sensitive to acid conditions. If clover and other legumes are grown in pure or mixed swards, you should maintain a pH of at least 6.0. Peat soils may be maintained at a rather lower pH than the majority of soils.

Soil nutrient content

29. To grow satisfactorily, plants need good supplies of the major nutrients: nitrogen, phosphorus, potassium, magnesium, calcium and sulphur. Sodium is also required by some crops. Smaller quantities of the trace elements: iron, manganese, copper, zinc, molybdenum, boron and chlorine are required. Trace elements will generally be supplied by the soil, but it may need to be supplemented by inorganic fertilisers and organic manures.

You should have the soil analysed regularly (every four to five years) to set a correct fertiliser policy. The correct balance of available nutrients is necessary to promote satisfactory plant growth. Nutrients are also deposited from the atmosphere, particularly sulphur, nitrogen and some of the trace elements. As a direct result of the amount of sulphur deposits being reduced, fertilisers which contain sulphur are now needed in many areas of the UK.

30. As long as the soil pH and organic matter content are maintained at appropriate values, most of the additional nutrient requirements of plants can be met by applying fertilisers or manures each year, or once in the rotation. If an agricultural soil is very low in nutrients, you can raise reserves of phosphorus and potash in two or three years by using fertilisers or manure generously, if it is appropriate to do so. However, take care to maintain the balance of all nutrients and avoid water pollution by nitrogen, phosphorus or organic matter (see *Code of Good Agricultural Practice for the Protection of Water*). You should not apply more than 250 kg/ha of nitrogen in livestock manures or other organic wastes in any one year.

Nutrient uptake into herbage is important for livestock health. Plant analysis is often necessary, possibly as well as soil analysis, to identify and correct any mineral imbalance.

31. In soils which are naturally deficient it can be difficult to raise available phosphorus reserves. In these situations, fertiliser phosphorus can bind strongly to the soil and is not available to plants. You may have to make many applications of organic or inorganic fertilisers to raise the available amount of phosphorus in the soil to a concentration suitable for general crop production. Once raised, you can maintain the available soil phosphorus content by regularly applying fertiliser.

32. Particular plants or natural habitats such as chalk grassland and flower-rich meadows may benefit from having low soil nitrogen and phosphorus contents, as this limits the growth of vigorous species such as ryegrass which compete with the natural species. Protect these habitats from direct application of fertiliser or run-off from nearby fertilised areas. Such principles have been introduced into the management regimes for some MAFF Environmentally Sensitive Areas.

33. Do not apply more phosphorus (in fertilisers or manures) than the crops in the rotation need. If soil particles with a high phosphorus content are eroded and deposited in rivers, lakes or the sea, the phosphorus content of the water will rise. This may cause eutrophication, making algae grow too fast, which uses up the oxygen in the water and can kill fish. Leaching (washing out) of soluble phosphorus compounds in drainage water can occur if a soil is nearly saturated with phosphorus. This is only likely to occur on sandy soils after many years of applying very large amounts of animal manures.

34. Do not apply more nitrogen (in fertilisers or manures) than the crop needs, as this can pollute the water with nitrate. Too much nitrate in surface water can cause aquatic plants to grow and contribute to other symptoms of eutrophication. Nitrate concentrations of more than 50 mg/l are undesirable in water for public supply and can trigger measures under the EC Nitrate Directive which affect agriculture.

NOTES:

Eutrophication

For the purpose of this Code, eutrophication is defined as the enrichment of water by nitrogen or phosphorus, causing algae and higher forms of plant life to grow too fast which disturbs the balance of organisms present in the water and the quality of the water concerned.

Organic matter

35. The amount and type of organic matter in the top layer of a soil influences its physical, chemical and biological properties. In particular, it affects its structural stability (and so the likelihood of erosion), how easy it is to cultivate, how much water it can retain and the nutrients available to plants. It also influences the behaviour of contaminants. Changes in management can result in increases or decreases in organic matter content.

36. A major aim should be to maintain the organic matter in a cultivated soil so that it can support plant growth. The amount that is needed will vary with the soil and farming system. The organic content of soil will fall with arable farming, particularly if the amount of plant residue returned to the soil is low. Organic matter may also be reduced by erosion, by removing topsoil which removes the organic rich layer, or by deep ploughing which dilutes the topsoil with subsoil which is low in organic materials.

Long-term trials show that, in arable systems, the highest yields are only possible when you take positive steps to maintain the level of organic matter in the soil.

37. If you do not have large quantities of bulky organic manures, such as farmyard manure, you can only increase the organic matter content in cultivated soil by changing the cropping. If you grow grass in previously cultivated land for a number of years, the soil organic matter may be increased. To maintain this higher level, your crop rotation may have to include grass. Returning crop residues to the land or applying bulky organic manures to land will gradually increase the organic matter content if you do this for several years. Following the ban on burning crop residues, ploughing straw into the soil is expected to have a small beneficial effect upon organic matter content in the short to medium term.

38. Significant increases in the organic matter content of arable soils will increase the amount of nitrogen available for crops. Adjust fertiliser rates or introduce other management practices to prevent an increase in leaching of nitrate (see MAFF Reference Book 209 *Fertiliser Recommendations*).

3. Physical Degradation

Introduction

39. Irreversible or only slowly reversible physical damage to soil is defined as physical degradation. This Section of the Code describes how this can be reduced or avoided by appropriate techniques. By taking action to control short-term problems you can control the more serious long-term degradation.

Soil compaction

40. Compaction of topsoils, or more especially subsoils, may seriously damage soils and can only be reversed very slowly. Compaction restricts root growth and reduces infiltration of water into soil. It can increase run-off which may lead to greater flooding, increased erosion and the transfer of potential pollutants (including nutrients and pesticides) to surface waters. As the air getting into the soil is also restricted, the biological activity is affected which reduces the fertility of the soil and more specifically the availability of plant nutrients. So it is important to minimise all forms of soil compaction.

41. Free-draining soils which are not regularly cultivated develop a soil structure which allows root growth and infiltration and drainage of water. Using agricultural or other machinery when the soil is too wet can seriously compact soil and restrict root growth. Allowing livestock to graze when the land is wet can also damage the soil structure and cause similar problems. Water movement is reduced and so plant growth is restricted. You should always take into account the condition of the soil when deciding what machinery to use, and when to use it. Large agricultural machinery is not necessarily a greater risk for normal work on undisturbed soils. This is because faster work rates allow the work to be completed under better soil moisture conditions. Using low ground-pressure tyres, dual wheels or tracked vehicles can be a great benefit. Axle load is an important factor and you should get professional advice to provide safe working guidelines for specific soil conditions, particularly on fine loamy, silty and clayey soils.

42. When choosing the crops to grow, you should take into account the ability to cultivate the land when necessary without causing unacceptable compaction. On clayey soils, cultivations for autumn crops are likely to cause less damage than cultivations for crops that are sown in the spring. You should also consider possible harvesting problems, in particular for root and vegetable crops. If winter harvesting is planned, take account of likely field conditions when deciding where to plant the crops. Advice on available work days for different soils is given in Regional reports from the Soil Survey and Land Research Centre.

43. In England and Wales, severe soil compaction is not a widespread problem. In areas where fine loamy or silty topsoils lie over clayey subsoils, plough pans and smearing can often be caused in wet conditions. When you have correctly identified these problems they can usually be corrected by ploughing or by subsoiling. Pay particular attention to compaction caused by repeated driving in tramlines or during harvesting. Regularly inspect vulnerable soils before cultivating to decide on any corrective measures that are necessary. However, if the structural damage is severe and is linked with low organic matter content, deep cultivation followed by several years in grass may be necessary to regenerate the soil. If damage is caused during soil restoration, the subsoil may become severely compacted and this can be very difficult, if not impossible, to correct (see Section 5). Whenever you are considering deep cultivation, take account of soil conditions and any work you will be carrying out later. Loosening the soil can make it more vulnerable to compaction by work that you do in the future.

Removing topsoil

44. The formation of fertile, humus-rich topsoil is a very slow natural process. Removal or erosion of topsoil reduces the productivity of the land by reducing the water and nutrients available to plants, and making the soil more likely to suffer from structural damage.

Shallow compact soils are less able to absorb rainfall and the risk of water erosion may be increased.

The loss of topsoil, either by direct action or indirectly as a result of management practices, should be kept to a minimum.

45. Stripping or removing topsoil for sale is an offence under the *Agricultural Land (Removal of Surface Soil) Act 1953* unless you have planning permission to do so (see paragraph 15). If you do not need any of the soil that is part of an agreed development project, you should move it somewhere else where it can be used.

46. Removing turf from agricultural land removes the surface layer of soil and its organic matter and plant nutrients. Although modern turfing techniques only remove a shallow layer of soil, you should avoid repeated cutting if this would restrict the future use of the land.

SOIL EROSION

47. Soil erosion is the loss of soil particles by the action of wind and water. Plants generally protect the soil against erosion but significant problems can occur on soils used for arable agriculture or after large areas of trees have been cut down. Risk of soil erosion is increased when soil organic matter content has decreased.

Repeated erosion results in a gradual loss of topsoil and reduces the fertility of the soil by selectively removing the fine soil particles which are rich in nutrients.

48. Apart from soil loss, damage can be caused to agricultural crops. Erosion can increase flooding and may cause contamination of surface waters by sediment and by the nutrients and pesticides in the eroded soil. Erosion may cause inconvenience and damage to non-agricultural interests and to the general public, for example by sediment being deposited on roads. The most obvious cases of erosion occur in lowland England and Wales, but significant problems can also occur in upland areas where over-grazing or recreational activities have removed the vegetation cover.

Erosion by water

49. Water erosion causes soil to be lost to some extent from all sloping arable land and land that is alternated between grass and arable crops. Sediment may be redeposited within the field or on roads, other properties or in water-courses and reservoirs. Severe erosion is uncommon in the UK but moderate erosion can occur on sands and light loams where heavy rainfall, slope and reduced infiltration combine to cause surface water to run-off. Erosion may be confined to run-off which contains fine soil particles, or it may be more serious and cut channels called rills or gullies. The significance of losing soil from land which lies on top of hard rock at shallow depth is much greater than where the underlying material is already weathered. Rooting depth and the quantity of soil water available for crops is reduced.

Water erosion in England and Wales has increased due to the increased area of arable cropping, the use of tramlines for spraying crops, the need for fine winter cereal seedbeds and the removal of hedgerows. Consider the possibility of soil erosion before you carry out any of these operations, particularly ploughing out pasture that is on sloping land.

Sandy soils in SW and SE England, East Anglia, the Midlands and South Wales are most at risk. Chalky soils on the South Downs, Wolds and in East Anglia are also prone to damage.

50. Water erosion may occur when the rate of rainfall is greater than the rate at which water soaks into the surface of the soil. Run-off then occurs. Appropriate management can greatly reduce the risk of this occurring. Avoid unnecessarily deep or numerous cultivations and working on the land when it is too wet. Compaction reduces the soil's ability to absorb water and this leads to ponding and run-off. You should correct this before you sow the next crop (see paragraphs 40 and 178–179). Careful planning should include the whole farm, pinpointing situations where there is a high risk of run-off and taking measures to reduce the risk in these areas. Pay particular attention to valley bottoms where run-off can accumulate. Reduce run-off from farm roads and tracks and from concreted areas by having adequate drains, ditches and soakaways. Control drainage water from fields by maintaining land drains, pipe outlets and ditches. Pay particular attention to removing sediment that has been deposited in ditches and drains.

51. If water erosion is a frequent or serious problem you may need to introduce grass into your crop rotation, create permanent grass strips as buffer areas, plant hedges or build new ditches to restrict run-off, or direct run-off water away from areas prone to erosion. Buffer areas of rough vegetation and hedges also encourage sediment to be deposited within or at the bottom of a field and so protect roads and watercourses.

52. Develop stable topsoils by applying bulky animal manures or other suitable organic materials where these are available (but see paragraph 30 and the *Code of Good Agricultural Practice for the Protection of Water*). In appropriate circumstances, consider introducing grass into arable rotations, or even having areas of permanent grassland. Government-supported schemes such as Environmentally Sensitive Areas or Nitrate Sensitive Areas are designed to help achieve this. Set-aside arrangements may also allow the most vulnerable areas of the field or farm to be protected by grass cover.

53. As plant cover is an important way of protecting the surface of land, planting winter crops early is very important where the risk of erosion is high. In such situations, drill winter cereals early and if possible without gaps for tramlines. Set up paths for spraying after the crops have emerged. If tramlines are left when you drill the crops do not use them until the spring. If this is not practical, due to your method of crop management, a shallow tine behind the wheel can break up any compacted soil and so reduce run-off.

54. Cultivating and planting crops in fields "on the contour" is recommended for controlling erosion in many parts of the world. For mechanised agriculture it is likely to be effective for crops grown in gently sloping fields with simple slope patterns which are present in arable land in England and Wales. For steeper sloping fields with complex slope patterns it is not practical to follow the contours accurately. In these fields, attempts at cultivations across the slope often lead to channelling of run-off water which can cause severe erosion. On steeper slopes, the risk of accidents from using machinery across fields is high. For row crops such as potatoes and sugar-beet, harvesters only work effectively up and down the slope. These crops may be unsuitable for sites that are particularly vulnerable to water erosion.

When using a reversible plough across the slope, always throw the soil up the hill to reduce the effect of erosion and soil creep.

55. You can protect bare ground by making sure that some chopped cereal straw is left at the surface during cultivations. You can do this by using tines or discs in place of ploughing. Rough seed-beds are more stable than fine tilths. Avoid rolling after autumn drilling on vulnerable sites (particularly when soils are wet) to help maintain the rate at which water is absorbed by the soil.

56. Cover crops such as rye, mustard or grass, sown in late summer or early autumn and ploughed in or killed off before drilling in spring, give good control of both water and wind erosion on sensitive soils. They may also reduce nitrate leaching.

57. Land which is ridged to grow potatoes and bed systems for vegetables in general are particularly at risk of increasing water erosion. Using soil walls to bridge furrows across the slope (tied ridges) and small pits (dikes) along furrow bottoms help to improve the soil's ability to absorb water, reduce run-off and so prevent erosion. These techniques are particularly valuable for irrigated crops.

Always apply irrigation water in a way that avoids erosion. Do not apply too much water, at too high a rate or with too great a droplet size. Avoid having leaking pipework and carefully drain water from disconnected equipment.

58. Land which is regularly and severely affected by water erosion and which cannot be controlled by changes in farming methods, cropping or by the other control measures outlined above should be put down to permanent grassland or woodland. Various Government-supported options are available, including set-aside and support for establishing farm woodlands.

59. Soils in upland areas with high rainfall are frequently shallow, often with a peaty topsoil that is not very fertile. When the plant cover is broken (by livestock, unsealed tracks, drainage ditches or recreational activities) they

are particularly prone to water erosion. When over-grazing has or is likely to cause a problem, you should reduce your stocking rates. Take care to limit the other activities mentioned in vulnerable areas. Protect eroding areas by encouraging the regeneration of plants to cover the soil.

60. When you are establishing any woodland or forestry areas, take precautions to avoid soil erosion. Keep a cover of plants where possible and avoid causing compaction by planting equipment, particularly on slopes, shallow soils and in upland peaty areas. (See *Forests and Water Guidelines*, Forestry Commission).

Erosion by wind

61. Wind erosion normally only affects bare sandy and peaty soils in exposed areas, especially between March and June. Arable soils that are planted in spring are commonly bare and dry during this period. The areas of highest risk are in parts of the East Midlands, Yorkshire and East Anglia. Wind erosion of exposed peaty soils can also occur in upland areas.

62. If your farming system and soil type together result in soil erosion, you should use control measures. You can control wind erosion by reducing wind speed at ground level, making the soil surface stable and trapping any soil particles which are already moving. Individual methods for control are described in the following paragraphs.

63. You can grow rows of trees or hedgerows to trap airborne particles and to provide protection for soil and for crops grown on the sheltered side. Shelters should allow 30–50% of the wind to pass through. Protection from the shelter reduces with distance and does not extend more than 20 times the height of the shelter. The benefit depends on the actual direction of any damaging winds. You can get information on the likely frequency and direction of damaging winds from meteorological records and you can use this information to help you decide where to put shelter belts. Shelters can also have important value for wildlife and should be planted accordingly.

64. Crops such as winter rye, winter barley or mustard can be grown as cover or nurse crops to provide protection for both soil and spring-sown crops. You can kill off cover crops before the spring crop is drilled, by cultivation or spraying, and nurse crops may be sprayed out during the early life of the crop. These methods are effective for peaty soils and for irrigated sandy soils.

65. On peaty soils, mechanised straw planting in rows may provide shelter for vegetable crops that you sow very early.

66. The traditional practice of marling to increase the clay content of peats and sands may provide a long-term solution to wind erosion. This technique is unlikely to be practical or economic unless suitable material is available close-by. You need to apply 300–1000 t/ha of suitable marling material to stabilise the surface of the soil. To be successful, the clay content of sandy topsoils should be increased to 8–10%. The marl should be left on the soil surface long enough for the lumps to break down by frost action before you cultivate it into the soil. After marling, you can lose the benefit if you plough the soil too deeply.

67. Applying mulches to the surface of seed-beds on sandy soils at 5–15 t/ha after drilling is an effective control measure. Organic manures, sugar beet factory lime and sewage sludge are suitable materials for mulches. When you use sewage sludge you must comply with the Regulations (see paragraphs 11–12) and any local water protection restrictions. Waste cellulose from paper production may be available locally and may be suitable for stabilising the surface. Other wastes must also comply with the appropriate Regulations (paragraphs 9–10). If you disturb the mulch by cultivating the land, the benefit is lost.

68. Synthetic stabilisers such as PVA (polyvinylacetate) emulsions or PAM (polyacrylamides) sprayed onto the soil surface of sands after drilling can provide temporary protection for high value crops. This method is unsuitable on peat soils. Appropriate professional advice should be obtained before you use these methods to control erosion.

69. Choosing cultivation practices carefully can provide effective erosion control for sandy soils. You can form an erosion-resistant surface by ploughing if there is enough silt and clay in the topsoil. Plough and press the soil at the same time before you sow the crop and drill it at right angles to the direction of pressing without cultivating the seed-bed any further. Adequate moisture is needed if pressing is to provide a stable surface. Uncultivated crop stubble also provides protection against wind erosion and a spring-sown crop can sometimes be drilled directly into the soil surface. However, you must take care as a compacted surface may increase run-off and cause water erosion. To ensure satisfactory crop growth, remove any compaction by loosening where necessary.

DEEP CULTIVATION AND MIXING OF SOIL

70. In certain situations, mixing the topsoil and subsoil may improve the physical characteristics of the soil by introducing clay into sandy soils or mineral matter into shallow and degraded peats. Usually, however, you should avoid diluting topsoil with subsoil brought to the surface as it will reduce fertility and cause physical degradation.

71. Do not plough deeper than 30 cm in silty and fine sandy topsoils with a low organic matter content, especially if the subsoil has an even lower organic matter content. If they are ploughed, the stability of the topsoil will be reduced even more. Crop establishment may be affected or wind and water erosion may be increased.

72. Avoid deep-ploughing shallow soils which lie over loose or weathered materials such as chalk. Deep ploughing will dilute plant nutrients, result in coarser seed-beds and slow down soil warming in spring. Increase the rooting depth by subsoiling rather than by ploughing.

73. Many heavy textured, poorly drained, grassland soils only have a well-developed structure of small aggregates in the top few centimetres. Ploughing these soils can dilute organic matter, destroy natural soil drainage and so increase the risk of damage by machinery and animals. The management of these soils will then be difficult for many years. If you need to reseed such swards, use surface seeding or shallow cultivation techniques.

74. Keep soil disturbance to a minimum when you remove trees from land by grubbing orchards, harvesting standard nursery stock trees, or clearing farm woodlands (including coppiced stands). Mixing subsoil can cause problems similar to those described in paragraph 70. Carry out all mechanised work when there is no risk of compacting the soil. Soil removed on the roots should be kept to a minimum.

75. A large part of our archaeological heritage is in the countryside, protected beneath the soil. These remains are easily disturbed and can be damaged or lost by ploughing, under drainage, subsoiling or other soil disturbance, including planting or uprooting of trees, shrubs or hedges. Such sites may be legally protected (see paragraph 17). You should make careful plans and obtain the necessary consent before undertaking any new work. You should read the Ministry of Agriculture and English Heritage booklet *Farming Historic Landscapes and People* and English Heritage's publication *Ancient Monuments in the Countryside*. A management agreement, including a small grant, may be available to help you to protect the site.

Not all ancient monuments are legally protected but they may still be of historic importance. If you have such sites on your land or you uncover remains or objects, you should contact your County Archaeological Officer (details from your local authority or English Heritage or CADW in Wales).

LOSS OF LOWLAND PEAT

76. Some lowland areas in England and Wales (such as in Humberside, the East Anglian Fens, Somerset Levels and Lancashire and Cumbria Mosses) have limited areas of peat deposits. In their original state, these deposits formed raised mires (domes of peat) or fen (sedge) peats. Areas of undrained, lowland peat-bogs with natural vegetation have become increasingly rare in England and Wales and many of these habitats are protected as Sites of Special Scientific Interest (SSSIs). You should leave undrained or virtually unaltered sites as natural or semi-natural areas, or as traditionally-managed pasture. You can receive grants under various conservation schemes to manage nearby land so as to reduce effects upon SSSIs.

77. Large areas of original peatland, especially in East Anglia and Lancashire, have been drained to form agricultural land. When drained and fertilised, these areas form very productive soil which is capable of producing high yields of root crops and vegetables. For effective drainage you need to lower the water table. This causes shrinkage of the land through the peat drying out and, together with repeated cultivation, it stimulates breakdown (oxidation) which leads to a reduction in the depth of peat. Several metres of peat have been already lost by these processes in parts of East Anglia. To maintain the peat depth, keep the water table as close to the surface for as long as possible consistent with the need to manage the land for food production. The processes of peat wastage can be slowed down or prevented only by reinstating natural peat mire conditions. This action would drastically reduce the value of the soils for growing crops. Land set aside for periods of one year will have little effect on the rate of wastage if water tables stay at low levels in surrounding fields.

4. Contamination

Introduction

78. This section describes the risks associated with the chemical contamination of soils and the measures that you need to take to avoid this happening. Man's activities may contaminate soil; either directly through applying materials such as industrial wastes, sewage sludge, pesticides, fertilisers or contaminated irrigation water; or indirectly by atmospheric deposition such as lead from car exhausts. Such activities usually result in contaminants building up slowly over many years and the timescale involved may mean that their significance is not easily recognised. Contamination may also occur quickly by more obvious and damaging events such as spillages, uncontrolled land spreading or dumping of wastes.

79. Soil may also become contaminated by natural processes which result in eroded materials that contain potentially harmful elements being deposited in the soil. Flooding by water from waste tips or mining sites can be a direct source of contamination. In such cases you may need to use short and long-term management techniques to protect the soil and the safety of livestock and humans who eat the crops grown there.

80. Land may already have been contaminated by natural processes or by man's activities. If large areas of soil are seriously polluted, realistic remedial measures may be too expensive for agricultural land. However, you can improve crop growth or reduce metal uptake of the crop by taking appropriate management measures such as liming the soil to raise its pH. For smaller areas, removal of contaminated soil to an appropriately licensed disposal site or covering it with a "clean" material may be appropriate. You should take professional advice on the best way of dealing with individual problems. Clean-up techniques which involve high-cost treatment are available for contaminated sites and have been reviewed in the Warren Spring Laboratory Report which is included in the list of further reading.

81. Contaminants can be considered under two headings:

- Inorganic materials—such as zinc, copper, lead and arsenic—which tend to remain in soil indefinitely, although their chemical or physical state may change with time.
- Organic materials—usually man-made chemicals such as pesticides or industrial solvents—which are broken down to a greater or lesser extent by micro-organisms in the soil. In some cases the result of the breakdown can be chemicals which are themselves contaminants. Even though the materials or their breakdown products are broken down, repeated applications may mean that a high concentration is present in the soil.

82. As inorganic and some organic contaminants occur naturally in soils, you need to analyse and assess the local background concentrations as well as the nature and origin of the various added contaminants. If background concentrations are low, deposits of trace elements such as zinc and copper, which

are essential for the growth of plants and animals, may increase the fertility of a soil.

83. Assess the risk associated with a particular contaminant in soil by considering the contaminant's effects on the following:

- soil biological activity;
- crop growth;
- concentration in human and animal diets; and
- surface water and groundwater quality.

84. To protect the long-term use of soil, you must recognise the many potential sources of contamination in order to assess their significance and then to take the necessary steps to prevent, limit or overcome their effects.

Whenever you apply waste materials containing potential contaminants to land, you must notify the Waste Disposal Authority.

A guide to acceptable concentrations and recommended management techniques is given in this section and in Annex I. You should protect soils from all avoidable contamination. Contaminants which were having no harmful effects may be taken up by the crop or leached from the soil if the soil becomes acid.

85. Whenever contamination is suspected, or you want to dispose of waste, professional advice should be obtained, based on analysis of the soil and of the waste materials.

Legal restrictions

86. As explained in Section 1, legislation which controls the application of sewage sludge to land sets limits for the concentration of certain contaminants in soil. Legislation does not prevent any particular soil being used for agriculture because of any contaminants in that soil. However, there are legal limits for concentrations of lead and arsenic in food and for a variety of inorganic and organic substances in animal feed. You need to take care not to exceed these limits when you produce food on soils with high concentrations of these contaminants.

87. Under the *Food and Environment Protection Act 1985* there are legal controls on advertising, selling, supplying, storing and using pesticides. There are also maximum residue levels (MRLs) for pesticides in food. The MRLs reflect maximum residues likely to arise from pesticides that are used correctly. Limits have also been set to reflect background levels for some persistent compounds which are no longer in use such as DDT, dieldrin and aldrin. Under the same Act, controls may be applied on food contaminated by other chemicals (such as dioxins) to prevent them entering the food chain.

Inorganic contaminants

88. Although soils may be affected by a wide range of contaminants, problems usually arise from a relatively small number of elements. Elements which can kill plants or reduce yields if they are present in high concentrations include zinc, copper, nickel, cadmium and arsenic. Elements which can be particularly harmful to animals or man include lead, arsenic, cadmium, mercury, copper, fluorine, selenium and molybdenum. In lower concentrations some of these elements may be essential trace elements for either plants or animals. With the exception of molybdenum and selenium, plants take up more of these substances from acid soils. Guidelines have been prepared for grazing old mining areas (Interdepartmental Committee on the Redevelopment of Contaminated Land (ICRCL) Guidance Note 70/90). Individual contaminants are discussed in Annex I.

NOTES:

Effects on Livestock

For most contaminants, but not molybdenum and selenium, the risk of poisoning livestock grazing on a contaminated soil depends almost entirely on the amount of soil swallowed and the concentration of the contaminant in that soil rather than the concentration in the grass. This concentration factor is more important than the fact that the contaminant may be released more easily from grass than from the soil once it is in the digestive system of the animal. The amount of soil contamination on grass will vary with the type of sward, its thickness, the time of year, weather conditions, stocking density and how grazing is managed. In a thick sward, or where there is a surface mat of grass, soil contamination of the diet may be less than 3% of the dry matter. In reseeded pastures, with an incomplete plant cover, soil contamination is often as high as 10% or more. Make sure that hay and silage is not contaminated with soil during harvesting. This means making sure that cutting equipment and pick-up reels are not set so low that they touch the soil.

The risk to livestock depends on:

- levels of contamination in the soil, and of soil contamination on the grass;
- levels of contaminants accumulated in the grass;
- variations in dietary intake over the year;
- differences in the uptake of the contaminant by livestock from their diet;
- the type, species, age and health of the animals;
- the length of time they are grazing; and
- supplementary food they are given.

There is a limited amount of reliable information on livestock tolerance to metals and other contaminants, particularly possible interactions between them. So it is only possible to give general guidelines on critical soil concentrations. It is based on expected metal concentration in or on the grass and the animals' intake, assuming that a specified proportion of soil is eaten as part of the diet. It is essential that you receive appropriate veterinary advice when you suspect that contamination is the cause of either acute (rapid) or chronic (long-term) deterioration of the health of your livestock.

Organic contaminants

89. Town refuse, other domestic and industrial wastes and, sewage sludge may contain organic chemicals which pose a threat to the environment. A large number of compounds could be involved and it is not possible to identify or monitor all of them while they are being applied to the land. Before you apply any wastes to land, they should have been analysed to see if any contaminants are likely to be present in large amounts. Without knowledge of specific contaminants, indicator a compounds should be used to assess the overall concentration of contaminants. Take specialist advice on these. More research is needed before it is possible to give general recommendations on maximum concentrations of organic contaminants. However, very few specific problems have been identified so far.

90. Most organic compounds are lost from soil by volatilisation into the air or they are broken down in the soil, but at different rates. The breakdown products may also be harmful. You must take precautions when you apply wastes or pesticides (see paragraph 112) to soil to make sure that there is no risk to water or the food chain. To protect soil over the long-term, applications should not affect soil organisms as this could damage soil fertility. The amount or frequency of application should not cause contaminants to build up in the soil. This is particularly important for compounds such as polychlorinated biphenyls (PCBs) and the more persistent pesticides which break down slowly in soils.

91. The following compounds give an indication of those which may be encountered. The group produced from benzene includes dichlorobenzene used in toilet disinfectants, and alkyl benzenes used in detergents. Polychlorinated biphenyls (PCBs) were used as electrical insulating agents but are no longer made in the United Kingdom. Polynuclear aromatic hydrocarbons (PAHs) are produced by burning and they occur at moderate levels in industrial wastes. Dioxins and furans may be present but usually only at very low concentrations.

92. Contamination of soil by mineral oils reduces plant growth by blocking soil pores and reducing the amount of oxygen available. Some oils are also directly poisonous to plants (see paragraphs 128–134 on Oil spillage).

Industrial contamination

93. It is important to identify any contamination of land previously used for industrial purposes including mining for metals, particularly where such sites are being returned to agriculture. Take care to prevent contaminants being spread on 'clean' sites or from entering ground or surface waters. You can obtain advice and guidance on contaminated land from a series of guidance notes published by the Department of the Environment on behalf of the ICRCL. Recommended threshold trigger concentrations for organic and inorganic contaminants are given according to the proposed use of the land. For gardens and allotments, action is suggested at lower concentrations than for recreational or amenity use where the risk of human exposure to the contaminants is much less.

Seek professional advice before you take any action to reclaim contaminated land.

94. The treatment processes are based on a range of physical, chemical and biological treatments which either remove the contaminants or make them harmless. The costs of these treatments are usually far greater than the value of land for agricultural purposes.

95. It is unlikely that industrial sites, other than some closed landfill sites or some in old mining areas, will be returned to agriculture. However, if the land is returned to agriculture, the ICRCL garden and allotment thresholds should apply, except in the case of grazing on old metal-mining sites where separate guidelines have been prepared. (ICRCL Guidance Note 70/90).

Atmospheric deposition

96. Atmospheric deposition is the term used to describe how contaminants in the air reach the soil as gases or are washed down in rain. These contaminants may arise from natural sources such as wind erosion or volcanic activity. In the UK, deposits of contaminants from natural sources have little effect. Contaminants which arise from human activities may cause large deposits near to a source such as an industrial complex. They may be dispersed more thinly over a wide area from activities such as coal burning.

Controls over industrial emissions to the atmosphere have increased in recent years. Although long-term deposition is less likely in future, continuing care is necessary, particularly to control organic contaminants. Care needs to be taken near industrial sites and you should take any necessary precautions to protect the environment and the food chain if an accidental emission occurs. You should seek professional guidance on what to do in any particular situation. Radioactive fall-out from a nuclear accident is dealt with by Government action according to the particular circumstances. General advice is not given in this Code.

Sewage sludge

97. It is a positive environmental benefit to recycle the carbon and plant nutrients that are in sewage sludge to agricultural land. Applying sludge to agricultural land is controlled by the *Sludge (Use in Agriculture) Regulations 1989* as amended, which implement EC Council Directive 86/278. Further guidance is given in the supporting Department of the Environment (DoE) *Code of Practice for Agricultural use of Sewage Sludge* (HMSO 1989). These are designed to protect the environment in general, and in particular the soil, when sewage sludge is used in agriculture (paragraphs 11–12). The risks have been evaluated and controls set, but they are kept under review and may need to be amended as a result of current research. Many other materials contain one or more of the contaminants present in sewage sludge and may cause similar problems. The concentration of contaminants in sewage sludge, in particular of heavy metals, has been greatly reduced in the last 10 years, mainly because of controls on industrial discharges. As a result, the nutrients needed by your crops should usually determine the application rates. It will usually take well over 100 applications of an average sludge before any of the metal concentration limits are reached. The limits are given in Annex II.

98. The producers of the sludge are responsible for keeping to the legal requirements on concentrations of metal contaminants. It is an offence to cause or knowingly allow sludge to be used on agricultural land when this does not meet the requirements of the Regulations. You should make sure that you know these requirements as explained in the DoE Code. Her Majesty's Inspectorate of Pollution (HMIP) enforces the Regulations.

99. The metals in sludge are from industrial discharges and domestic sources. They remain in soils virtually forever and their effects may increase as the associated organic matter is broken down by natural soil processes. If uncontrolled, these effects would include reductions of crop growth, increased intake of metals by animals and man through food, and reductions in the activity of microbes in the soil.

To avoid these potential problems, the UK has had established guidelines for sludge use in agriculture since 1976.

Further explanatory notes are given in the following paragraphs.

100. There are legal restrictions on zinc, copper, nickel, cadmium, lead, mercury and chromium which control the amount applied and the ultimate concentration in the soil in samples taken to a depth of 25 cm, or the depth of topsoil if less. The UK Code of Practice also recommends that the concentrations should not be exceeded in soil samples taken to a depth of only 15 cm in arable land or to the depth at which sludge may be injected. The Code also gives recommended limits (not legally-set ones) for applying molybdenum, selenium, arsenic and fluoride. Any other inorganic contaminants present in sludge should not be a problem, as long as you keep within the limits set for these major contaminants.

101. The Code also provides recommendations for the maximum concentration of contaminants in the top 7.5 cm of soil under grass. These are intended to limit the risk to grazing animals and to reduce the damage to plants whose roots may concentrate in this surface layer. If these concentrations are exceeded at 7.5 cm, cultivate the soil to disperse the metals before further applications are made.

102. Different metal limits apply according to the acidity (pH) of the soil. It is important that you keep the pH of the soil at the appropriate level both during and after applying sludge. Most metals become more available in acid soils and any adverse effects will then increase. The availability of selenium and molybdenum to plants increases in alkaline soils. When sludge is applied up to the allowed limits, you will need to maintain the pH for an indefinite period. Sludge should not be applied to agricultural land with a pH below 5.0.

103. The Regulations and Code referred to in paragraph 97 only relate to agricultural land. They do not apply to forests, reclaimed land, amenity or service areas. A separate Code of Practice has been issued by the Forestry Commission for sludge use in forests. This recommends that the concentration limits in Annex II of this Soil Code relating to pH 5.0–5.5 should apply. This allows for the acidic nature of many forest soils. For other types of land, the metal concentration limits in Annex II for the appropriate pH should apply.

Other industrial and domestic wastes

104. The disposal of wastes subject to the *Control of Pollution Act 1974* are regulated by the *Collection and Disposal of Waste Regulations 1988*. Such wastes can be applied to land without a licence only if the material is applied "for the purpose of fertilising or otherwise beneficially conditioning that land". In these cases notification is required to the local Waste Regulatory Authority. As stated in paragraph 9, new waste management controls are being developed by the DoE.

There is no definition of a fertiliser in this context but the elements that may be considered as fertilisers in agriculture in England and Wales are identified in paragraph 29 as those essential for plant growth. At least part of the content of these elements should be available, or become available, for plant uptake within three years.

Apart from consideration of whether a waste is a fertiliser, the amount applied should not exceed the nutrient requirement of the crop or rotation of crops being grown. Applications must not pollute water-courses or have other harmful effects on the environment.

105. Beneficially conditioning the land should be regarded as a long-term physical improvement. The temporary increase in soil moisture through the water in dilute wastes should not be considered as beneficial conditioning. Even if a waste can be said to be fertilising or beneficially conditioning, it should not be applied to land if it contains unacceptable quantities of potential contaminants.

106. Contaminants applied to soil may subsequently affect water quality if they are leached or eroded into ground or surface waters. Application of wastes containing contaminants should always be undertaken so that the risk to water quality is minimised by avoiding losses to the aquatic environment. (See *Code of Good Agricultural Practice for the Protection of Water* and *National Rivers Authority Policy and Practice for the Protection of Groundwater*).

107. When wastes are known, or suspected, to contain elements not specifically covered in this Code, all relevant information should be assessed and professional guidance sought to decide if land application is desirable and if so at what rate.

Animal manures

108. The main contaminants in animal manures are copper and zinc. EC legislation has reduced the concentration allowed in animal feed, so the quantities in manures have now been reduced. On fields which receive repeated applications of animal manure, you should check the content of these metals in pig and poultry manures and slurries and the concentrations in the soil. Take samples to a depth of 15 cm for arable land and 7.5 cm for grassland. If the soil values approach the limits in Appendix II, get professional advice about applying manure to this land in the future.

109. Animal manures contain relatively high quantities of the main plant nutrients. When you apply manures according to the *Code of Good Agricultural Practice for the Protection of Water*, the amount of contaminants added to the soil will be limited and damaging concentrations are unlikely. However, you should take precautionary samples as outlined in paragraph 108. The *Code of Good Agricultural Practice for the Protection of Water* includes a maximum guide figure for total nitrogen in organic manures of 250 kg/ha per year which you should keep to, but you should also consider the phosphorus and potassium needs of the crops. Adjust the amount of inorganic fertiliser that you apply to take account of any manures you have applied.

Inorganic fertilisers

110. Base the amount of inorganic fertilisers you use on soil analysis and follow the principles of the detailed fertiliser recommendations given in MAFF/ADAS Reference Book 209 *Fertiliser Recommendations for Agricultural and Horticultural Crops*. Avoid potentially harmful build-ups of nutrients, and also avoid applying too much lime.

111. Materials you use as inorganic fertilisers (such as rock phosphate) may be applied in a relatively unprocessed form or after chemical and physical treatment. These treatments may affect the quantity or availability to plants of any contaminating materials which are present. Manufacturers should monitor the concentration in fertilisers of any contaminants so that the soil will be protected from any unacceptable contamination. Cadmium and, to a lesser extent, fluorides and uranium in phosphate fertilisers are of particular concern.

Pesticides

112. Pesticides in England and Wales are controlled under Part III of the *Food and Environment Protection Act 1985* (FEPA). The *Control of Pesticides Regulations 1986* (COPR) provide legal controls over advertising, selling, supplying, storing and using pesticides in England, Scotland and Wales. The MAFF/HSC statutory *Code of Practice for the Safe Use of Pesticides on Farms and Holdings* (1990) provides guidance on all aspects of using pesticides, including disposing of wastes and washings, containers, packaging and other contaminated materials. Practical guidelines to avoid pesticides polluting water are given in the MAFF *Code of Good Agricultural Practice for the Protection of Water* and in the DoE *Guidance for Control of Weeds on Non-Agricultural Land*. Guidance on avoiding pollution of water is directly relevant to avoiding pollution of soil. Read both of these Codes when you are finding out about protecting soil.

113. Most pesticides are organic compounds which are broken down in the soil by physical and chemical processes and by micro-organisms. By law, these compounds must only be applied at a rate and in the way specified in their authorisation. This is granted on the basis that, when correctly used, the chemical will have no unacceptable long-term effect upon the environment. Regularly using certain pesticides (such as some soil-acting herbicides) may leave residues which take several years to break down.

114. Some pesticides that are currently approved contain copper. Although these are no longer widely used, repeated applications over many years may raise the copper concentration in some soils. In these rare situations, you should have your soils analysed and compare the copper content with the figures given in Annex II to find out if you should continue to use the pesticide.

Dredging materials

115. If there is reason to believe that materials dredged from settlement ponds or natural waters such as ponds, lakes, rivers, etc. contain potential contaminants, they should not be spread on agricultural land until any such contaminants have been identified, professional advice sought and a satisfactory programme of land application and subsequent management established. Local enquiries should be made on potential contaminants and identification should be confirmed by analysis of the material. The source of the contaminants, e.g. geological or industrial wastes, will determine their likely affect on crops or livestock. Appropriate action will vary accordingly. Contaminated dredging material may be subject to Hazardous Waste legislation. In addition, new waste management controls being developed by the Department of thc Environment may affect the spreading of such materials.

Remedial treatment

116. Take all possible steps to avoid contaminating soil. When accidental or natural events cause contamination, obtain professional advice and put action programmes in place to limit the damage. Where possible you should treat the soil to improve its condition. Two situations where problems can be solved by relatively straightforward management practices are in the cases of sea water flooding and oil spillages.

Sea water flooding

117. When sea flooding occurs, it is important that the water on the soil surface drains back to the sea or river as quickly as possible in order to minimise residues of sodium and chloride in the soil. When possible, dig surface channels by hand to help remove the water from low-lying areas. If large areas have been flooded it might be more practical to use mechanical diggers with low ground-pressure tyres. You can also remove sea water by pumping. The sooner surplus water is removed, the sooner the recovery process can start.

118. In freely-draining soils, average winter rainfall in England and Wales can remove most of the chloride left in the soil in one winter. If flooding occurs in late winter or spring, the chloride will not be removed until the end of the next winter. This process may be quicker if you do not plant a crop in the soil for the first summer after flooding. You should also prevent the growth of any weeds.

119. On soils that are not so well drained, washing out the excess chloride may take two or three winters. If the soil is very poorly drained, with little or no water moving through the soil, the soil may remain contaminated. This is a particular problem if the soil is very dry at the time of flooding, so that salt water penetrates deep into the soil. The soil is usually already wet when it is flooded and in this condition the salt water will not penetrate deep down into the soil.

120. Soils with pipe drainage will recover naturally as long as the system is working properly. The number of winters needed to leach the excess chloride will depend on the structure of the soil and the effectiveness of the leaching process.

121. If soils contain more than 1200 mg/l of water-soluble chloride in the top 20 cm, grow tolerant plants such as barley or ryegrass rather than more sensitive species such as legumes or brassicas.

122. As water moves through the soil, the soil sodium concentration will be reduced by leaching. If sodium taken up by the clay particles is not immediately replaced by calcium or magnesium, the clay particles will disperse and the soil will become very difficult to cultivate. Soils with a high silt or clay content are most at risk of deterioration. Peaty and coarse sandy soils are less prone to damage.

123. To maintain a satisfactory structure, the soil must contain a supply of calcium or magnesium. This may come from a high natural content of calcium carbonate or from added gypsum. Gypsum is calcium sulphate which is more soluble in water than lime (calcium carbonate). On cultivated soils which are susceptible to structural deterioration and have been flooded with sea water, you should apply finely ground gypsum at 5 t/ha as soon as possible after the soil has dried out. This is likely to improve the soil even if it already contains some calcium carbonate. Gypsum is most effective if it is left on the soil surface and not ploughed in. You may need to make another application on clay soils which do not contain lime and which have been flooded for a long time.

124. Soils in grassland should only be treated with gypsum if they have a weak structure and contain no lime. Do not treat peaty and coarse sandy soils as you will get very little benefit.

125. Use of gypsum in this way may be subject to the new Waste Management Controls being developed by the Department of the Environment.

126. For rapid recovery from flooding damage, do not carry out cultivations in wet conditions. Avoid sowing crops in the spring until the soil structure is fully restored.

127. Apply adequate fertiliser because any nutrient shortage will increase the problem. If there is a drought, irrigate the land with non-saline water where possible.

Oil spillage

128. When there is a significant oil spillage, the main concern is to reduce the fire hazard and prevent the oil from entering sewers, water-courses or groundwater. Tell the National Rivers Authority about the spillage immediately so that they may assess any risks to surface or groundwaters. The next step is to remove as much of the spillage as possible and dispose of it safely, so reducing the amount left to be broken down by micro-organisms in the soil or to be lost by evaporation. Only dispose of the contaminated soil to a site licensed to receive special waste.

129. If light oil such as diesel or heating oil penetrates the topsoil but is held up by the subsoil or the water table, it may be possible to dig holes, allow the oil to drain into them and then pump it out. The hole should not penetrate the layer that is holding up the oil. Do not apply water or detergents to try and flush the oil from the soil and do not try to burn oil on the soil surface.

130. Crude and heavy oils will stay on the soil surface. Scrape them up and remove them from the site, taking as little topsoil as possible. This may be easier if you let the oil solidify first. It will also reduce the risk of machinery damaging the soil during the clean-up operation.

131. The next stage in restoring the soil is to make sure that the conditions for the remaining oil to be broken down by micro-organisms are as favourable as possible. All soils contain micro-organisms that can break down oils. The soil needs to have a pH of about 7, be at an adequate temperature, and contain water, oxygen and nutrients. If the soil is in a suitable state, cultivate the surface to improve the oxygen supply to the micro-organisms. Mixing the soil and oil will increase the rate of breakdown.

132. For heavily contaminated soils, apply inorganic nitrogen and phosphorus fertiliser before cultivating so the micro-organisms have an adequate nutrient supply. Do not add organic manures to oil contaminated land as these increase the micro-organisms' need for oxygen, and plants could be damaged.

133. The time it takes for the soil to completely recover depends on the type and quantity of oil contamination. Spillages of light oil will generally affect the soil for one to two years. After this period plant growth is not likely to be affected. Spillages of crude and heavy oil may take 5 years or longer before the soil can be used to grow a wide range of plants again.

134. Commercial companies offer services for cleaning up soil contaminated with oil and other organic contaminants, using microbiological and other appropriate techniques. Get professional advice on the correct course of action for the particular contaminant which has to be treated. Detailed guidance is given in a *Code of Practice for the Investigation and Mitigation of Possible Petroleum-Based Land Contamination*, published by The Institute of Petroleum.

5. Restoring Disturbed Soils

Introduction

135. This section of the Code gives advice on measures to reduce the effect of soil disturbance by extraction of minerals, landfill, laying pipelines and other civil engineering works. It provides information on safeguards that need to be taken to make sure that the long-term quality of the soil is protected. The main responsibility for applying most of the measures and safeguards described will rest with the developers, contractors and site operators as well as with planning authorities.

136. This Code does not provide comprehensive guidance on detailed planning or operational practices. It aims to provide you, the farmer, or your advisers with an outline of operational standards and conditions that are likely to be placed upon operators. It also advises you on measures you may take to make sure that appropriate controls are applied and on the "aftercare" which is necessary to make sure that disturbed soils are restored to satisfactory standards for farming.

137. The overall aim is to make sure that if land is going to be restored for agricultural use:

- soil damage is minimised;
- soil is restored wherever practical to its original quality (the MAFF Agricultural Land Classification (ALC) grading is normally used); and
- restored soil is not damaged by inappropriate farming practices.

If planning permission has been given for restoring land for use other than agriculture, other measures for restoring the soil may be appropriate. However, the measures described here may be relevant to some other uses.

LEGISLATION

Extracting minerals and landfilling

138. Virtually all development to extract minerals or for landfill waste needs planning permission under the *Town and Country Planning Act 1990* (as amended by the *Planning and Compensation Act 1991*). When an application is made, the landowner and any tenant of the land involved will be notified. If you have any questions about the application, or you want to make any comments, you should contact the Planning Authority within 21 days of receiving the notification.

If consent is given, it is normally subject to planning conditions which control working of the site, how it must be restored and aftercare. These conditions are applied to make sure that land is restored to an appropriate standard. Detailed guidance on these aspects is given in the DoE Mineral Planning Guidance, Note 7 *The Reclamation of Mineral Workings* and will also be in future *Good Practice Guidelines* that will be published by the DoE.

As well as planning permission, landfill sites which take controlled wastes also need waste management licences (currently under the *Control of Pollution Act 1974*, to be replaced in due course by the *Environmental Protection Act 1990*).

139. The site operator is responsible for making sure that the planning conditions are met. The Minerals Planning Authority is responsible for enforcing the conditions. Landfilled sites will also need to be monitored for several decades after they have been closed, under the Waste Management Licensing system. The Waste Regulation Authority is responsible for enforcing the licence conditions.

140. If you are the landowner, you should be aware that, although such cases are rare, if a site operator fails to meet their commitments in any way, and the authority concerned cannot take enforcement action against that operator, then any necessary enforcement action may be taken against you as the landowner.

So you should consider whether the operator can provide evidence of how they have managed, restored and cared for a similar site; whether the operator follows any best practice guidance or codes issued by the relevant trade associations; and whether these associations have any restoration guarantee fund.

If appropriate, landowners can try to negotiate legally-binding agreements to make sure that practices meet your personal requirements, including provisions to protect you against default by the operator or any third party involved in the working of the site. However, these are private contractual arrangements between you and operators, and entirely separate from any planning permission or conditions.

Pipelines

141. Legislation is contained in several Acts which are often specific both to the material being carried (oil, gas, water) and the status of the promoting organisation (private or public agency). The main laws are the *Pipe-lines Act 1962, Gas Acts 1965* and *1972, Water Industry Act 1991, Water Resources Act 1991* and the *Town and Country Planning Act 1990*.

142. Detailed operational requirements are given in BS 8010—*British Standard (BS) Code of Practice for Pipelines.*

143. Codes of practice have been prepared by individual water companies and approved by the DoE. The BS Code gives detailed recommendations for stripping, storing and reinstating soil. The BS Code is not a legal document and it is important to make sure that you observe all legal obligations which may mean more than just following the BS Code.

144. Engineering and restoration works are carried out by contractors for a pipeline operator who has got exclusive rights for the temporary use of the land, possibly having used compulsory powers to buy land or get licences to carry out the work. So you usually have little or no control over the work being done. As the landowner or occupier you should make a note of all activities to help make sure that restoration is a success. Contractors may offer you private agreements for offices, soil storage facilities or for the disposal of surplus soil materials. If you accept these, take care to make sure that any land affected is properly restored.

PLANNING THE WORK

145. For all sites, good planning requires attention to detail. No short-cuts should be attempted. If soil is seriously damaged it may not be possible to restore it at reasonable cost. All reasonable steps should be taken to avoid damage, as without due care restored land may be unsuitable for profitable agriculture.

146. All work should be planned and carried out without staff or equipment having to go onto surrounding farmland. This is important to minimise soil disturbance and also to prevent any plant and animal diseases in the soil from being spread. Further guidance is given in the MAFF booklet *Preventing the Spread of Plant and Animal Diseases—a Practical Guide.*

147. Before work starts, the developer or pipeline operator should carry out a survey of the site to provide a detailed inventory of the soils and potential soil-forming materials (including topsoil and subsoil depths) to provide an assessment of the quality of the land. It is important that this information is accurately prepared, as it will highlight potential problems with future working and provide the basis of the operator's proposals for handling the soil in the site working and restoration scheme that they will send to the Minerals Planning Authority for approval.

148. When preparing schemes, consideration should be given to:

- intended soil stripping depths;
- using available soils and soil-forming materials to get the best possible restoration;
- ways of keeping different soils apart;
- methods of handling the soil, including proposals to minimise dust nuisance at all stages of the work;
- the location and height of soil mounds and how long they will be present;
- proposals for reinstating soils including the location, depth and composition of reinstated soil profiles, and the contours of the restored land;
- installing appropriate pipe drainage and methods for restoring any disrupted land drains; and
- commitments for undertaking necessary restoration works according to an assessment of soil conditions made after reinstatement for example soil loosening or de-stoning operations.

149. There may also be a risk of off-site flooding where slopes or drainage patterns have been altered or disrupted. Flooding can cause considerable damage to soils in surrounding areas, and surface run-off may cause pollution. If this may occur, the proposals should also include plans to deal with any disruption of water-courses and underdrainage systems, and deal with any increased surface run-off to minimise all risks of water pollution.

150. Before approving a scheme for extracting minerals, the Minerals Planning Authority should discuss the proposals with all interested parties, including the landowner, the occupier and MAFF or Welsh Office in Wales, if the land is to be restored for agricultural use. MAFF or Welsh Office will try to make sure that the soil depths, stripping and storage proposals are adequate to protect the soil quality before these requirements are written into planning conditions.

151. As well as any planning conditions and private agreements (see paragraph 140), the operator should prepare a method statement to translate the working arrangements approved by the planning authority into practical instructions which can be used by those involved in the day-to-day working of the site. This is important as techniques for reinstating soil for agriculture often differ from techniques for preparing the ground for building.

SITE WORKING

152. The quality of the restoration depends on the standard of work of people on the site. The operator must make sure that all work which affects the soil proceeds in accordance with the working scheme and method statement. If you believe that these conditions are being broken, you should tell the operator. If the matter cannot be resolved satisfactorily, you should bring it to the attention of the Minerals Planning Authority if the planning conditions have been broken. You should also tell the land agent, liaison officer or other person involved in working on the site that the authority has been told that the conditions may have been broken. Private legal action may be appropriate if a private agreement with the operator is broken. However, actual conditions and operational requirements rarely match up to those anticipated. Allowance should be made for adjustments that may be necessary in order to achieve the best results. For example, changing weather conditions may require changes to soil handling operations. The following provides a general indication of good practice for the different stages of site working and restoration.

Soil stripping

153. Operations should only strip topsoils and subsoils to the depths agreed in the planning consent. Agricultural topsoil is the dark surface layer which normally varies in depth from 20 to 40 cm (but may be less). Subsoil is the underlying, usually lighter-coloured soil material which should be removed to at least 1.2 metres below the original ground surface, unless rock or other materials make this impossible or undesirable. If different soil types have been identified, strip them separately. If the upper layers of the subsoil are of significantly better quality than the lower layers, they should also be stripped separately.

154. Operators should only strip and transport soils when they are in a dry and friable condition (when they crumble easily). Site working should be planned to fit with the expected weather. Take care to make sure that machinery does not go across unstripped soils or storage mounds unnecessarily.

Soil storage

155. If restoration is already taking place elsewhere on the site, operators should not store soils unless it is essential. Instead, re-instate them immediately. However, on many sites, immediate replacement is not always practical and soil has to be stored. If this is the case, topsoil, subsoil and any other soil-forming material should be stored separately. Also, different soil types should be stored separately, for example sands separate from clay soils. Do not let them be moved from the site unless this is specifically agreed in the scheme of working and planning conditions.

156. Before the operator builds subsoil storage mounds, they should remove the topsoil from the area where the mound will be. Topsoil and subsoil should be removed from areas used for storing other materials (for example clays and shales). The height of storage mounds will depend on operational and planning requirements.

157. If soils will be stored for more than 6 months, mounds should be seeded with grass to minimise erosion and weed growth. Control any excess weed growth, preferably by mechanical methods. Appropriate measures, such as settlement lagoons, may be necessary to prevent eroded materials in run-off from polluting water-courses.

Soil reinstatement

158. Soils should be reinstated in dry conditions on appropriately contoured and prepared ground as specified in the restoration scheme. They should also be replaced in correct sequence; subsoils first and then topsoils to the depths previously agreed. Care must be taken to avoid soil losses or contamination with other materials. After soils have been replaced, they should be thoroughly loosened to remove any compaction. After they have settled, soil depths should normally match those of the original undisturbed profile without leaving low spots in which water may settle. Wherever possible, try to provide 1.2 metres of cover for crop growth and to allow drains to be laid.

159. For most modern landfill sites, current good practice requires a "low-permeability cap" (usually of clay or synthetic materials) above the wastes to provide a seal to stop water entering and to enable proper management and control of any leachate or gas generated. Also, systems of pipework wells and vents for control and possible flaring of gas may be installed. It is therefore very important to provide an adequate depth of soil to allow normal agricultural operations such as underdrainage and subsoiling. Such agricultural operations should not damage the clay cap or other leachate or gas control systems. If it is not possible to provide enough soil cover, then agricultural restoration is unlikely to be possible and alternative afteruses should be considered.

160. For pipelines, the depth of the reinstated soil should be at least 0.9 metres above the top of the installed pipe. It is not unusual to have surplus soil after reinstatement. Any surplus subsoil should be spread on the excavated strip before the topsoil is replaced. All topsoil should normally be used on site. Disposing of it off-site should be agreed between the landowner and the operator. Particular attention should be given to the interception and reinstating of existing underdrainage systems and the need to install additional underdrainage as part of the reinstatement process.

161. Regular site meetings should be held between all interested parties to inspect the work and assess the need for remedial treatments such as levelling, loosening to remove soil compaction, removing stones and additional drainage.

AGRICULTURAL "AFTERCARE"

162. Soil that has been reinstated may take several years to get back to normal. Restored soils usually suffer some structural damage and need a period of specialised aftercare before they are suitable for normal agricultural use. The aftercare period should be used to assist the recovery of soil structure in restored soils rather than trying to increase productivity immediately. The length of time during which you need to take particular care will vary greatly. It will not usually be less than four years and may be 10 years or more.

163. On restored minerals sites, agricultural management is normally controlled by planning conditions for five years from the soil being replaced. Information on the legislation and guidance on conditions for aftercare and the preparation of aftercare schemes is given in paragraphs 138–140.

164. Although the operator is responsible for aftercare, there are many options for managing the land during the aftercare period. Operators may choose to manage the land themselves, or they may employ agricultural contractors. Licences and short-term lettings may be used, or share-farming arrangements may be made. It is important that aftercare management is carried out promptly and effectively and that everybody involved understands the need to restore land for the longer term and not for short-term gain.

165. The operator may offer you the opportunity to take over responsibility for the aftercare. Before you take up this option, carefully consider the cost of meeting the aftercare obligations laid down by the Minerals Planning Authority, as any private agreement between you and the operator will be legally binding and you will then be liable for any penalties and costs for non-compliance with the aftercare scheme.

166. Although legal aftercare obligations apply to most sites, there may be some sites which do not have to meet this legislation. However, even on sites where legal obligations do not apply but land is to be restored to agriculture, you should still take account of the following guidance to make sure the land recovers properly.

Cropping

167. It is not possible to make standard recommendations for aftercare cropping as a lot will depend upon the site, soil and climatic conditions. As a general rule, crop cover should be established as soon as possible after restoration, and maintained to protect sites from soil erosion and assist the recovery of soil structure. Planting a crop early allows roots to penetrate cracks and fissures. These roots will help the soil to dry out during the spring and summer, improving ground conditions for other farming operations and remedial treatments.

168. When choosing aftercare crops, remember that the structural properties of restored soils are usually not as good for crop growth or farming operations as soil that has not been disturbed. Nutrient reserves may be lower and the amount of air in the soil and the drainage poorer. Choose crops which can grow in these conditions.

169. Grass is the preferred option for aftercare cropping, especially for clay soils in areas that have a high rainfall. You must control grazing carefully and remove livestock when the soil is wet. Where possible cut grass rather than letting it be grazed. Avoid over-grazing as this may lead to soil erosion. However, you may have difficulty making use of the grass in an arable area and winter cereals may be an appropriate alternative, except on heavy soils or in areas that have a high rainfall. Do not grow winter barley on acid soils.

170. Avoid sowing spring cereals except on well drained land in dry areas. This precaution is due to the increased risks of damage to soil structure by spring cultivation and the problem of establishing a satisfactory crop in wet years. Oilseed rape and other combine-harvested crops are not recommended unless the soil conditions are good and an effective underdrainage system has been installed.

171. Do not grow root crops such as potatoes and sugar beet, as late harvesting will normally prevent remedial subsoiling and may result in bare land over the winter. There is also the risk of causing serious damage to the soil structure when harvesting in wet years.

Cultivations

172. In the early stages, restored soils are generally more sensitive than undisturbed land to damage by wheeled machinery. Take particular care over the timing and number of cultivations and minimise axle loads and wheel slip. You should give disturbed soils a high priority when you are planning farm work as there are normally fewer suitable days available for cultivations on restored land.

Lime and fertiliser

173. Soil pH and available nutrient contents, especially phosphorus, can fall if soil is stored for a long time. As it is important to establish crop cover as quickly as possible, lime or nutrient deficiencies should be corrected by applying lime, fertilisers and (on well drained sites) organic manures. To ensure that you use appropriate applications, the soil should be analysed immediately after soil replacement and repeated every two years throughout the aftercare period.

174. During the aftercare period, you should apply fertiliser to help the roots to grow vigorously and so help the soil structure to recover, and build up nutrient reserves to levels suitable for normal cropping at the end of the aftercare period. Avoid large single applications at high rates to minimise losses by leaching or surface run-off, which could cause water pollution.

Drainage

175. Establishing satisfactory soil drainage is an important part of aftercare.

Poor drainage can affect crop growth, reduce work days, shorten the grazing period and generally increase the chance of agricultural operations causing damage to the soil.

176. You will normally need underdrainage if there was artificial drainage before the soil was disturbed. It will also be needed where soils have been damaged during working or where other materials that water cannot pass through have been introduced below the topsoil. The system should be designed to control the water table at least 500 mm below the surface for arable crops and 300 mm for grass within 48 hours of rain. On clay and compacted soils, you will normally need to carry out mole drainage or subsoiling, or both, to achieve this.

177. On most sites, underdrains should be installed as soon as possible after soil reinstatement as long as conditions are suitable, but not if the drainage work will cause more damage. This will increase opportunities for carrying out essential remedial treatments and reduce the risk of the soil structure deteriorating in wet conditions.

Subsoiling

178. Frequent subsoiling is usually necessary to improve the soil's ability to absorb water and help root penetration. It should be carried out in late summer or early autumn when the subsoil is relatively dry, using a single or multi-bladed "winged tine" machine. When you carry out subsoiling in grassland, take care to minimise damage to the sward. Decide the depth, choice of machine and spacing after thoroughly inspecting the soil.

179. Where compaction is serious, agricultural subsoiling is generally only effective to depths of about 350 mm. However, deeper benefits can be achieved by progressively increasing subsoiling depth over a number of years. Inspect the soil profile to assess the need for subsoiling and the most appropriate depth of working. You may need professional advice on this. You should carry out a further inspection immediately before starting work to confirm that the subsoil is dry enough. Also, inspect while the work is going on to make sure that the cultivation is effective. On pipeline sites, note the soil conditions under the running track where compaction may be severe and deep.

Grazing management

180. To reduce surface compaction and poaching, only graze with sheep and young cattle. It is preferable to cut the grass for hay or silage but only when topsoil conditions are suitable. Graze the aftermath carefully to avoid damaging the soil. Remove livestock from the land over winter and in wet conditions. Keep farm machinery off the land whenever the soil is wet.

Monitoring

181. Carefully monitor the soil structure throughout the aftercare period. For restored minerals sites, annual site review meetings may need to be held between the site operators, Minerals Planning Authorities and other interested parties to agree the detailed aftercare programme for the coming year and the need for remedial treatments. A final meeting may also be necessary at the end of the aftercare period to make sure that all planning conditions have been met.

Long-term management

182. Once the land is released from aftercare, it is still important to maintain good soil-management practices. Do not suddenly increase agricultural use. Base decisions to grow more demanding crops or increase stocking rates on proven experience gained from farming the restored land. A cautious approach is usually best in the long term. Otherwise you may cause serious damage and this can be slow and expensive to put right.

Annex I

INORGANIC CONTAMINANTS OF SOILS IN ENGLAND AND WALES

The concentration of potential contaminants in soils in England and Wales has been reported in a *Soil Geochemical*

Atlas by McGrath and Loveland based on samples taken on a 5 km grid survey. The table below shows the most commonly occurring concentrations (median value) together with the values below which 10% of soils fall (ten percentile) and above which 10% fall (90 percentile). The average concentration (arithmetic mean) is also shown.

Concentrations (mg/kg dry matter) of metals in soils of England and Wales

Metal	Ten percentile	Median	Ninety percentile	Arithmetic mean
Zinc	38	82	147	97
Copper	9	18	37	23
Nickel	7	23	42	25
Cadmium	0.2	0.7	1.4	0.8
Lead	20	40	131	74
Chromium	15	39	64	41

This table reports total metal concentrations in topsoils. The table does not represent particular conditions or levels of contamination to be expected on any one site, and it is not a substitute for a site assessment if you suspect or know of contamination.

(i) Zinc

Zinc is an essential trace element for crop growth but in high concentrations it is toxic to plants. It is easily taken up by plant roots and moves to the leaves. Too much zinc restricts plant growth and affects how the plant deals with elements such as iron, resulting in a severe yellowing of the whole plant. These symptoms usually occur at concentrations well below those which cause any risk to an animal's health. It affects animals by interacting with other elements, such as copper.

Concentrations of zinc (up to 2000 mg/kg of soil) from materials such as minespoil may be tolerated by certain plants depending on the pH of the soil and other factors. For clover and productive grass species at a pH of 6.0, the maximum recommended concentration is 1000 mg/kg. Zinc from industrial wastes, atmospheric deposition or sewage sludge is more available to plants, and sensitive species may be affected above about 300 mg/kg of zinc in the soil when the pH is between 6 and 7.

Zinc alone is unlikely to affect animals until they eat more than 300–1000 mg/kg of dry food, depending on the type of animal, the form of the zinc and the balance of other nutrients in the diet. Concentrations in herbage that are greater than about 220 mg/kg of dry matter are likely to have a significant effect on copper metabolism in grazing livestock.

(ii) Copper

Copper is held by organic matter in the soil and is not as easily taken up into the leaves of plants as zinc, but it can accumulate in the roots. Soil pH has little effect on the amount of copper the plant takes up, except in very acid conditions (less than pH 4.5) when it appears to be more available and is taken up by acid-tolerant species. Although copper is an essential plant nutrient, it can be toxic to plants at high concentrations. If material containing copper (such as pig slurry) is applied to a growing crop, copper can be directly absorbed by the leaves. The resulting forage may be a health risk to grazing sheep.

At a soil pH of 6.0 or above, a total soil concentration of copper from geological materials up to 500 mg/kg of dry solids would allow the growth of productive grasses, but clovers and other sensitive species may be affected at 250 mg/kg. The effect of a given concentration of copper on livestock depends upon its chemical form and on how it interacts with other elements. When the concentration of copper in soil is more than 500 mg/kg, the soil and plants are likely to exceed the toxic threshold and may poison susceptible animals, especially sheep and lambs. A copper concentration in the diet greater than 10 mg/kg of dry food is toxic for the most susceptible breeds of sheep. If you have to let livestock graze on contaminated land, they should only be grazed for short periods and with adequate herbage on offer so that the amount of soil eaten is kept to a minimum. Cattle are unlikely to be affected by copper.

(iii) Lead

Lead in soils with a pH of above 6.0 is not usually toxic to plants but eating soil-contaminated herbage can be dangerous to livestock. Monogastric animals (pigs, poultry and horses) are considerably more at risk of lead poisoning than are ruminants such as cattle and sheep. Consider precautions where soils have a natural total lead concentration greater than about 300 mg/kg of dry solids.

In alkaline soils (pH of more than 7), lead is not available to plants. If contaminated soil is eaten by grazing animals, the lead may be absorbed by them whatever the soil pH. The chemical and physical form of the lead will affect its absorption.

Lead contamination of crops is unlikely to exceed the legal limit for food of 1 mg/kg of lead in dry matter, except when vegetables are grown and sold from a soil which contains lead at more than about 300 mg/kg of dry solids. Under these circumstances you should take care that the crop is not contaminated by soil to ensure that this limit is not exceeded.

(iv) Cadmium

Cadmium is often found with geological deposits of lead and zinc. It is taken up by plant roots and moved to the leaves and seeds. This effect is greater at low pH and varies with the type of plant. If a grazing animal ingests cadmium, it builds up in that animal, especially in the kidneys and the liver. The guideline concentration of 3 mg/kg of cadmium in soil is set to protect the food supply of animals and man. Plant growth is not affected at this level. The amount of cadmium that plants take up varies according to the physical and chemical form of the cadmium and the species of plant. The total cadmium concentration limit in soil of 3 mg/kg of dry solids must not be exceeded when you apply sewage sludge to agricultural land and you should observe this limit in other situations. If land is contaminated by wastes from lead mines, the high concentrations of zinc and lead will have a much greater effect on plants and animals than the cadmium. Much of the cadmium added to agricultural soils comes from phosphate fertilisers.

(v) Arsenic

Plant roots absorb and store arsenic. In high concentrations, it may kill them. However, it does not move freely to leaves or stems. An arsenic concentration of 250 mg/kg of dry soil is not likely to cause any ill effects to plants or animals. Concentrations above 500 mg/kg can result in animals eating sufficient soil whilst grazing to increase the arsenic in their offal and, in extreme cases, to poison them. Contamination of fresh produce offered for sale should be kept to a minimum. Soil concentrations of arsenic in land used to grow fresh produce should not exceed 50 mg/kg of dry soil. This will minimise the risk of exceeding legal limits in food (generally 1 mg/kg).

(vi) Fluoride

Fluoride in soils is normally present as insoluble calcium fluoride. In this form it is not readily taken up by plant roots. If soil that is high in fluoride, or grass that is contaminated by fluoride, is eaten over a long period, the teeth and bones of livestock can suffer due to a condition called fluorosis.

A total concentration of fluoride, from whatever source, of 500 mg/kg of dry soil could result in the diet of grazing animals exceeding the safe limit of 30 mg/kg of dry matter.

(vii) Nickel

Nickel is toxic to plants. In order to protect against damage to crops or animals, a limit for nickel of 75 mg/kg of dry soil exists for soil at pH 6–7 receiving sewage sludge. Other limits apply for different soil pH values. (See Annex II).

(viii) Chromium

There has been some concern about chromium being added to soil because the chromate (VI) ion is toxic to plants and animals. However, due to the conditions found in organic waste materials or in soil, it will only exist as the relatively inactive chromic (III) ion.

Chromium (III) is unlikely to be toxic to plants except in extremely acidic soils. Land which has sewage sludge applied to it must contain chromium at less than 400 mg/kg of dry soil.

(ix) Mercury
The amount of mercury in soil which will kill plants is far greater than that which arises under natural conditions or from any likely form of contamination. Plant roots do not take up mercury very effectively. However mercury is one of the most poisonous elements to many animals and man. Soil concentrations of mercury should not be greater than 1 mg/kg of dry soil.

(x) Selenium
Where soils are contaminated by selenium the safe concentration of 2 mg/kg of dry matter in plants can be exceeded. Livestock are not normally poisoned until they take in selenium at more than 5 mg/kg of dry food. To minimise risk, the concentration of selenium in soil should be kept below 3 mg/kg. Soils naturally high in selenium are very rare in England and Wales but may be a risk to grazing livestock where they occur.

(xi) Molybdenum
High molybdenum levels in soil may result in the need to take precautions to limit the amount taken in by livestock. High molybdenum in plants (more than 5 mg/kg of dry solids) reduces the availability of copper to livestock and may cause a copper deficiency. Do not apply waste materials to land if this would raise soil concentrations of molybdenum above 4 mg/kg of soil. However, if the concentration in the soil is naturally higher than this value, and livestock are receiving copper therapy, you can apply sewage sludge which only contains trace levels of molybdenum. Obtain veterinary advice before you take any action. Some clay and shale soils naturally contain molybdenum at more than 100 mg/kg of soil.

(xii) Sodium and Chloride
Plants growing on sea-flooded land may be damaged by lack of oxygen or by the soil around their roots being disturbed. Salt water deposits sodium and chloride in the soil. High chloride levels restrict plant growth and decrease the root system's ability to take up water from the soil. High levels of sodium in the soil will disperse clay particles and cause problems in soil structure, especially in non-calcareous soils.

Annex 2

MAXIMUM PERMISSIBLE CONCENTRATIONS OF POTENTIALLY TOXIC ELEMENTS (PTES) IN SOIL AFTER APPLICATION OF SEWAGE SLUDGE TO AGRICULTURAL LAND AND MAXIMUM ANNUAL RATES OF ADDITION

PTE	Maximum permissible concentrations of PTE in soil (mg/kg dry solids)				Maximum permissible average annual rate of PTE addition over a 10-year period (kg/ha)[3]
	pH[1] 5.0–5.5	pH[1] 5.5–6.0	pH 6.0–7.0	pH[2] >7.0	
Zinc	200	250	300	450	15
Copper	80	100	135	200	7.5
Nickel	50	60	75	110	3
	For pH 5.0 and above				
Cadmium	3				0.15
Lead	300				15
Mercury	1				0.1
Chromium	400 (Provisional)				15 (Provisional)
*Molybdenum[4]	4				0.2
*Selenium	3				0.15
*Arsenic	50				0.7
*Fluoride	500				20

* These parameters are not subject to the provisions of Directive 86/278.

1 For soils in the pH ranges 5.0–5.5 and 5.5–6.0 the permitted concentrations for lead, zinc, copper, nickel and cadmium are provisional and will be reviewed when current research into their effects on certain crops and livestock is completed.

2 The increased permissible PTE concentrations in soil of pH greater than 7.0 apply only to soils containing more than 5% calcium carbonate.

3 The annual rate of application of PTE to any site shall be determined by averaging over the 10-year period ending with the year of calculation.

4 The accepted safe concentration of molybdenum in agricultural soils is 4 mg/kg. However, there are some areas in the U.K. where, because of local geology, the natural concentration of this element in the soil exceeds this level. In such cases there may be no additional problems as a result of applying sludge, but this should not be done except in accordance with expert advice. This advice will take account of existing soil molybdenum levels and current arrangements to provide copper supplements to livestock.

Appendix 4

FARM WASTE MANAGEMENT PLAN

ORCHARD LODGE FARM

UPTON MAGNA

FARM DETAILS

Name:	A & O Rogers, Orchard Lodge Farm, Upton Magna, Somerset. TA3 7PW
Telephone:	01456 76543
Holding No:	50/111/76
O.S. Grid ref:	6578E9876N
Prepared by:	A. R. Larpent M I Soil Sci M.B.I.A.C Fieldfare Associates Orchard Lodge Ashbrittle Wellington Somerset TA21 0LH
Telephone:	01398361326
Fax	01398361535

Date of site visit and field assessment.31st May 1996

Report date: 16th July 1996

1. INTRODUCTION:

Orchard Lodge Farm is a traditional dairy farm at the foot of the Blackdown Hills 3 miles west of Upton Magna. The farm carries a milking herd of 90 cows which are cubicle housed in the winter for 150 days. Appendix 1 is a Farm Waste Management Plan, discussing soil types, slurry production, nitrogen loading and dirty water production. A set of colour coded maps indicating the risk of spreading under normal and field capacity conditions is included in appendix 2 with various cropping constraints and water features map.

2. CURRENT WASTE DISPOSAL METHOD.

The cubicle sheds are scraped to a slurry lagoon with an estimated capacity of $1654m^3$. The lagoon is dewatered via a strainer box to two dirty water pits, one settling and one pumping. From the pumping section, it is irrigated via a low rate irrigation system to fields.

4. THE SOILS AND CLIMATIC DATA.

4.1 CLIMATIC DATA.

Altitude: AOD

Nat Grid Ref 3341E 1124N

The estimated field capacity period		
Type of year	Return date	End date
Normal year	Mid October	End April
Wet year	Mid-End September	Mid May
Dry year	Mid November	Early April

The field capacity period is that period when the soils are replete with water and any excess moves under the influence of gravity to land drains, ground water or over the surface, to water courses. On the soil types found on Orchard Lodge, windows of opportunity during the winter will be narrow, so careful management of wastes is essential.

4.2 THE SOILS.

The soils on Peasmarsh are a loamy silty clayey soil over a clay loam. Some of the soils were slightly mottled, indicating they could lie wet during the winter months. As stated previously, careful management of wastes is essential and the risk maps should be adhered to with a cross reference to the management notes.

TYPES OF POLLUTION RISK

N NON SPREADING AREAS

Within 10 metres of a water course, or where there is a danger of wind blowing material into a water course.

Within 50 metres of a spring, well or borehole used for human consumption or in farm dairies.

Other areas may not be available due to problems caused by aerosols or management agreements.

VH VERY HIGH RISK OF POLLUTION 1

VHI May be flooded in month following application.

VH2 May be waterlogged due to slowly permeable soils. 3

VH3 May be waterlogged due to ground water. 3

VH4 Steep slope. 2 3

VH5 Moderate slope (4-7^0) and slowly permeable soil. 2 3 4

VH6 May be severely compacted. 3

VH7 Slope of more than 7^0

VH8 constraints due to aerosols

Other very high risk areas may apply from time to time:

If ground is frozen hard.

If ground is waterlogged. 3

If severely surface compacted. 3

If drained or moled in the last twelve months.

If subsoiled over drains in the last twelve months.

If drained and the soil is cracked to drains or backfill.

If depth over fissured rock is less than 30cm and soil is cracked

H HIGH RISK OF POLLUTION 1

H1 Moderate ($4-7^{0}$) slope 2 3

H2 Slowly permeable soil or slight risk of waterlogging 2 3 4

H3 Soil depth over fissured rock is less than 30cm

H4 Soil is liable to crack to drains and backfill

H5 Soil is permeable and contains drains. 2 3

H6 Slope over 7^{0}

H7 Constraints due to aerosols

L LOWER RISK OF POLLUTION 1

L1 Light topsoil (S. LS. SL. SZL. ZL.)

L2 Medium topsoil (CL. ZCL. SCL.)

L3 Heavy topsoil (C. ZC. SC. Heavy CL. ZCL.)

NOTES

1 Dominant risk in that part of the field during the time specified. Other risks may apply from time to time or locally (e.g waterlogging, old drains, compaction)

2 Applies when the soil is at field capacity. This is when more rain would cause the drains to run

3 When the field is adjacent to a watercourse, spring or borehole.

4 A slowly permeable soil which has a compacted subsoil. When fully wetted further, runs off laterally rather than down through the soil.

PLANNING WASTE APPLICATIONS

1. AREAS WHERE WASTE SHOULD NOT BE SPREAD AT ANY TIME

Leave an untreated strip at least 10 metres wide next to all watercourses. An uncultivated buffer strip will help reduce the risk of causing pollution. Irrigation systems should work so that there is no chance of their spray coming within 10 metres of a watercourse, or of wind blowing material into a watercourse.

To reduce the risk of polluting groundwater, livestock wastes and other organic wastes should not be applied within 50 metres of a spring, well or borehole that supplies, or could supply, water for human consumption or is to be used in farm dairies. In some cases a bigger distance may be needed.

Material might not be able to be spread on some areas of the farm because of the nuisance that could be caused by smell, or because of management agreements.

2. MATCHING LAND AREA TO NITROGEN IN WASTE

As a general guide there should be enough land where waste can be spread to make sure that the amount of total nitrogen in livestock wastes and other organic wastes that are applied, is less than 250 kg/ha/yr (kilograms each hectare each year). This figure does not include manure deposited while livestock are grazing. Lower amounts may be appropriate in sensitive catchments, such as Nitrate Sensitive Areas.

The available nitrogen in organic wastes applied to the land should not be more than the crop needs. This available nitrogen should be taken into account when assessing fertiliser needs.

3. ESTIMATING THE RISK OF POLLUTION FROM SPREADING

3.1 **VERY HIGH RISK AREAS** - Do not apply waste when certain conditions apply

Fields likely to flood in the month after the waste is applied

Fields that are frozen hard

Fields next to a watercourse, spring or borehole where the surface is badly compacted

Fields next to watercourses, springs or boreholes that are waterlogged

Fields next to a watercourse, spring or borehole that have steep slopes and are at field capacity

Fields next to a watercourse, spring or borehole that have a moderate slope, a slowly permeable soil and the soil is at field capacity

Fields that are pipe or mole drained in the last twelve months

Fields that are pipe or mole drained and the soil is cracked down to the drain or backfill

Fields that have been subsoiled over a pipe or mole drainage system in the last twelve months

Fields where the soil depth over fissured rock is less than 30 cm and the soil is cracked

3.2 **HIGH RISK AREAS** - Do not apply more than the recommended amounts

On areas not ruled by the above and under the following conditions, do not put on more than the amounts of livestock wastes or other organic wastes recommended below

Fields next to a watercourse, spring or borehole that have a moderate slope and the field is at field capacity

Fields next to a watercourse, spring or borehole with a slowly permeable soil and the soil is at field capacity

Fields where the soil depth over fissured rock is less than 30 cm

4. APPLICATION RATES

Not more than 50m3 / ha (4500 gallons/acre) of slurry or 50 tonnes / ha (20 tons per acre) of manure at one time should be applied.

To reduce the risk of pollution in these situations, the amount of diluted liquid livestock waste applied by pumped irrigation systems should not be more than :

an application rate of 50m3/ha (4500 gallons/acre) for travelling irrigators

a precipitation rate of 5mm/hour (0.2 inches/hour) with sprinklers moved regularly to suit conditions.

FIELD SOIL DESCRIPTION.

Field No	Description
NG 6382	Silty clay loam to 8″ over slowly permeable, reddish, slightly stony loam. 4° slope to water course, soil compacted
NG 8417	Silty clay loam to 11″ over slowly permeable, stony clayey soil. (under drained)
NG 8100	Clay loam to 8″ over slowly permeable, mottled clay soil
NG 0088	Silty clay loam to 13″ over well mottled dark clayey soil, subject to water logging (slopes to water courses)
NG9400	Loamy clay soil to 12″ over stony silty clay loam
NG0024	As above
NG0002	Loamy clay soil to 14″ over stony silty clay loam
NG1835	Dark greyish brown, slightly stony silty clay loam to 8″ over slightly mottled, yellowish, silty clay loam
NG3559	As above
NG1971	Dark greyish brown, slightly mottled silty clay loam to 9″ over mottled clay loam
NG0573	As above
NG0250	Greyish brown, slightly mottled silty clay loam to 7″, over slightly stony silty clay loam
NG8438	Loamy clay soil to 11″, over slowly permeable clay loam.

FIELD ANALYSIS. *(10 metre buffer zones around all water courses deducted)*

Field Number	Hectares	Normal Risk	Field capacity Risk
NG 6382	6.10	6.10 LR	6.10 HR
NG 8417	3.42	3.42 LR	3.42 HR
NG 8100	3.13	3.13 LR	3.13 HR
NG 0088	3.68	3.68 HR	3.68 NS
NG 9400	1.59	1.59 HR	1.59 NS
NG 0024	1.74	1.74 LR	1.74 HR
NG 0002	5.00	5.00 LR	5.00 HR
NG 1835	4.95	3.14 LR 1.82 VHR	3.14 HR 1.82 NS
NG 3559	3.19	3.19 HR	3.19 VHR
NG 1971	4.61	4.61 HR	4.61 VHR
NG 0573	3.02	3.02 HR	3.02 VHR
NG 0250	2.58	2.58 LR	2.58 HR
NG 8438	0.52	0.52 HR	0.52 VHR

TOTALS HECTARES 43.54

NORMAL RISK %		**FIELD CAPACITY %**	
Lower Risk	**25.11 ha**	**Lower Risk**	**0.00**
Higher Risk	**16.61 ha**	**Higher Risk**	**25.11 ha**
Very High Risk	**1.82 ha**	**Very High Risk**	**11.34 ha**
No Spreading	**0.00 ha**	**No Spreading**	**7.1 ha**

Please refer to the management guidlines for spreading information

RAINFALL DATA SUPPLIED BY MET OFFICE

The average annual rainfall is 939.8 mm.

January	February	March	April	May	June	July
110.6	81.8	79.5	65.4	57.6	55.9	69.0
August	September	October	November	December		
9.0	74.6	87.1	91.3	108.9		

RAINFALL RETURN PERIOD DATA

The once in five year maximum rainfall amounts for various periods of time as required by the code are :

Duration	Rainfall (mm)
1 Hour	19.2
2 Hours	24.3
3 Hours	27.7
4 Hours	30.4
24 Hours	53.3
48 Hours	66.1

The once in five year maximum rainfall for a four consecutive month period during the six months from October to March is 549.0 mm.

The highest average annual rainfall expected once in five years is 1085 mm.

LIVESTOCK DETAILS

1 DAIRY COW = 1.00 Livestock Unit (LSU)

90 animals = 90LSU's

1 BULL = 0.65 Livestock Unit (LSU)

1 animals = 1LSU's

1 ZERO TO ONE YEAR = 0.34 Livestock Unit (LSU)

6 animals = 2LSU's

TOTAL LSU's = 93

Total nitrogen production from 93 LSU's

93 LSU's	= 5.3 m^3
150 days housed	= 780.0 m^3
780.0 * 5kg 'N'	= 3900 Kg 'N'
3900 ÷ 250	= 15.60 ha

All young stock and followers are housed and straw bedded, so for the following calculations, volumes of slurry are based on 90 Livestock units.

90 LSU's housed for 150 days

Slurry production from 90 LSU's	= 770 m^3
770 m^3 * 5kg 'N'	= 3848 kg 'N'
3848 kg 'N' ÷ 250	= 15.39 ha

90 LSU's grazed for 215 days

Slurry production from 90 LSU's	= 184 m^3
184 m^3 * 5kg 'N'	= 919 kg 'N'
919 kg 'N' ÷ 250	= 3.68 ha

Total land requirement for all 'N' production= 19 ha. *from livestock scources*

SILAGE EFFLUENT PRODUCTION *(estimated)*

Capacity of silo	= 1038 m^3
20 litres per m^3 for the first 1500m^3	= 20.76m^3
6.7 litres per m^3 for the balance	= 0.00m^3
Total effluent produced	= 20.76m^3

The silage effluent will be directed into into the dirty water store.

SAFETY NOTE

Do not add silage effluent to slurry in enclosed, below ground tanks, or tanks inside buildings, as it gives off lethal gases, which can cause instantaneous death.

NB. Do not apply silage effluent to non-spreading areas, or land in the very high risk category. Dilute silage effluent with the same amount of water, before you apply it to the land. Do not apply more than 50m^3/ha (4500gallons/acre).

DIRTY WATER AND SLURRY VOLUMES

Month Rain	Parl/Dairy Washings M^3	Yrd/Water M^3	Slurry M^3	Total Volumes M^3
Jan 110.6mm	54	224.0	156	434
Feb 81.8mm	54	165.6	156	376
Mar 79.5mm	54	161.0	160	375
Apr 65.4mm	54	132.4	26	212
May 57.6mm	54	116.6	26	197
Jun 55.9mm	54	113.2	26	193
Jul 69.0mm	54	139.7	26	220
Aug 9.0mm	54	18.2	26	98
Sep 74.6mm	54	151.1	26	231
Oct 87.1mm	54	176.4	26	256
Nov 91.3mm	54	184.9	152	391
Dec 108.9mm	54	220.5	156	430

DIRTY WATER PRODUCTION

Total dirty water production in a year

Total yard area	= 1651 M^2
Total Lagoon area	= 374 M^2
Total dirty water area	= 2025 M^2
2025 M^2 x 1085 mm	= 2197 M^3
18% Strainings from lagoon	= 173 M^3
Dairy and parlour washings	= 657 M^3
Total dirty water over 12 months	= 3027 M^3

Total dirty water production for 4 month period

Total yard area	= 1651 M^2
Total Lagoon area	= 374 M^2
Total dirty water area	= 2025 M^2
2025 M^2 x 549 mm	= 1112 M^3
18% Strainings from lagoon	= 112 M^3
Dairy and parlour washings	= 216 M^3
Total dirty water over 4 months	= 1440 M^3

Total dirty water production in a 48 hour return period

Total yard area	= 1651 M^2
Total Lagoon area	= 374 M^2
Total dirty water area	= 2025 M^2
2025 M^2 x 66 mm	= 134 M^3
18% Strainings from lagoon	= 2 M^3
Dairy and parlour washings	= 4 M^3
Total dirty water over 48 hours	= 138 M^3

DIRTY WATER PRODUCTION continued

Total dirty water production in a 24 hour return period

Total yard area		= 1651 M^2
Total Lagoon area		= 374 M^2
Total dirty water area		= 2025 M^2
2025 M^2 x 53 mm		= 108 M^3
18% Strainings from lagoon		= 1 M^3
Dairy and parlour washings		= 2 M^3
Total dirty water over	24 hours	= 112 M^3

Total dirty water production in a 1 hour return period

Total yard area		= 1651 M^2
Total Lagoon area		= 374 M^2
Total dirty water area		= 2025 M^2
2025 M^2 x 19 mm		= 39 M^3
Total dirty water over	one hour	= 39 M^3

METRIC TO IMPERIAL CONVERSIONS

APPROXIMATE

Millimetres to inches	:	x 0.0394	25 mm = 1 inch
Metres to feet	:	x 3.29	10 m = 33 feet
Hectares to acres	:	x 2.471	10 ha = 25 acres
Litres to gallons	:	x 0.220	1000 l = 220 gallons
Litres to cubic metres	:	- 1000	1 m^3 = 220 gallons
			455m^3 = 1000,000 galls
Tonnes to tons	:	x 0.984	100 t = 98.40 tons
Tonnes/ha to tons/acre	:	x 0.405	50t/ha = 20 tons/acre
m^3/ha to gallons/acre	:	x 89.033	1m^3/ha = 90 galls/acre
			50m^3/ha = 4500galls/acre
Kilograms/ha to units/acre	:	x 0.8	125kg/ha = 100 units/acre

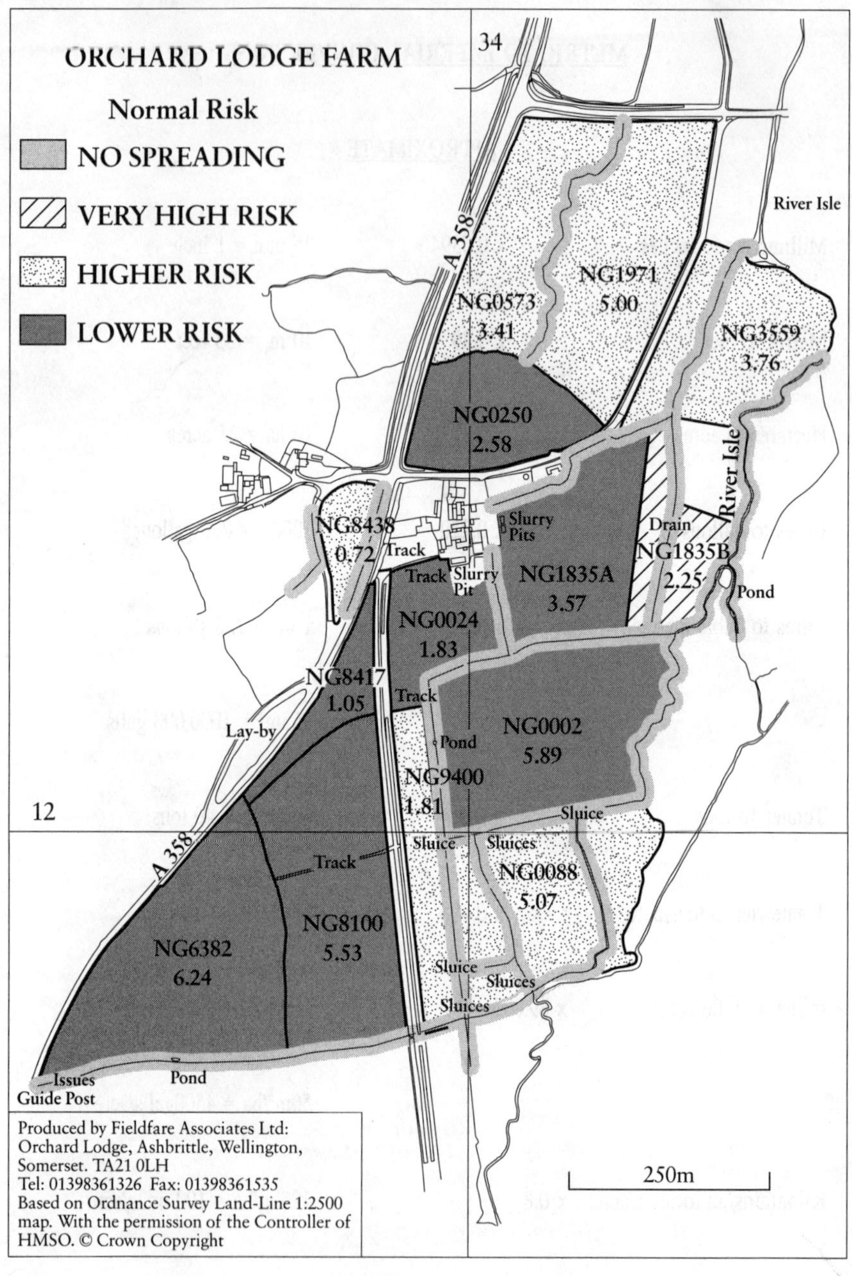
ORCHARD LODGE FARM
Normal Risk
NO SPREADING
VERY HIGH RISK
HIGHER RISK
LOWER RISK
34
12
A 358
A 358
River Isle
River Isle
NG0573
3.41
NG1971
5.00
NG3559
3.76
NG0250
2.58
NG8438
0.72
Track
Slurry Pits
Drain
NG1835A
3.57
NG1835B
2.25
Pond
Track
Slurry Pit
NG0024
1.83
NG8417
1.05
Track
Lay-by
Pond
NG0002
5.89
NG9400
1.81
Sluice
Sluice
Sluices
Track
NG0088
5.07
NG8100
5.53
NG6382
6.24
Sluice
Sluices
Sluices
Issues
Pond
Guide Post
250m
Produced by Fieldfare Associates Ltd:
Orchard Lodge, Ashbrittle, Wellington,
Somerset. TA21 0LH
Tel: 01398361326 Fax: 01398361535
Based on Ordnance Survey Land-Line 1:2500
map. With the permission of the Controller of
HMSO. © Crown Copyright

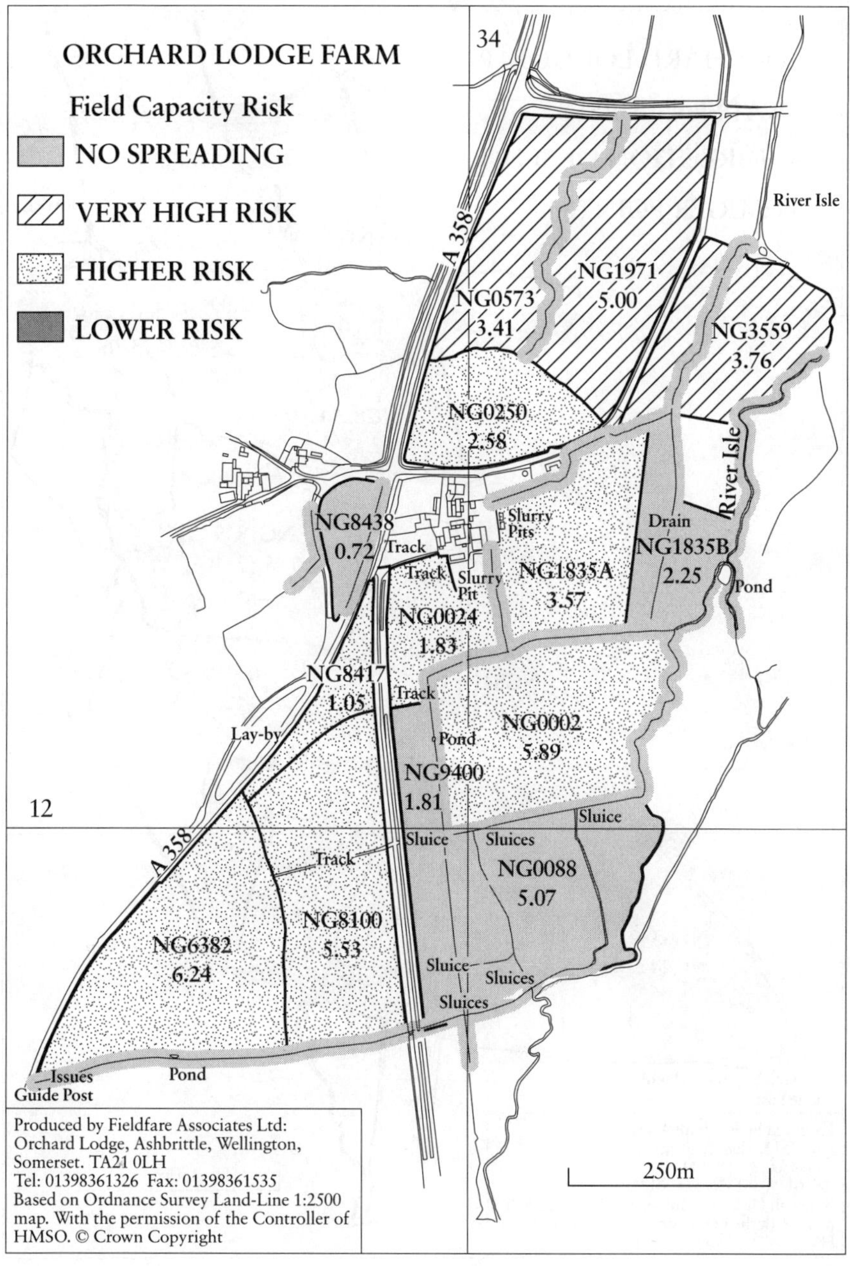
ORCHARD LODGE FARM
Field Capacity Risk
NO SPREADING
VERY HIGH RISK
HIGHER RISK
LOWER RISK
34
12
A 358
River Isle
NG0573
3.41
NG1971
5.00
NG3559
3.76
NG0250
2.58
NG8438
0.72
Track
Slurry Pits
Slurry Pit
NG1835A
3.57
Drain
NG1835B
2.25
Pond
NG0024
1.83
NG8417
1.05
NG0002
5.89
NG9400
1.81
Lay-by
Sluice
Sluices
NG0088
5.07
NG8100
5.53
NG6382
6.24
Issues
Guide Post
250m
Produced by Fieldfare Associates Ltd:
Orchard Lodge, Ashbrittle, Wellington,
Somerset. TA21 0LH
Tel: 01398361326 Fax: 01398361535
Based on Ordnance Survey Land-Line 1:2500 map. With the permission of the Controller of HMSO. © Crown Copyright

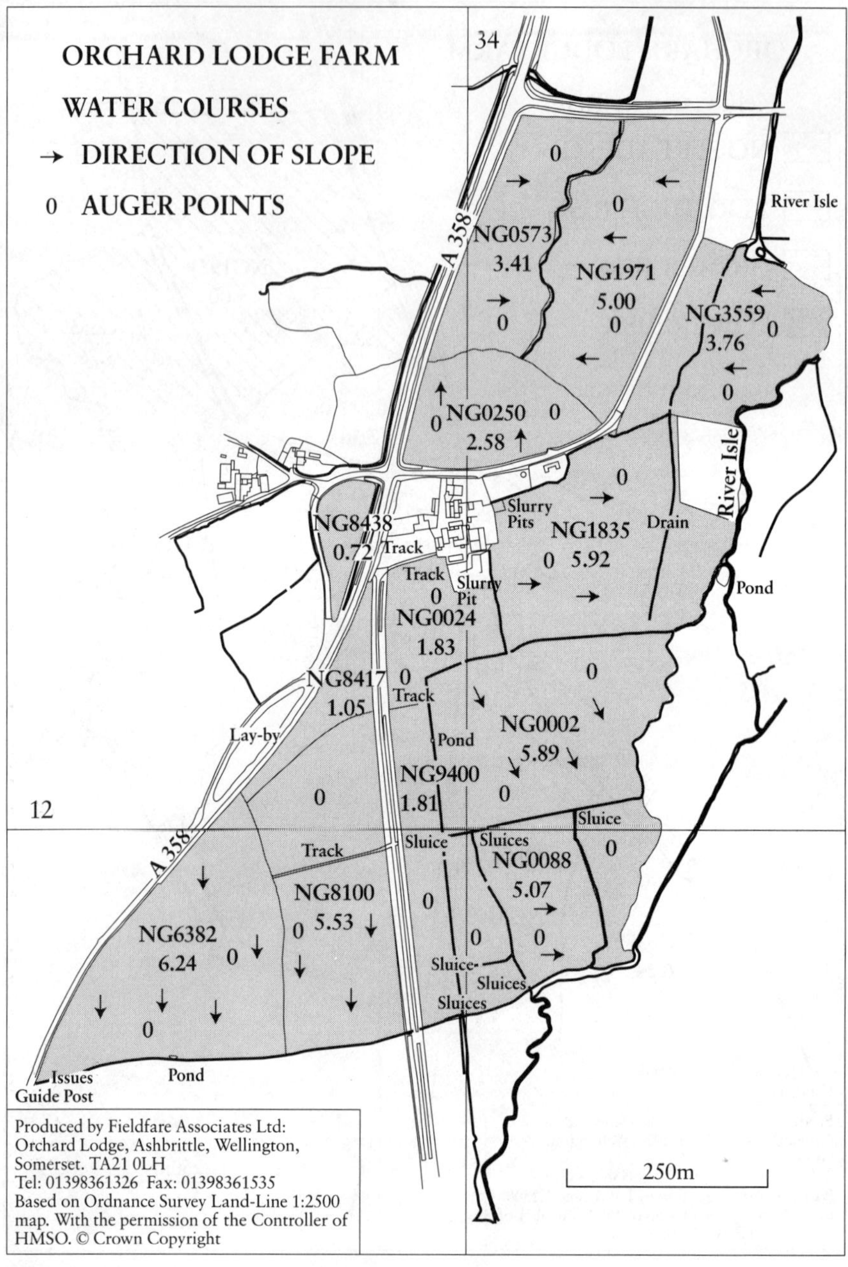
ORCHARD LODGE FARM
WATER COURSES
→ DIRECTION OF SLOPE
0 AUGER POINTS
34
12
A 358
River Isle
NG0573
3.41
NG1971
5.00
NG3559
3.76
NG0250
2.58
Slurry Pits
NG1835
5.92
Drain
Pond
NG8438
0.72
Track
Slurry Pit
NG0024
1.83
NG8417
1.05
NG0002
5.89
Lay-by
NG9400
1.81
Sluice
Sluices
NG0088
5.07
NG8100
5.53
NG6382
6.24
Issues
Guide Post
250m
Produced by Fieldfare Associates Ltd:
Orchard Lodge, Ashbrittle, Wellington,
Somerset. TA21 0LH
Tel: 01398361326 Fax: 01398361535
Based on Ordnance Survey Land-Line 1:2500
map. With the permission of the Controller of
HMSO. © Crown Copyright

Appendix 5

The Environment Agency Enforcement Code of Practice.

Policy Statement

Introduction

1. This policy statement and its accompanying and complementary guidance on enforcement practice, sets out the principles that the Environment Agency (the "Agency") will adopt for its enforcement activities. It takes account of:
   - — the principal aim of the Agency, as provided by section 4(1) of the Environment Act 1995, that is:

     "It shall be the principal aim of the Agency (subject to and in accordance with the provisions of this Act or any other enactment and taking into account any likely costs) in discharging its functions so to protect or enhance the environment, taken as a whole, as to make the contribution towards attaining the objective of achieving sustainable development mentioned in subsection (3) . . . that Ministers consider it appropriate to make . . .," and
   - — the principles of the Government's Code of Practice for enforcement agencies (Working with Business) and Schedule 1 of the Deregulation and Contracting Out Act (1994). In particular these principles are reflected through a commitment that the Agency's warranted officers,[1] will explain to any person upon whom enforcement action is contemplated of the:
     - — suggested remedial action,
     - — intention to take immediate enforcement action,
     - — right to make representations, and
     - — right of appeal if applicable to formal enforcement action.
2. The statement sets out the general principles and approach which the Agency will adopt. It is written for the enforcement of the Environment Act 1995 and those other Acts which the Agency enforces[2] and their relevant statutory provisions.

General principles

3. The Agency will endeavour to secure compliance with the law. Much of its dealings with those on whom the law places duties (businesses and persons engaged in potentially polluting activities) are informal. At an early stage in such endeavour, the Agency's warranted officers will seek to advise and inform those it regulates, offering relevant information, advice and support—face to face, as well as in writing—by confirming the availability of relevant formal guidance publications and by specific, activity related advice.
4. Warranted officers will also assist businesses and individuals to understand the legal requirements, the obligations these impose and the specific environmental concerns in their locality. They will seek to encourage good environmental practices by businesses, including encouraging voluntary initiatives both individually and in cooperation with similar enterprises. They will be sensitive to

[1] Warranted officers are Agency enforcement staff authorised under the Environment Protection Act 1995, s. 108. They include water resource and pollution control officers and bailiffs, pollution inspectors and other enforcing officers from the former constituent bodies of the Agency (see 4).

[2] The Acts which impose regulatory duties upon the Agency are listed in Annex 1 of the associate general Guidance.

the needs of business including its requirement for prompt responses, transparency of action and the imposition of minimum burdens consistent with regulatory compliance.

5. Warranted officers also use formal enforcement mechanisms, as set out in the relevant legal provisions. They include; warnings, cautions, enforcement and works notices where a contravention needs to be remedied, prohibition notices where there is an imminent risk of serious environmental damage, suspension or revocation of environmental licences[3] variations of licence conditions, injunctions and, finally, prosecution.
6. This statement applies to all dealings contributing to securing compliance, whether formal or informal, between warranted officers and all those that they regulate.
7. The Agency's view of enforcement derives in part from its former, constituent bodies[4] as influenced by the pursuit of harmonisation and integration of earlier regulatory regimes and the obligations placed upon the Agency by the Environment Act 1995 and the Department of the Environment's Management Statement for the Agency.[5] It is fully accepted that there should be a quick and effective response to serious breaches of the law and a discriminating and efficient approach to other breaches.
8. Much modern environmental protection law is goal setting. It sets out what must be achieved, but not how it must be done. Some ways of achieving the goals are set out in guidance describing good practice, prepared for enforcement staff by the Agency's constituent bodies. Neither codes nor guidance are in terms which necessarily fit every case. In considering whether good practice has been adopted, the Agency's warranted officers will take relevant codes and guidance into account, using professional judgment about the extent of the risks and the effort that has been applied to counter them. More is said about this below.
9. Sometimes the law is prescriptive—spelling out in detail what must be done. For example, controlled waste may not be disposed of, water abstracted, potentially polluting matter discharged to water or prescribed processes operated, without an environmental licence. Prescriptive law requires that both licenceholder and enforcer meet its requirements precisely and removes the opportunity for discretion—by either party—in the way the law is brought into effect.

Scope

10. EM Agency's regulatory powers are extensive, ranging from pollution control to the management of water resources, flood defence, fisheries and navigation. These powers will be enforced within the spirit of this statement but the application of the procedures described in associated guidance may only be appropriate to activities undertaken at fixed locations, such as:
    — water abstraction,
    — the removal of waste from land, and
    — by holders of environmental licences,

    and in response to point source emergencies and pollution incidents.
11. The procedures are unlikely to be appropriate for the regulation of such activities as:
    — navigation,
    — land drainage consents,
    — responses to notices requiring the provision of information, or furnishing of documents,

[3] Environmental licences include: authorisations, registrations, licences, consents, etc., issued by the Agency or its former constituent bodies (see 4).

[4] The National Rivers Authority, Her Majesty's Inspectorate of Pollution and the Waste Regulations Authorities of England and Wales.

[5] Relevant extracts from the Management Statement are set out below.

— actions required by enforcement notices, and
— angling.

Principles of Enforcement

12. The enforcement of environmental protection law should be informed by the principles of:
— *proportionality*, in applying the law and securing compliance,
— *consistency* of approach,
— *targeting* of enforcement action, and
— *transparency* about how the regulator operates and what those regulated may expect.

Proportionality

13. Proportionality means relating enforcement action to the risks and costs. Those whom the law protects and those on whom it places duties expect that action taken by the Agency to achieve compliance should be proportionate to any risks posed to the environment and to the seriousness of any breach of the law or relevant licence or consent.

14. Some duties are specific and mandatory. However, others require action in line with the principles of "reasonableness" or "appropriateness" and the regulatory system often includes the concept of proportionality through such principles. Deciding what is reasonable or appropriate to control risks, involves the exercise of judgment by licenceholders and, where the law permits, discretion by enforcers, based on sound professional judgment. When a licenceholder and enforcer cannot reach agreement, final determination of what is reasonable in particular circumstances is usually made by the courts.

15. When the law requires that risks be controlled by "appropriate" conditions or as "thought fit" by the Agency—in considering prevention measures taken by licenceholders, the Agency will take account of cost, to the environment as a whole and to regulated organisations, as well as the degree of risk. The Agency may legitimately expect that relevant good practice will be followed. Where good practice, in particular circumstances, is not clearly established, the modern approach to environment protection requires licenceholders to assess the significance of the risks, in terms of both their extent and likelihood, to determine the action that needs to be taken to satisfy the Agency that the action complies with the law.

16. Some irreducible risks may be so serious that they cannot be permitted irrespective of the economic consequences while, at the other extreme, some risks may be so environmentally inconsequential that it is not worth spending more to reduce them. In general, risk-reducing measures will be weighed against the associated costs, the licenceholder taking appropriate ameliorating measures—unless the cost of particular actions is excessive when compared with the benefit of the risk reduction in terms of its magnitude or probability.

17. Although not precisely defined, costs are an implicit element of practicability. Existing methodologies, such as those for assessing the Best Available Technique Not Entailing Excessive Costs (BATNEEC) and the Best Practicable Environmental Option (BPEO), will be used and further refined as practical tools for evaluating the Agency's specific duty to have regard to costs and benefits in exercising its powers.

Consistency

18. Consistency of approach does not mean uniformity. It means taking a similar approach in similar circumstances to achieve similar ends.

19. Environmental licenceholders managing similar risks expect: consistency from the Agency in the advice tendered, the use of powers, decisions on whether to prosecute and in the response to pollution incidents.

20. The Agency recognises that, in practice, consistency is not a simple matter. Warranted officers are faced with many variables; the degree of pollution, the

attitude and actions of management and the history of pollution incidents and flood risk. Each may vary between businesses which otherwise appear similar. Decisions on enforcement action are a matter of sound professional judgment and the Agency, through its officers, should exercise discretion. It will continue to develop arrangements—including standard procedures—to promote consistency within and, where practicable and necessary, between legislative regimes in the exercise of discretion. These will include effective arrangements for liaison with other enforcing authorities, such as periodically reviewed memoranda of understanding.

Transparency

21. Transparency means helping licence and consent holders and others to understand what is expected of them and what they should expect from the Agency: not only what they have to do but, where this is relevant, what they don't. It also means making clear why an officer intends to, or has taken enforcement action. In turn, these mean distinguishing between statutory or compulsory requirements on the one hand and advice or guidance about what is desirable—but not compulsory—on the other.
22. This statement sets out the general policy framework within which the Agency will operate. Licenceholders need to know what to expect when a warranted officer calls and what rights of complaint are open to them: an explanatory leaflet will be provided to licenceholders during a visit or when enforcement action is contemplated. The Agency's initial approach will reflect those of its constituent bodies, variously produced in response to initiatives such as the Citizen's Charter and reflecting the principles of the government's "Code for enforcement agencies". The Agency's intention is to harmonise any differences in its approach as practicability and experience demonstrates is necessary.

Targeting

23. Targeting means making sure that inspection is directed primarily towards those whose activities give rise to the most serious environmental damage or pollution, or where the hazards are least well controlled. And that action is focused on lawbreakers or those directly responsible for the risk and who are best placed to control it.
24. The Agency has inherited systems for prioritising inspection visits. They range from responses to complaints from the public about regulated activities to assessment of the risks posed by a licenceholder's operations taking account of the hazards and nature and extent of the risks. In all cases, management actions are important. A relatively low hazard site or activity poorly managed can entail greater risk to the environment than a higher hazard site or activity where proper control measures are in place. There are, however, high hazard sites (*e.g.* nuclear installations, major hazardous waste disposal facilities) which will receive regular visits so that the Agency can be sure that remote risks continue to be effectively managed. The Agency will pursue the development of risk assessment models and tools to enhance risk comparison within and between regulatory regimes.
25. When formal enforcement action is necessary, those responsible for creating an unacceptable risk to the environment will be held to account for it. The licence/consentholder will be an individual or the owner or occupier of the premises or site. Where several licenceholders share the responsibility, the Agency will take action against those who can be shown to be in breach.

Prosecution

26. The Agency will use discretion in deciding whether to initiate a prosecution. Other approaches to enforcement can often reduce actual or likely environmentally damaging practices and promote good environmental practice more effectively. But, where circumstances warrant it, prosecution without prior

warning and recourse to alternative sanctions, such as revocation of a licence, may be appropriate.

27. The decision to prosecute will take account of the criteria set down in the Code for Crown Prosecutors as published by the Crown Office, *e.g.* evidence and public interest tests.

28. The Agency will consider prosecution when:
- it is appropriate in the circumstances as a way to draw general attention to the need for compliance with the law and the maintenance of standards required by law, especially where there would be a normal expectation that a prosecution would be taken or where, through the conviction of offenders, others may be deterred from similar failures to comply with the law; or
- there is judged to have been potential for considerable environmental harm arising from breach; or
- the gravity of the offence, taken together with the general record and approach of the offender warrants it, *e.g.* apparent reckless disregard for standards, repeated breaches or persistent poor standards.

Prosecution of Individuals

29. Subject to the above, the Agency will identify and prosecute individuals, including company directors and managers, if they consider that a conviction is warranted and there is a reasonable prospect of success.

Encouraging Action by the Courts

30. Environment protection law gives the courts considerable scope to punish offenders and to deter others. Unlimited fines and, in some cases, imprisonment may be imposed by higher courts. The Agency will continue the efforts of its constituent bodies to raise courts' awareness of the gravity of pollution offences and encourage them to make full use of their powers. Examples of the sanctions/penalties presently available to the courts for pollution and environmental damage offences are[6]:

    Magistrates' Court—up to six months imprisonment and/or £20,000 fine.

    Crown Court—up to five years imprisonment and/or an unlimited fine.

[6] As at April 1996. These penalties may change from time to time.

The Environment Agency: Management Statement

The Agency is a non-departmental public body; as such, its management is given broad freedom to exercise its responsibilities within a clearly defined framework. The Department of the Environment's Management Statement for the Agency presents Ministers' aims and objectives for the Agency, its duties and powers, the responsibilities of its Chairman, Board and Chief Executive, and its relationship with Ministers, Government Departments and other bodies.

Among its provisions, the Management Statement specifies how the Agency conducts its external relations—including with regulated organisations—as detailed in the following extract.

"External Relations

Regulated organisations

Ministers expect the Agency to implement environmental regulations in ways which deliver environmental objectives while not imposing unnecessary burdens on those it regulates. To do so, the Agency should seek constructive relationships with regulated bodies (or whose business activities are otherwise affected by its work) and their representatives. This should include provision of advice on regulations, including its approach to enforcement and how to comply with requirements.

The Agency should develop a Code of Practice on the exercise of its regulatory responsibilities. This should promote fairness, proportionality, transparency and consistency of enforcement. It should reflect the principles of the government's code of enforcement agencies ("Working with Business") and Schedule 1 of the Deregulation and Contracting Out Act 1994, while enabling the Agency to maintain effective environmental protection and to take immediate enforcement action where this is justified.

In preparing the Code, the Agency should consult representatives of regulated organisations, and other bodies as appropriate. The Agency should discuss this list of consultees beforehand with the Department, whose approval to the Code is also required.

The Agency should ensure that its staff are aware of the Code, and implement its principles in their work. It should also publish the Code so that it is readily available to regulated organisations. It should monitor compliance with the Code, and have arrangements for reviewing complaints of non-compliance.

Other regulators

The Agency should liaise with other regulators to minimise duplication and conflict in applying legislation, guidance and standards. The Agency should agree a memorandum of understanding with the Health and Safety Executive. It will less also need to liaise with local authorities on matters relating to local air pollution control, contaminated land and environmental health; and with the Marine Safety Agency of the Department of Transport."

The Environment Agency Enforcement Practice Guidance for Warranted Officers

Introduction

1. This is general guidance on the procedures to be followed by Agency warranted officers when enforcing environment protection and pollution prevention legislation[1] in line with the principles of the Agency's enforcement policy.[2] Complementary guidance or more specific regulatory activities will be prepared in due course.

Important Note

2. **This guidance does not weaken the environmental protection afforded by the relevant Acts and their Regulations. It does not affect a warranted officer's duties and powers to take immediate enforcement action against businesses and individuals, or to require them to take immediate remedial action, in any a case where it appears to warranted officers to be necessary to take such action or impose such a requirement.**
3. The guidance does not apply to prosecutions. In considering prosecutions, warranted officers should refer to guidance given in the Agency's Enforcement Policy Statement until the comprehensive prosecution policy for the Agency has been prepared.
4. The Agency's policy gives business the following rights:

   (a) the right to a letter, on request, explaining what needs to be done and why—when warranted officers express an opinion that something should be done—without taking formal action;

   (b) the right to a "**minded to**" **notice** and an entitlement to **have a point of view heard** by the Agency before formal action is taken;

   (c) when **immediate action** is taken, the right to a written statement explaining why this is necessary (*i.e.* why immediate rather than another course of action, and the consequences of failing to take action); and

   (d) the right to be told exactly what rights of **appeal** it has when formal action is taken.

   These rights reflect the principles set out in the Deregulation and Contracting Out Act 1994.

Enforcement practice

5. The following are, in the Agency's view, the key elements of good enforcement practice, much must be applied.
6. At the end of a visit, warranted officers should explain what further action, if any, they are going to take and give information on the rights to: written confirmation of suggested remedial action; make representations; appeal; or complain. The information should be confirmed at the same time by the provision of the leaflet "*Your rights when Environment Agency warranted officers take action*". The leaflet may also be used to provide information to businesses, individuals or their representatives on the action required of them. The text of the leaflet is reproduced at Annex 2.

Letters

7. If warranted officers intend or are asked to write they should do so as soon as practicable and should say when a letter can be expected. Letters should make

[1] See Annex 1, below.

[2] See Enforcement Policy Statement PGSO1.

the status of the advice clear. Where a letter requires remedial action it should set out what needs to be done, why, within what period, and what law applies. It should be explained that there are 10 working days to make representations to the warranted officer's manager if it is thought that the action required is not justified.

8. Warranted officers should not take formal enforcement action during the 10 working-days period for making representations beginning on the date of the letter—unless immediate action is justified by the risk.

Enforcement notices

9. If a warranted officer intends to issue an enforcement notice, an operator has a right to know and to understand what needs to be done to comply and within what timescale. Unless immediate action is necessary, the opportunity should be given to make representations to the warranted officer's manager if it is considered that the proposed notice should not be issued, or should be changed.
10. Warranted officers should discuss with the operator what the breaches of the law are and the action which will be needed to comply. As well as complying with any statutory provisions, warranted officers should give the operator a written summary covering the reasons for the proposed notice, what constitutes the failure to comply with the law, outlining what needs to be done to comply and by when—together with the leaflet explaining business' rights. The summary must be enough to enable the operator to make representations.
11. The operator has 10 working days—from receiving written notice of the intention to issue an enforcement notice—to make representations to the warranted officer's manager if it is thought that the requirements should be changed or the notice should not be issued. Warranted officers and their managers should take a fair and fresh look at the proposed action in the light of representations.

Immediate action

12. Whenever warranted officers need to take immediate enforcement action, they should provide a written statement as soon as practicable explaining the reasons. Prohibition notices should include such explanation where they do not already do so.
13. In the case of their power to "seize and make safe" warranted officers should send a written explanation as soon as practicable.
14. Immediate action should, where practicable, be discussed with operators at the time and the views expressed taken into account.

Appeals

15. Warranted officers must give an operator written information on how to appeal when issuing notices, explaining the grounds, how, where and within what period an appeal may be brought. And, where applicable, that action on an enforcement notice is suspended while an appeal is pending.

Monitoring

16. The Agency will introduce systems to monitor that a leaflet has been provided to every operator they visit, that where warranted officers intend to issue enforcement notices they confirm their intention in writing and that any representations are properly considered.
17. The Agency's Board and Executive will ensure that this guidance is applied fairly and effectively.

Start date

18. This guidance will be adopted forthwith.

Annex 1 (to the Enforcement Practice Guidance for Warranted Officers)

The Environment Agency—Enforced Acts

Each Act has associated statutory instruments, orders and the like—not listed.

WATER MANAGEMENT
WATER RESOURCES
Water Resources Act 1991
Water Industry Act 1991

FLOOD DEFENCE

Water Resources Act 1991
Land Drainage Act 1991
Land Drainage Act 1976
Flood Defence Byelaws

FISHERIES
Diseases of Fish Act 1937
Sea Fisheries Regulation Act 1966
Salmon & Freshwater Fisheries Act 1975

Wildlife & Countryside Act 1981
Diseases of Fish Act 1983
Salmon Act 1986
Water Resources Act 1991

NAVIGATION
Water Act 1989
Water Resources Act 1991
Land Drainage Act 1976
Sea Fish Industry Act 1951
Pilotage Act 1987
Harbour Docks & Piers Clauses Act 1847
Anglian Water Act 1977
Southern Water Authority Act 1980
Thames Conservancy Acts 1932, 1950, 1959, 1966, 1972

POLLUTION REGULATION
DISCHARGES TO WATER
Water Act 1989
Water Resources Act 1991
Water Industry Act 1991

Salmon & Freshwater Fisheries Act 1975
Environmental Protection Act 1990

WASTE REGULATION
Control of Pollution Act 1974
Control of Pollution (Amendment) Act 1989

Environmental Protection Act 1990

INTEGRATED POLLUTION CONTROL
Environmental Protection Act 1990

AIR POLLUTION
Health & Safety at Work etc. Act 1974
Alkali etc. Works Regulation Act 1906
Environmental Protection Act 1990

RADIOACTIVE SUBSTANCES
Radioactive Substances Act 1993

GENERAL
The Environment Act 1995
European Communities Act 1972

Annex 2 (to the Enforcement Practice Guidance for Warranted Officers)

The Environment Agency—Your Rights When Agency Warranted Officers Take Action

The Environment Agency's Enforcement Policy Statement sets out the principles to be followed in enforcing environmental protection legislation

If a warranted officer:

— **intends to take immediate action,** for example by issuing a notice prohibiting a certain action, you have a ***right to a written explanation as soon as practicable*** of why this is necessary. Prohibition notices normally include such explanation;

— **tells you to do something,** you have a **right, *if you ask,* to be given a letter** explaining what needs to be done, when and why. On receipt of the letter, you have 10 working days to make representations to the warranted officer's manager. You may be asked to agree to a shorter period as an alternative to taking immediate action;

— intends **to issue an enforcement notice,** you have a ***right to a written explanation of what is wrong, an outline of what needs to be done, and by when.*** You have a right to have your point of view heard by the warranted officer's manager if you consider that the notice should be changed or should not be issued. You have 10 working days in which to make representations, which will be considered on a fair and fresh basis.

When a notice is issued you will be told in writing about your ***statutory right of appeal*** and given the appropriate form to use to appeal. You will be told:

— how to appeal;

— where and within what period an appeal may be brought;

— the grounds upon which an appeal may be brought; and

— where the law requires it, that the action required by the notice is suspended while an appeal is pending.

The procedures and rights outlined abovc provide ways for you to have your views heard if you are not happy with the warranted officer's action. If these procedures have not been followed, you should let the officer's manager know.

You can speak or write to the warranted officer's manager who will investigate your grievance and tell you what is going to be done about it. Experience has demonstrated that most grievances will be settled in this way, very often immediately. If you are not satisfied that your grievances has been handled in accordance with this procedure, you can contact the Agency's Regional General Manager or write to the Chief Executive at the Agency's headquarters (address below) who will see that your complaint is followed up promptly and fairly. You can also write and ask your Member of Parliament to take up your case with the Agency or with Ministers. Your M.P. may also ask the independent Parliamentary Commissioner for Administration (Ombudsman) to review your concerns.

Appendix 6

Farm Waste Management Plan

The ADAS step by step guide for farmers

Name
Farm Address
Date

MAFF/WOAD Farm Waste Management Plan Sept 1994

Introduction

These guidelines have been designed to help you produce a plan for spreading manure, slurries and other organic wastes on your farm. This plan will help you to minimise the risk of causing water pollution. The background to the plan is described in the Code of Good Agricultural Practice for the Protection of Water which is available free of charge from your local office of the Ministry of Agriculture, Fisheries and Food or Welsh Office Agriculture Department. The Code also gives advice on the handling and storage of manures and slurries.

You should not forget that other materials used on farms such as pesticides, fuel oil and fertilisers can also cause water pollution. You should also follow the Code of Good Agricultural Practice for the Protection of Water for these materials.

The guidelines have been divided into five easy steps.

The first four steps enable you to complete a **coloured map** of your farm showing where manures can safely be spread during the **winter**. Notes are provided to help you at other times of the year.

- **Step 1** helps you identify how much land you have for spreading manures and where manures should not be spread
- **Step 2** helps you identify any restrictions on manure spreading
- **Step 3** helps you work out the minimum area of land you need for spreading
- **Step 4** gives you guidance on applying sewage sludge and other organic wastes
- **Step 5** helps you work out whether you need extra storage for slurry and dirty water

The guidance that we have given may not cover every circumstance on your farm. Please discuss any problems with your ADAS contact.

If you wish to use this plan to support proposals for an installation affected by the Control of Pollution (Silage, Slurry, and Agricultural Fuel Oil) Regulations 1991, you will need to obtain advice from the National Rivers Authority.

Reducing the risk of pollution from land spreading

Complete the first four steps in the following pages to produce a plan. Carry out the recommendations and you will minimise the risk of causing water pollution from spreading animal manures and organic wastes on your farm.

To complete this plan you will need to do some calculations. These are easier to do in metric units but we have provided conversion figures to help you if your information is in imperial.

To draw up the plan you will need:

1 Your total farm area in hectares (1 hectare = 2.5 acres).

2 A map of the farm that clearly shows:

- every field and watercourse (including all ditches)
- field areas in hectares
- any boreholes, springs or wells that supply water for farm dairies or human consumption including any on neighbouring land near to your boundary

If these features are not marked on your map, please draw them in.

Note: If you use a 1:2500 scale map, 1 grid square = 1 hectare and 1 side of a square = 100 metres.

3 Stock details:

- the average number of each type of stock housed on the farm over the whole year, (eg. pigs, poultry and beef cattle) and/or over the winter period only, (eg. dairy cattle)
- the average time for which each type is housed

4 Coloured pens or pencils - red, orange, yellow and green

5 A calculator

In the following pages we give you the necessary steps to draw up a successful plan.

As you complete the steps you will notice letters beside some boxes. These letters are used to identify figures which recur throughout the document. They are a guide to help you when transferring figures from one box to another in certain calculations. You should find the steps easy to follow.

Colour coding of pollution risk areas

Your plan will contain some or all of the following coloured areas:

- **Red areas** must never be used for spreading
- **White areas** are not normally used for operational reasons but may be brought into use in the future.
- **Orange areas** cannot be used when certain conditions apply, but they will usually be available at some other times of the year. For example fields which cannot be used when they are at field capacity in winter may be used in spring. However they may also be at very high risk if the soil cracks over drains in summer.
- **Yellow areas** may be used for spreading at most times of the year but application rates must be no more than 50m^3/ha when certain conditions apply.
- **Green areas** may be used for spreading at most times of the year.

Step 1

Calculating the area of crops and grass available for spreading animal manures

Areas where animal manures should never be spread

These areas are described below. Pick out those areas which occur on your farm, and colour them on your map in **red**. Where an area is an unusual shape, for example circular areas around wells, mark off a square or 'practical' shaped area of the field.

Areas on which manures and slurry should never be spread are:

Ditches and watercourses

- Within at least 10 metres (11 yards) of either side of any watercourse including ditches and piped ditches. This will avoid direct spreading into the watercourse and also reduce the risk of run-off reaching the watercourse. Do not forget to include watercourses that form the boundary of your farm.

Other non-spreading (red) areas

- Within at least 50 metres (55 yards) of any spring, well, borehole or reservoir that supplies water for human consumption or farm dairies.
- Very steep slopes where run-off is a high risk throughout the year.
- Any areas where you may not be allowed to spread for reasons such as a tenancy agreement, an abatement notice due to smell, set-aside land, SSSIs, ESAs.

After colouring in these areas on your map, use Table 1, opposite, to help you calculate the total number of hectares where you should never spread animal manures.

Areas on which manures and slurry should never be spread

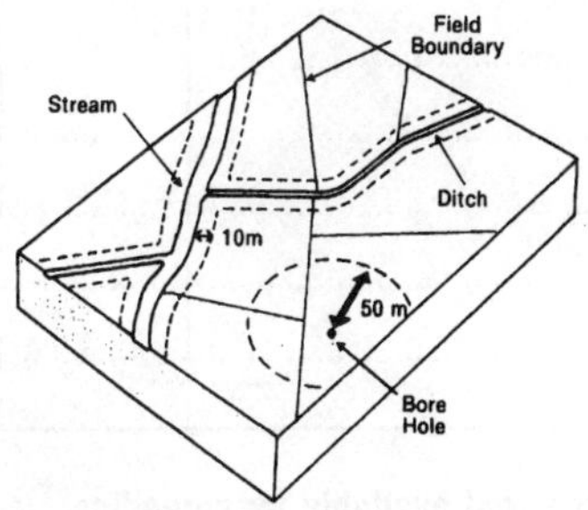

Other areas where you do not normally spread slurry

We suggest that you leave these areas **white** on your map. Enter their areas into Table 1.

This may be because of:-

- non farmed areas - buildings, roads, tracks.
- particular land use such as orchards, woodlands etc.
- location eg they are too far from the farmstead
- the surface is rocky or uneven so that your equipment cannot be used effectively or safely.

Table 1 - Calculating the area not available for spreading
List in this table **only** your fields which have red or white areas. Remember ditches and watercourses have two sides.

Field name or number	Whole field area in hectares (ha)	Ditches & watercourses		Other red areas (ha)	White areas (ha)
		Total length in metres (m)	* Metres ÷1000=ha		

Areas not available for spreading:	**Totals**	**x**	***y***	**z**

** This calculation is derived from ditches x 10m (red area) ÷ 10 000 to give hectares. If we do not multiply by the 10m first, we only need to divide by 1 000.*

Note: If you use a 1:2500 scale map, 1 grid square = 1 hectare and 1 side of a square = 100 metres

Total farm area ***A*** [ ] ha

Area available for spreading: A minus (x + y + z) = ***B*** [ ] ha

Step 2

Identifying areas where manures should not be spread under certain conditions or where rates should be restricted

Some areas of the farm will be unsuitable for spreading at certain times of the year, particularly in winter. This could vary from year to year. Other areas may receive manure at any time of the year but the rate and frequency of application needs to be carefully limited. The conditions which restrict the timing, rates and frequency of applications are listed in Table 2 below.

Table 2 - Identifying very high risk (orange) and high risk (yellow) areas

Any field which meets both orange and yellow conditions should be coloured orange

Key	Conditions leading to very high and high risk areas	Colour Map
1	Fields or part fields next to a watercourse, spring or borehole when the surface is severely compacted† or waterlogged.	Orange
2	Fields or part fields that are likely to flood sometime in most winters	Orange
3	Field or part fields next to a watercourse, spring or borehole when the soil is at field capacity* (in winter) and there is:-	
	• a steep slope	Orange
	• a moderate slope and a slowly permeable soil (ie a clay soil or one through which water passes only slowly)	Orange
	• a moderate slope and a well-drained soil	Yellow
	• a slight slope and a slowly permeable soil	Yellow
	All fields** or part fields with effective pipe or mole drains (but see extra limitations below)	Yellow
	Shallow soils over gravel or rock eg limestone, chalk, slates and shales	Yellow

Notes

† **Severely compacted is when rain stays on the surface after rainfall**

* **Field Capacity is when the soil becomes fully wetted and more rain would cause water loss by drainage. This normally happens in autumn and lasts until the spring.**

** **Fields or part fields which in the last 12 months have been pipe drained, mole drained or subsoiled over drains should not be used for spreading.**

Drained or mole drained fields should not be used in summer if they are cracked down to the drains or backfill.

Areas for spreading (subject to restrictions)

Identify areas which meet the conditions in **Table 2** and mark them on your map in **orange** (very high risk) or **yellow** (high risk) as indicated.

Number the orange areas on your map using the reasons and number key from Table 2. Number the map with all the conditions affecting it.

Colour the remaining areas of crops and grass **green** (lower risk). Remember you may need to leave some areas white (Step 1).

Slurry and manure should never be spread when:

- The ground is frozen hard as a subsequent thaw or rainfall can cause a significant risk of run-off.
- The fields are so wet that tractor-drawn machinery will damage the soil.
  You may consider that areas you have marked yellow are not available during the winter for this reason.

Attach the key below to your map to help you identify areas more easily.

Colour Key

- **Red areas**
  Land where waste should never be spread
- **Orange areas**
  Very high risk
- **Yellow areas**
  High risk
- **Green areas**
  Lower risk
- **White areas**
  Land not normally used for spreading

Orange areas number key

1. Do not spread on these fields when the surface is compact or waterlogged
2. Do not spread when there is a risk of flooding
3. Do not spread when the soil is at Field Capacity ie when the soil is fully wetted

Step 3

Calculating the minimum area of land needed for spreading animal manures

This calculation ensures that no more than 250 kg/ha (200 units /acre) of total nitrogen in animal manure is applied in any one year. *(This is the guide figure given in the Code of Good Agricultural Practice for the Protection of Water).*

Follow these steps in **Table 3**.

- Fill in your stock numbers in column A
- Enter the number of months cattle are housed in column B
- Carry out the multiplication using the figures in columns A, B and C and record the result in column D.
- Finally add up the column D to get the total area needed.

If you spread slurry or manure from other farms on your land, include these livestock numbers as well. If you spread sewage sludge or other organic wastes, see Step 4. Details for other classes and weights of stock are given in annex 1 page 16.

Table 3 - Stocking Calculation

Stock Unit	A Number of stock units		B Months housed		C Hectares needed per stock unit		D Total area needed (ha)
1 Dairy Cow		x		x	0.031	=	
1 Suckler Cow		x		x	0.024	=	
1 Beef Bullock		x		x	0.011	=	
1 Follower/Young Stock		x		x	0.009	=	
1 Calf (to 6 months)		x		x	0.0025	=	
1 Breeding Sow Place, including piglets to 4 weeks				x	0.060	=	
1 Weaner Place				x	0.015	=	
1 Pig place (20 - 90 kg)				x	0.042	=	
1000 Laying hens				x	2.500	=	
1000 Broiler places				x	2.400	=	
				x		=	
				x		=	

Total = Minimum land needed ***C*** [ ] ha

Area available for spreading manure (Transfer B from page 5) ***B*** [ ] ha

If C is bigger than B:

Extra area is needed to spread animal manures (C minus B) [ ] ha

- You may wish to consider if some of the white areas on your map which are used for cropping could be safely used for spreading to make good the difference.
- Alternatively you should make arrangements to spread the excess manures on another farm or dispose of it in other ways. You should always follow the Code of Good Agricultural Practice.

Step 4

Guidelines for spreading sewage sludge or other organic wastes

You only need to read this page if you spread sewage sludge or bring other organic wastes onto your farm.

The Farm Waste Management Plan you have drawn up should also be used to guide you when spreading sewage sludge or other organic wastes. The risk of causing pollution is very similar to the risk that occurs when spreading animal manures.

The recommended annual limit of 250 kg/ha N in organic manures applies to the total organic nitrogen applied during the year from all sources. Therefore you should only spread sewage sludge and other waste if you have more land suitable for spreading than you need for your animal manures.

Before deciding whether you wish to spread these materials check that there will be some land available for spreading after you have spread all your animal manures. The amount of land remaining will be given by:

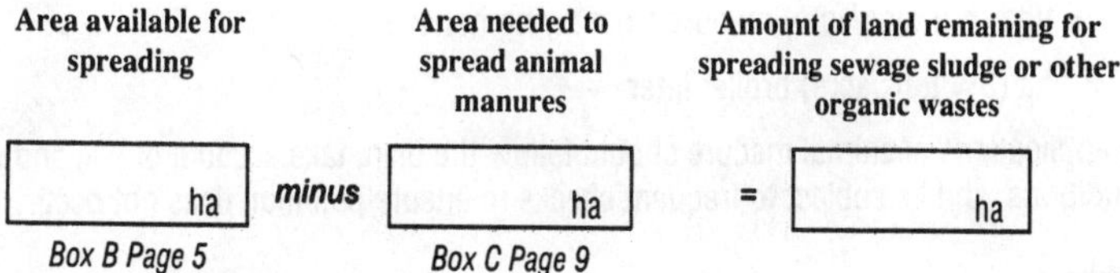

The simplest way to avoid applying excess nitrogen is to avoid spreading on fields where you plan to spread animal manures. A single application of sludge commonly contains at least 250 kg/ha N. To help you avoid applying more than 250kg/ha N, the rate of application should not be more than that given below. However, sludge from a particular source may contain more or less nitrogen than the average analyses on which these figures are based. The supplier should provide you with an analysis and interpretation.

Type of sewage sludge	Maximum rate of application	
Liquid undigested	138	m³/ha
Liquid digested	125	m³/ha
Sludge cake undigested	33	t/ha
Sludge cake digested	33	t/ha

All other organic wastes should be spread at rates which take account of their nitrogen content and polluting potential.

Using this plan

These pages help you use your plan to avoid pollution

Red areas

These should never be used for spreading manure as it would cause water pollution, damage natural habitats or in some cases break a legal obligation.

White areas

You have judged these unsuitable for various reasons. It may be possible to spread manure safely at some time in the future. You should use the guidance in Table 2 and the notes on page 6 to make this decision.

Maximum annual applications to all areas

- The amount of animal manure applied to a given area in a 12 month period should not contain more than 250 kg/ha total N (200 units/acre).

  This is equivalent to a maximum of:

  - $50 m^3$/ha (4500 gallons/acre) undiluted cow slurry or undiluted slurry from liquid-fed pigs
  - 40 t/ha (16 tons/acre) fresh cattle FYM
  - 16 t/ha (6½ tons/acre) manure from laying hens
  - 8 t/ha (3¼ tons/acre) broiler litter.
- All applications of animal manure should follow the plan, take account of soil and weather conditions, and be subject to frequent checks to ensure pollution does not occur.

Remember:

- **Slurry and manure should never be spread on any areas which are frozen hard**
- **Risks can be reduced by applying wastes at lower rates than those recommended above**
- **Do not spread wastes when the soil is so wet tractor-drawn machinery will damage the soil**
- **The maximum annual application of animal manures also applies to land used for growing maize**

Using orange areas

Do not apply to these areas in the winter or when severely compacted or in summer if cracked over drains.

Using yellow areas

Provided your machinery does not damage the soil these areas can be used for spreading at most times of the year. When the soil is at field capacity you should follow the guidelines below:

Do not	apply more than 50 m^3/ha (4500 galls/acre) of diluted slurry or other effluent at any one time.
Do not	apply more than 50m^3/ha by travelling irrigators at any one time.
Do not	apply more than 5mm/hour ($^1/_5$"/hr) dirty water with sprinklers.
Do	move sprinklers regularly to suit conditions. On drained soils take particular care that polluting material does not pass into a watercourse.
Do	leave an interval of at least 3 weeks between applications.

These rules also apply to drained and shallow soils throughout the year.

- **Risks can be reduced further by applying waste at lower rates than those recommended above**
- **Remember that some drained fields which are high risk (yellow) in winter may crack in summer. They should not be used for spreading when in this condition.**

Using green areas

Provided your machinery does not damage the soil these areas can always be used for spreading, with a lower risk of causing pollution. Low dry matter slurries or other dilute effluents may be applied at more than 50 m^3/ha at any one time, but always taking care that run off does not occur.

Drained soils

In orange, yellow, and green areas, drained soils may be used provided the limiting rates given above for yellow areas are observed - but check drain outfalls to ensure no pollution occurs.

You should not use any drained fields when they are cracked in summer, or within 12 months of installation of drains or of moling or of subsoiling.

Silage effluent

The amount of effluent produced will vary from year to year according to the moisture content of the grass when it is ensiled. **Silage effluent is highly polluting and should be diluted with the same amount of water before application to land. Do not apply more than 50m^3/ha of diluted effluent.** Apply according to the criteria for different areas above. Avoid drained land wherever possible to reduce the risk further. Take account of its nitrogen content in your fertiliser policy.

Using manures

Use your map together with your cropping plan and grazing schedule to decide when to apply to a particular field. The fertiliser value of manures should be maximised by applying according to crop needs and to complement your inorganic fertiliser applications. MAFF booklet RB209, Fertiliser Recommendations for Agricultural and Horticultural Crops gives further guidance.

Step 5

Assessing whether extra storage is needed for slurry and dirty water

You may wish to use this step to help you assess your storage need.
It does not apply to farms where only solid manures are produced

Using the assessment of spreading risks made in steps 1 to 4, together with your experience of spreading over winter, step 5 will enable you to estimate whether extra storage of slurry and dirty water will be needed to minimise the risk of causing pollution.

It is assumed that solid manures will remain in buildings or be stored at a suitable outside location if you do not have enough land available for winter spreading.

Complete the boxes below with your best estimate of existing slurry and dirty water storage capacity.

Storage capacity available - slurry **D_1** [mths]

Storage capacity available - dirty water **D_2** [mths]

OR

Storage capacity available - slurry and dirty water together **D_3** [mths]

From your coloured map, add the total green and yellow areas and enter the figure in box E.

E [ha]

Complete Tables 4 (and Table 5 where necessary) overleaf using the above information. Pay particular attention to the notes below each table before completion.

Slurry Storage

Table 4 Assessing whether extra slurry storage is needed (see notes below)

	A Do you apply slurry during these months? YES or NO	B If the answer in column A is Yes, do you have enough suitable land available on your plan for spreading in these months? YES or NO	C If the answer in column B is No, do you need more storage in these months? YES or NO
September October			
November December			
January February			
March April			
May June			
July August			

Column A

- The answers in column **A** should reflect typical current practice. If you sometimes use these months, answer YES.

Column B

- Consider whether the map you have prepared shows adequate land available for each 2 month period for which you answered YES in column **A**. **Remember that you should not exceed the safe application rate on each field.**
- Use your knowledge of cropping and grazing together with the information in Box **D1** (or **D3**) and Box **E**. You will also need to consider whether soil conditions will allow field machinery to operate.
- You may wish to refer to Annex 2 , page 17 to estimate the minimum monthly area needed for spreading slurry (Box **F**).

Column C

- If you answered **NO**, it means that you can overcome the shortage of land for spreading in these months by some other means eg. spreading on a neighbouring farm.
- If you answered **YES**, the size of additional slurry storage will need to be calculated. You may need to take professional advice.

Dirty Water Storage

Table 5 Assessing whether extra dirty water storage is needed (see notes below)

	A Do you apply dirty water during these months? YES or NO	B If the answer in column A is Yes, do you have enough suitable land available on your plan for spreading in these months? YES or NO	C If the answer in column B is No, do you need more storage in these months? YES or NO
September October			
November December			
January February			
March April			
May June			
July August			

Column A

- The answers in column A should reflect typical current practice. If you sometimes use these months, answer YES.

Column B

- Consider whether the map you have prepared shows adequate land available for each 2 month period for which you answered YES in column A . **Remember that you should not exceed the safe application rate on each field.**
- Use your knowledge of cropping and grazing together with the information in Box **D2** and Box **E**. You will also need to consider whether soil conditions will allow field machinery to operate.
- You may wish to refer to Annex 2 , page 17 to estimate the minimum six monthly area needed for spreading dirty water (Box **K** or **L**).

Column C

- If you answered **NO**, it means that you can overcome the shortage of land for spreading in these months by some other means.
- If you answered **YES**, the size of additional dirty water storage will need to be calculated. You may need to take professional advice.

Annex 1

Hectares needed per stock unit for other classes and weights of stock

Stock Unit	Table 3 Column C Hectares needed per stock unit
Calves, 6 months - 1 year	0.006 per month
1 mature sheep	0.002 per month
1 fattening lamb	0.001 per month
1 pig place (20-65 kg) dry meal fed	0.036 per year
1 pig place (20-65 kg) liquid-fed	0.036 per year
1 pig place (20-110 kg) dry meal fed	0.048 per year
1 pig place (20-110 kg) liquid-fed	0.048 per year
1000 free range laying hens	1.250 per year
1000 turkeys (male)	5.160 per year
1000 turkeys (female)	2.420 per year

Annex 2

Estimating minimum areas needed for spreading slurry and dirty water

Area needed for spreading slurry

For a typical month when all livestock are housed calculate the area needed to spread the slurry that is produced that month.

Table 6 Calculating the areas needed to spread slurry during months when all livestock are housed

Stock Unit on **slurry based system**	**A** No. on slurry or part slurry-based system		**B** Proportion of waste collected as slurry		**C** Hectares needed per stock unit per month		**D** Area needed for month (ha)
1 Dairy Cow		x		x	0.031	=	
1 Suckler Cow		x		x	0.024	=	
1 Beef Bullock		x		x	0.011	=	
1 Follower/Young Stock		x		x	0.009	=	
1 Calf (to 6 months)		x		x	0.0025	=	
1 Breeding Sow Place, including piglets to 4 weeks		x		x	0.005	=	
1 Weaner Place		x		x	0.001	=	
1 Pig Place (20-90kg) dry meal fed		x		x	0.0035	=	
		x		x		=	
		x		x		=	

Total area needed per month = ***F*** [ ] ha

Calculating dirty water production (six months winter period)

To estimate likely production of dirty water you will need:

1. A rough plan of the open yards and silage clamps with dimensions to enable calculation of the total dirty yard area from which run-off is collected.
2. The average annual rainfall for your farm.
3. A calculator.

Use your plan of open yards to work out the total dirty area in square metres. **Exclude** covered areas if rain falling on these roofs is collected and discharged to a clean drain. If rainfall onto roofs or clean concrete also mixes with dirty water then include this roof or yard area. Also **include** the area of uncovered silage clamps and dungsteads and weeping wall stores if the liquid drains to the dirty water store.

In the calculations below, parlour washings are based on a standard figure of 18 litres (4½ gallons) per cow per day. If you know the total amount of parlour washings (litres) on a daily basis multiply by 0.18† and enter directly into box **H**.

	Total yard area in m2		Typical winter rainfall (annual rainfall x 0.6)			
Run-off:	m2	X	mm	÷ 1000 * =	**G**	m3
			Number of cows			
Parlour washings:				x 3.24 ** =	**H**	m3

Estimate any other foul run-off in the winter 6 months e.g. use of hosepipe or pressure washer : **I** [ ] m3

Total winter volume of dirty water = G + H + I = **J** [ ] m3

1 square yard = 0.84 m2, 1 inch = 25.4 mm, 220 gallons = 1m3

† **Multiplying by 0.18 converts litres per day into cubic metres per 6 months**

* **Dividing by 1000 converts rainfall from millimetres into metres**

** **Multiplying by 3.24 gives the volume of parlour washings over 6 months**

Minimum area needed for spreading dirty water in winter

Six month (winter) volume of dirty water (transfer **J** from above)		Minimum area needed for spreading dirty water in winter
J [ ] m3	**divided by 1000* =**	**K** [ ] ha

* divided by 1000 because up to 1000 m3 of dirty water may be applied to a hectare without applying more than 250 kg/ha N. Dirty water contains 0.25 kg N/m3 (on average), 250 ÷ 0.25 = 1000.

The nitrogen concentration of dirty water is increased if you add to it the liquid that drains from weeping-wall stores or strainer boxes. If this is the case you will need to increase the area for spreading. To do this multiply the figure in box **K** by 4 and enter into box **L**.

Appendix 7

E.C. Nitrate Directive 91/676 Annex III—Measures to be Included in Action Programmes as Referred to in Article 5(4)(a)

1. The measures shall include rules relating to:
   (1) periods when the land application of certain types of fertilizer is prohibited;
   (2) the capacity of storage vessels for livestock manure; this capacity must exceed that required for storage throughout the longest period during which land application in the vulnerable zone is prohibited, except where it can be demonstrated to the competent authority that any quantity of manure in excess of the acrual storage capacity will be disposed of in a manner which will not cause harm to the environment;
   (3) limitation of the land application of fertilizers, consistent with good agricultural practice and taking into account the characteristics of the vulnerable zone concerned, in particular:
      (a) soil conditions, soil type and slope;
      (b) climatic conditions, rainfall and irrigation;
      (c) land use and agricultural practices, including crop rotation systems;

   and to be based on a balance between:
      (i) The foreseeable nitrogen requirements of the crops, and
      (ii) the nitrogen supply to the crops from the soil and from fertilization corresponding to:
         — the amount of nitrogen present in the soil at the moment when the crop starts to use it to a significant degree (outstanding amounts at the end of winter),
         — the supply of nitrogen through the net mineralization of the reserves of organic nitrogen in the soil,
         — additions of nitrogen compounds from livestock manure,
         — additions of nitrogen compounds from chemical and other fertilizers.

2. These measures will ensure that, for each farm or livestock unit, the amount of livestock manure applied to the land each year, including by the animals themselves, shall not exceed a specified amount per hectare.

   The specified amount per hectare be the amount of manure containing 170 kg N. However:
   (a) for the first four year action programme Member States may allow an amount of manure containing up to 210 kg N;
   (b) during and after the first four-year action programme, Member States may fix different amounts from those referred to above. These amounts must be fixed so as not to prejudice the achievement of the objectives specified in Articles 1 and must be justified on the basis of objectives criteria, for example:
      — long growing seasons,
      — crops with high nitrogen uptake,
      — high net precipitation in the vulnerable zone,
      — soils with exceptionally high denitrification capacity.

   If a Member State allows a different amount under subparagraph (b), it shall inform the Commission which will examine the justification in accordance with the procedure laid down in Article 9.

3. Member States may calculate the amounts referred to in paragraph 2 on the basis of animal numbers.
4. Member States shall inform the Commission of the manner in which they are applying the provisions of paragraph 2. In the light of the information received, the Commission may, if it considers necessary, make appropriate proposals to the Councils in accordance with Article 11.

Welsh Office/DoE/MAFF Consultation Document November 1995

E.C. Nitrate Directive 91/676 Proposed measures to apply in Nitrate Vulnerable Zones and draft regulations transposing the Directive in England & Wales

Action programme

The left-hand column below shows the basic requirements in Nitrate Vulnerable Zones which it is proposed to incorporate into regulations. They follow, with some minor amendments, the outline Action Programme published in the 1994 Consultation Document. The centre column gives some further explanation of the requirement. The right-hand column explains what extra guidance needs to be given in the literature to farmers to ensure the action programme is effective.

Inorganic (Chemical) Nitrogen Fertiliser Use

ENFORCEABLE REQUIREMENT	EXPLANATION OF REQUIREMENT	EXTRA GUIDANCE TO BE GIVEN
Do not apply between 1 September and 1 February unless there is a specific crop requirement during that time.	Inorganic nitrogen applied during this autumn/winter period is not generally required by crops and if applied is often poorly utilised and available for leaching. Hence the basic rule will be to forbid applications during this period. However, some crops, *e.g.* over-wintered cauliflower, do require modest amounts of nitrogen fertiliser at this time of year, and it is proposed that the regulations should make it admissible to meet the particular needs of such crops.	Information about the circumstances in which it will be accepted that nitrogen fertiliser is necessary during the closed period will be given, as well as procedures for establishing in advance that such applications are admissible.

Do not apply when the soil is — **waterlogged** — **flooded** — **frozen hard** — **snow covered.**	The basic rule is to prohibit applications under these conditions. Technical definitions of these conditions will, however, be avoided in the regulations.	The guidance material will help the farmer identify the conditions when applications are prohibited. Thus an example of frozen hard would be when the soil is frozen for more than 12 hours. Days when soil is frozen overnight but thaws out during the day would not be regarded as frozen hard.
Do not apply to steeply sloping fields.	The basic rule is to prohibit applications under these conditions. Technical definitions will again be avoided, since slopes are rarely simple features of the landscape. It is not practicable to define critical angles of slope.	The guidance material will help the farmer identify the conditions when applications are prohibited. Fields in the steeply sloping category are unlikely to be cultivated.
Do not exceed crop requirement for quantity of nitrogen fertiliser on each field each year, taking account of crop uptake and soil supply from soil organic matter, crop residues and organic manures.	This obligation requires that an assessment is made of the amount of fertiliser required by each crop on each field each year. The factors listed are taken into account by most fertiliser recommendation systems. MAFF RB209 'Fertiliser Recommendations, for agricultural and horticultural crops' 6th edition 1994, is one authoritative source but it is not the only source of information on crop nitrogen requirement.	The guidance literature will emphasise the need to plan fertiliser applications by taking account of the nitrogen already available in the soil from soil organic matter, previous crop residues and from applications of organic manures. Techniques for calculating these residues will be explained.

Do not apply fertilisers in such a way that they will enter directly into surface water.	The basic requirement is for fertilisers to be spread accurately on the cropped area without directly contaminating surface waters.	It will be pointed out that full width machines should present few problems. Spinning disc and oscillating spout machines will need careful operation. Headland deflector plates may be appropriate. The need for proper calibration of spreaders will be stressed.
Organic Manure Use **Applications of organic manures shall not exceed 250 kg/ha of total nitrogen each year averaged over the area of grass on the farm and 210 kg/ha of total nitrogen each year averaged over the area of the farm not in grass. These rules apply to all farms, whether producting or receiving organic manures.**	These limits apply to all organic manures, including deposition while grazing, and to all the agricultural land on the farm in the NVZ. They include sewage sludges and other organic wastes. The limits do not include inorganic nitrogen fertiliser. The Directive allows a derogation to the level of 210kg where justified by objective criteria. The lower leaching from grassland justifies a higher limit of 250kg/ha. It is expected that the 210 kg/ha limit on fields not in grass will subsequently be reduced to 170 kg/ha.	Assistance will be given with assessing the nitrogen content of manure and the typical numbers of different types of animals that equate with these limits. The actual number of animals equating to a limit on a particular farm may vary depending on feeding and other details of the production system.

On sandy or shallow soils do not apply slurry, poultry manure or liquid digested sludge: **— between 1 September and 1 November to grass fields** **— between 1 August and 1 November to fields not in grass.**	Nitrate leaching risk is greatest in these situations. Other types of organic manure (such as farmyard manure) contain a much lower proportion of their nitrogen in a form that is readily converted to nitrate. Very dilute wastes such as parlour washings and yard run-off on dairy farms are also excluded. The months when application is banned are the most crucial ones. August application on grassland allows time for nitrate produced to be taken up by the growing crop. Other crops are less effective. Applications after 1 November will result in very limited conversion to nitrate in most winters.	Guidance will be given on how to tell whether a field is covered by the ban on autumn application or not. Broadly speaking, it will apply to sandy (sand or loamy sand to 40 cm depth and sandy to 100 cm) and shallow soils (mineral soils over chalk, limestone or other rock within 40 cm of the surface).
Do not apply when the soil is **— waterlogged** **— flooded** **— frozen hard** **— snow covered.**	Again, the basic rule is to prohibit applications, but without laying down a technical definition.	The same guidance on frozen hard as used for inorganic fertiliser applications will be provided.

Do not apply to steeply sloping fields.	Run-off risk following organic manure application is similar to that for inorganic fertilisers.	Guidance will be given on rapid incorporation. This will usually be the day of application.
Do not apply within 10 m of surface water.	The requirement is to ensure that spreaders and irrigators do not apply any organic manures, effluents or wastes within 10 m of surface waters. This will minimise the risk of direct application to surface water and provides a buffer against run-off.	
Storage of Slurry and Silage		
All new, substantially reconstructed or substantially enlarged installations for the containment of slurry and silage must conform with The Control of Pollution (Silage, Slurry and Agriculture Fuel Oil) Regulations 1991.	These Regulations are currently being reviewed, but the main changes proposed relate to field silage making. The NRA already have powers under these Regulations to require changes to facilities built before 1 September 1991 if they are causing or likely to cause pollution.	Assistance is available for farmers who undertake general waste management planning, and specific guidance will be given in NVZs on planning in relation to these restrictions.

The storage capacity available for those animal manures which cannot be applied during the autumn must be sufficient to cover this period unless other environmentally acceptable means of disposal are available.	The practical minimum storage period to enable the spreading ban on slurry to be met is 3 or 4 months for grass and non-grass farms respectively. This assumes that slurry is being produced throughout, is not being exported outside the zone and that winter application is both practicable and environmentally acceptable.	
Fertiliser Records		
All farms must keep records of use of inorganic nitrogen fertiliser and organic manures.	Records of the amounts used are essential to monitor compliance with the Action Programme.	A simple paper recording system will be available to those who do not already have an adequate recording system. The mandatory records form a part of a systematic approach to fertiliser management and planning which will be explained.

BIBLIOGRAPHY

ADAS: *A review of methyl bromide use in horticulture 1996* (December, 1996).

Benjamin *et al*: Stomach NO synthesis, (1994), *Nature*, Vol. 386, p. 502.

Bockman, Kaarstad, Lie and Richards: *Agriculture and Fertilisers*, (Norsk Hydro, Oslo, 1990).

DoE: *Disposal of Sewage sludge to land—Standing technical committee report No. 20* (HMSO, 1981).

DoE: *The Ozone Layer* (HMSO, 1991).

DoE: *The Potential effects of climate change in the U.K.* (HMSO, 1991).

DoE: "1995—Hottest year on record", *Climate Change*, Issue 6, (HMSO 1996).

DoE: *Digest of Environmental Statistics 1995*, (HMSO, 1996).

DoE: *Indicators of sustainable development in the United Kingdom*, (HMSO, 1996)

ENDS (Environmental Data Services): The ENDS Report—various issues.

Foy and Withers: *The contribution of agricultural phosphate to eutrophication*, Fertiliser Society Proceedings No. 365, (1995).

MAFF: *Review of the Rules for Sewage Sludge Application to Agricultural Lands. Soil fertility aspects of potentially toxic elements*, The Report of the Independent Scientific Committee, Bradshaw (1993).

MAFF: *Sewage Sludge—general information on the application of sewage sludge to agricultural land*, PB 2568, (HMSO, 1996).

MAFF/DoE/Welsh Office: *E.C. Nitrate Directive Consultation Document—Proposed measures to apply in nitrate vulnerable zones*, (November, 1995).

McGrath and Loveland: *The Soil Geochemical Atlas of England and Wales*, (1992).

Parliamentary Office of Science and Technology: *Drinking water quality*, (May, 1993).

Powlson and Goulding: "Agriculture, the nitrogen cycle and nitrate", in *Nitrate control policy: agriculture and land use—Proceedings of the 4th Professional Environmental Seminar*, (White Horse Press, 1995).

Royal Commission on Environmental Pollution: *Freshwater quality (16th Report)*, (HMSO, 1992).

Royal Commission on Environmental Pollution: *The sustainable use of soil (19th Report)*, (HMSO, 1996).

U.K. Climate Change impacts Review Group: *Review of the Potential effects of climate change in the United Kingdom*, (HMSO), 1996).

WHO: *Letter to Fertiliser Manufacturers Association*, (October 3, 1989).

WHO: *Guidelines for drinking water quality*, Vol. 1 (1993).

INDEX